KT-412-567

TOWER HAMLETS LIBRARIES

Information Services

Reference Library
REFERENCE SECTION
NOT FOR LOAN

For AQA Specification A

Understanding GCSE Geography

FOUNDATION

Ann Bowen

John Pallister

Heinemann Educational Publishers

Halley Court, Jordan Hill, Oxford OX2 8EJ

A division of Reed Educational and Professional Publishing Ltd

Heinemann is a registered trade mark of

Reed Educational and Professional Publishing Ltd

OXFORD MELBOURNE AUCKLAND
JOHANNESBURG BLANTYRE GABORONE
IBADAN PORTSMOUTH NH (USA) CHICAGO

Text © Ann Bowen, John Pallister

Copyright notice

All rights reserved. No part of this publication may be reproduced in any
material form (including photocopying or storing it in any medium by
electronic means and whether or not transiently or incidentally to some
other use of this publication) without the prior written permission of the
copyright owner, except in accordance with the provisions of the Copyright,
Designs and Patents Act 1988 or under the terms of a licence issued by the
Copyright Licensing Agency Ltd, 90 Tottenham Court Road, London W1P
0LP. Applications for the copyright owner's written permission to reproduce
any part of this publication should be addressed to the publisher.

First edition published 2002

02

10 9 8 7 6 5 4 3 2 1

British Library Cataloguing in Publication Data

A catalogue record for this book is available from the British Library

ISBN 0 435 35170 2

Typeset and designed by Oxford Designers & Illustrators, Oxford

Printed in Great Britain by Bath Press Colourbooks, Glasgow

TOWER HAMLETS
LIBRARIES

HEA £14.99

04 DEC 2002

LOCN. CLASS
BOWD J910

ACC. No.
C1195205

Contents

Features of the book:		
Activities	Tasks catering for the need of foundation students	
i	A panel giving extra information on a particular topic or theme	
There are Case Studies in each chapter, both integrated within the text and as separate pages, providing further real examples of the topic.		

Acknowledgements

The publishers would like to thank the following for permission to reproduce copyright material:

Photographs

Ace Photos, (p. 137) Aerofilms, (p. 26, Fig. 1; p. 70, Figs 3 & 4; p. 123 & p.186, Fig. 2) AP (p. 5p. 14, Fig. 2) APEX photo agency (p. 62, Fig. 3) APS (UK) (p. 73, Fig. 2) Ardea (p. 149, Fig. 5) Ardea (p. 91, Fig. 1) Collections (p. 147, Fig. 5, p. 170, Fig. 1, p. 85, Fig. 4) Collections/Hamish Williamson (p. 135, Fig. 5) Collections/Iain McGowan (p. 26, Fig. 2) Collections/John D Beldon (p. 153, Fig. 4) Collections/Michael Allen (p. 68, Fig. 2) Collections/Mike Kipling (p.169, Fig. 5) Collections/Paul Watts (p. 20, Fig. 2) Collections/Robin Weaver (p. 29, Fig. 5) Colorific/Ray Nelson (p.79, Fig. 4) EOSAT (p. 96, Fig. 1) FLPA (p. 111, Fig. 5) FLPA (p. 157, Fig. 2) FLPA/Tony Wharton (p. 18, Fig. 2, p. 9, Fig. 4) GSF (p. 93, Fig. 3) Ian Hay, Daily Telegraph (p. 135, Fig. 6) Network Photographers/ Peter Jordan (p. 205, Fig. 4, p. 207, Fig. 3) Oxfam/Badal (p. 227, Fig. 4) PA News/John Giles (p. 61) Panos (p. 119, Fig. 5, p. 166, Fig. 1) Panos/Chris Towers (p. 101) Panos/Howard Davies (p.116, Fig. 2) Panos/Jeremy Hartley (p. 227, Fig. 3) Philip Wolmuth (p. 224, Fig. 2) Planet Earth/Andre Bartschi (p. 36, Fig. 2) Popperfoto (p. 17,Fig. 4, p. 46, Fig. 1) Robert Harding (p. 149, Fig. 4, p. 20, Fig. 1, p. 34, Fig. 2) Robert Harding/Adam Woolfit (p. 132, Fig. 1) Robert Harding/JHC Wilson (p. 162, Fig. 4) Robert Harding/M. Black (p. 23, Fig. 3) Robert Harding/Roy Rainford (p. 31, 35, Fig. 3) Roger D Smith (p. 165) Roger Scruton (p. 134, Fig. 1, p. 68, Fig. 1, p. 70, Fig. 2) Science Photo Library (p. 39, Fig. 3) Silvia Pitcher (p. 47, Fig. 3) South American Pictures (p. 97, Fig. 3) South American Pictures/Tony Morrison (p. 140, Fig. 1, p. 142, Fig. 2) Still pictures (p. 89) Still Pictures/Mark Edwards (p. 105, Fig. 4) Still Pictures/Gerard and Margi Ross (p. 105, Fig. 5) Still/Hartmut Schwarzbah (p. 122, Fig. 2) Still/Jorgen Schytte (p. 164, Fig. 1 & 2) Still/Mark Edwards (p. 114, Fig. 2, p. 159, Fig. 2) Still/Ron Giling (p.160, Fig. 1, p. 167, Fig. 3) Tony Stone/James Balog (p. 7, Fig. 5) Tony Waltham (p. 56, Fig. 3) Trip/H.Rogers (p. 153, Fig. 6) Univ of Dundee (p. 83, Fig. 2, p. 85, Fig. 2); All other photographs are the copyright of the authors, Ann Bowen and John Pallister.

Maps, diagrams and extracts

BP Statistical Review of World Energy, 1996, (Fig. 1, p. 190); Bunce, V. (ed.), Longman Geography for GCSE, (Fig. 1, p. 102), (Fig. 3, p. 162); Carr, Patterns, Process and Change in Human Geography, Macmillan, (Fig. 3, p. 120); Dickenson et al, Geography in the Third World, Routledge, (Fig. 2, p. 212); Dobson & Virgo, Elements of Geography, Hodder and Stoughton, (Fig. 1, p. 8); European Union, (Fig. 2, p. 152); Financial Times, (Fig. 2, p. 223); Galbraith and Wigand, An Introduction to Geomorphology, OUP, (Fig. 4 p. 13); GeoActive, series 4, Stanley Thornes Ltd., (Fig. 5, p. 156); Kidron and Segal, The State of the World Atlas, Myriad Editions LTD, Penguin, (Figs. 2 & 3, p. 118); Knapp, Ross and McCrae, Challenge of the Human Environment, Longman, (Fig. 1, p. 114); Longman Atlas for Secondary Schools, (Fig. 3, p. 115); New Internationalist, (Fig. 2, p. 194), (Fig. 2, p. 196); Nixon, B., British Isles, Bell & Hyman, (Figs. 1 & 2, p. 80); Northern Echo, Newsquest, (Fig. 3, p. 71); Philip's Geographical Digest, (Fig. 4, p. 120); Philip's Heinemann School Atlas, (Fig. 3, p. 235); Population Concern, (Fig. 3, p. 205), (Fig. 1a, p. 234); Ross, S., Longman Coordinated Geography, 'People and Physical Environment', (Figs. 3 & 4, p. 7); The Daily Telegraph, (Fig. 2a, p. 110), (Fig. 3, p. 112), (Fig. 6, p. 135), (Fig. 3, p. 139); The Guardian, (Fig. 3, p. 63), (Fig. 4, p. 87), (Fig. 3, p. 109), (Fig. 6, p. 183), (Fig. 4, p. 193), (Fig. 3, p. 205), (Fig. 1, p. 214), (Fig. 2, p. 218), (Fig. 4, p. 219), (Figs. 1-3, p. 228); This product includes mapping data from Ordnance Survey® with the permission of the Controller of Her Majesty's Stationary Office©, Crown Copyright. All rights reserved. Licence no. 100000230, (Fig. 4, p. 27), (Fig. 4, p. 29), (Fig. 2, p. 40), (Fig. 4, p. 41), (Fig. 5, p. 53), (Fig. 4, p. 55), (Fig. 2, p. 124), (Fig. 4, p. 125), (Fig. 5, p. 125). (Fig. 3, p. 131), (Fig. 2, p. 173), (Fig. 3, p. 175), (Fig. 1, p. 200); Time International Magazine, (Fig. 2, p. 190), (p. 204); UN Population Division, 1995, (Fig. 4, p. 125); Unwin, T. (ed.), Atlas of World Development, Wiley, (Fig. 3, p. 225); Waugh, Geography an Integrated Approach, Nelson, (Fig. 2, p. 22); Waugh, North and South America, Nelson, (Fig. 3, p. 143); Waugh, The UK and Europe, Nelson, (Fig. 3, p. 151); Waugh, Wider World, Nelson, (Fig. 4, p. 117), (Fig. 5, p. 121), (Fig. 3, p. 146), (Fig. 1, p. 162); Whynne-Hammond, C., Elements in Human Geography, Unwin Hyman, (Fig. 1, p. 108); Williams, J., The Weather Book, Vintage Books, (Figs. 1 & 2, p. 88); WWF, Data Support Sheet for Education 24, (Fig. 1, p. 194); Yorkshire Life, (Fig. 4, p. 201); Young & Lowry, The British Isles, Hodder and Stoughton, (Fig. 1, p. 150).

The publishers have made every effort to trace the copyright holders, but if they have inadvertantly overlooked any, they will be pleased to make the necessary arrangements at the first opportunity.

Chapter 1

Tectonic activity

The Soufrière Hills volcano on the island of Montserrat in the Caribbean erupted in 1997. It caused massive damage to a large part of the island. Why do volcanoes occur in certain parts of the world?

Key Ideas

The Earth's crust is unstable:
- the tectonic plates may move together or move apart
- earthquakes, volcanoes and fold mountains occur at plate boundaries
- there are different types of volcano – composite or shield.

Tectonic activity influences human activity:
- human activities in fold mountain areas are a result of the physical conditions
- there are advantages and disadvantages for settlement in areas of tectonic activity
- tectonic activity has different effects in rural or urban areas and in rich and poor countries.

TOWER HAMLETS LIBRARY

The Earth's tectonic plates

The Earth's structure is shown in **Figure 1**. It has three layers:

- the **core** at the centre
- the **mantle** of molten rock surrounding the core
- the thin **crust** at the surface.

The Earth's crust is broken up into tectonic **plates**. There are seven large plates and many smaller ones. The plates may move as a result of **convection currents** inside the mantle. The movement is greatest where two plates meet – the plate boundary. Areas away from the plate boundaries tend to be stable.

The movement of the plates

The plates move in three different ways:

- they move apart – this is called a tensional plate boundary
- they move together – this is called a compressional plate boundary
- they slide past each other – this is called a passive plate boundary.

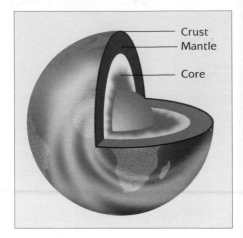

▲ **Figure 1** The structure of the Earth.

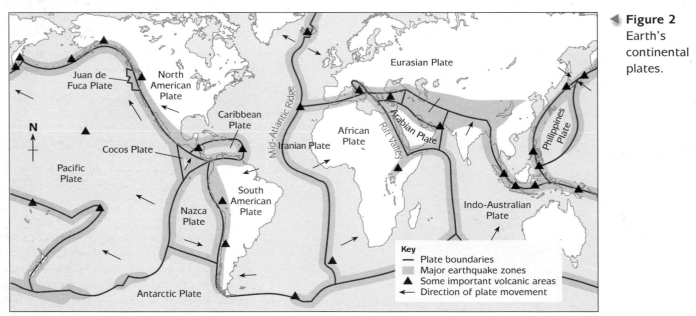

◀ **Figure 2** Earth's continental plates.

Key
— Plate boundaries
▨ Major earthquake zones
▲ Some important volcanic areas
← Direction of plate movement

Activities

1 a Draw a labelled diagram to show the structure of the Earth.
  b Describe how the Earth is like an apple – mention the core, the 'fleshy' part and the skin.

2 Use an atlas to place the following countries in two lists – countries that are liable to suffer tectonic activity and countries not liable to suffer tectonic activity.
  - Japan
  - Britain
  - Canada
  - Brazil
  - Morocco
  - Finland
  - Australia
  - Chile
  - Alaska (USA)

3 a How many large tectonic plates exist?
  b Why do the plates sometimes move?
  c Where does the movement take place?

4 Complete a table like the one below – the first set of answers have been done for you.

Type of plate boundary	Type of movement	Example of plate boundary
Passive	Plates slide past each other	Pacific and North American plates
Tensional		
Compressional		

Types of plate boundary

Compressional plate boundaries

- At a **compressional plate boundary** the plates move together.
- One of the plates is forced to sink below the other.
- As it sinks into the mantle the plate melts in the subduction zone.
- The heat and pressure in the **subduction zone** sometimes cause an earthquake.
- The molten rock or magma may also be forced to the surface causing a volcanic eruption. The plate that does not sink is crumpled by the pressure and forms fold mountains.

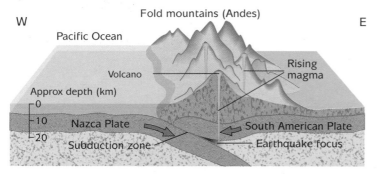

▲ **Figure 3** A compressional plate boundary.

Tensional plate boundaries

- The plates move apart at a **tensional plate boundary.**
- Most of these plate boundaries are under the oceans.
- As the plates move apart magma rises up from the mantle to fill the gap.
- The rising magma forms shield volcanoes.
- The ends of the plates crumple up to form ridges.

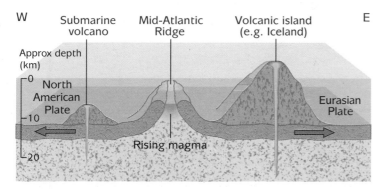

▲ **Figure 4** A tensional plate boundary.

Passive plate boundaries

Plates slide past each other at a **passive boundary**. An example of a passive plate boundary is the San Andreas fault in California. Earthquakes occur along the fault.

▲ **Figure 5** The San Andreas fault, California. What has happened to the ground where the fault is?

Activities

5 Copy and complete the sentences below. The missing words are:

fold mountains   subduction   Nazca   volcano
together   earthquake   magma

Compressional plate boundaries

The plates are moving _____ . The N_____ plate is sinking into the mantle. In the mantle the plate melts in the _____ zone. The molten rock is called _____. The molten rock may erupt at the surface forming a _____. The great pressure may be released causing an _____. The edge of the South American plate is crumpled upwards to form _____ _____.

6 Draw a diagram to show a compressional plate boundary.

7 a How do the plates move at a tensional plate boundary?
  b Where are most tensional plate boundaries?
  c Name two features formed at a tensional plate boundary.

8 Use an atlas to answer these questions.
  a Find a map of South America and name the range of fold mountains formed where the Nazca plate meets the South American plate.
  b Find a map showing the Atlantic Ocean and name a volcanic island formed along the Mid-Atlantic ridge.

Fold mountains

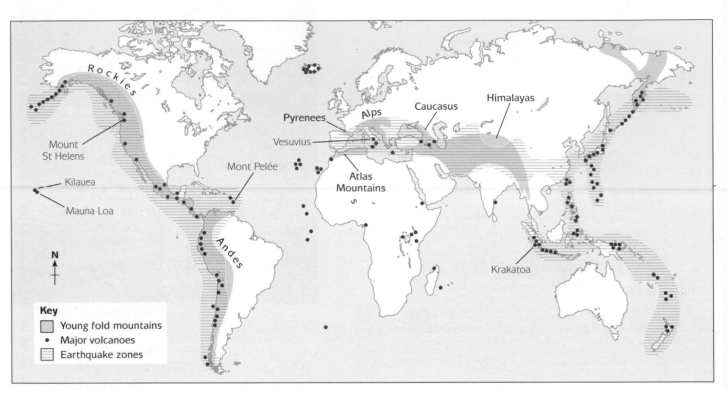

▲ **Figure 1** The world distribution of young fold mountains, active volcanoes and earthquake zones.

Fold mountains form along compressional plate boundaries where the plates are pushed together. This happens during mountain-building periods. The most recent period created the Alps, Andes, Himalayas and Rockies so these are often called young fold mountains. The formation of fold mountains is shown in **Figure 2**.

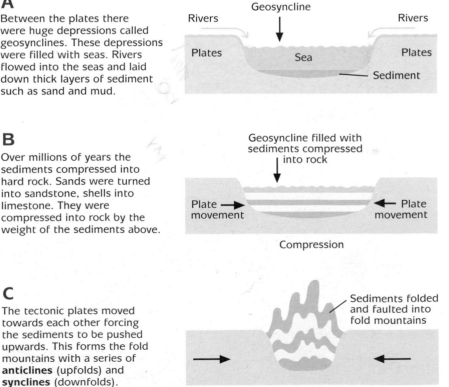

A
Between the plates there were huge depressions called geosynclines. These depressions were filled with seas. Rivers flowed into the seas and laid down thick layers of sediment such as sand and mud.

B
Over millions of years the sediments compressed into hard rock. Sands were turned into sandstone, shells into limestone. They were compressed into rock by the weight of the sediments above.

C
The tectonic plates moved towards each other forcing the sediments to be pushed upwards. This forms the fold mountains with a series of **anticlines** (upfolds) and **synclines** (downfolds).

▲ **Figure 2** The formation of fold mountains.

The Alps

The Alps are young fold mountains. They were formed 30–40 million years ago when two plates moved together. The rocks were folded upwards to form two parallel ranges.

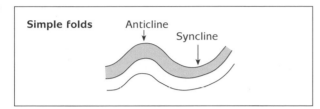

▲ **Figure 3** Simple folds.

ℹ️ The Alps

- The highest peak is Mont Blanc, 4810m
- Other peaks include the Matterhorn and the Eiger
- Some of Europe's largest rivers begin in the Alps, e.g. the Rhône and the Rhine
- The Alps have been eroded by ice forming huge U-shaped valleys, peaks and ridges (**Figure 4**)
- The ice also helped to form large ribbon lakes, e.g. Lake Como and Lake Garda in Italy.

Activities

1. On a blank world map mark and label four areas of fold mountains. Add a title to your map.
2. Copy the diagrams in **Figure 2** and complete the following sentences to describe how fold mountains are formed.

   Between two plates there was a big depression called a _____. The depression filled up with sediment brought by _____. The sediment was _____ into solid rock, e.g. _____. The plates moved _____ folding the sediments upwards into _____ _____ e.g. the Andes and _____.

3. a How long did it take the Alps to form?
   b Using an atlas draw a sketch map to show the location of the Alps. Label the countries through which the Alps pass.
   c List four physical features of the Alps.

4. Draw and label a sketch of **Figure 4**. Add a title. Here are some ideas for labels:

   steep slopes   bare rock   snow-capped peaks woodland   settlement   grassland

▲ **Figure 4** Alpine view – the Jungfrau region of the Lauterbrunnen Valley.

Human activity in the Alps

In the Alps land uses and vegetation are zoned because as the altitude increases the climate becomes colder. The main human activities in the Alps are connected with tourism, dairy farming, forestry, HEP and industry (see **Figure 1**).

Tourism

Many new resorts, such as St Moritz and Chamonix, developed in the 1950s when tourism and especially skiing expanded. The tourist industry encouraged the building of new roads, tunnels, avalanche shelters, hotels, restaurants, cable cars and other facilities. Some of these have benefited the farmers and other local people.

The area attracts skiers, climbers and walkers. Attractions include:

- beautiful winter scenery with glaciated mountains, snow-capped peaks and forests
- lakeside summer resorts, such as Lucerne and Garda
- extensive winter sports facilities, such as ski slopes, ice rinks and toboggan runs
- good communications – close to international road and rail routes using Alpine passes such as the Simplon and St Gotthard, as well as international airports at Geneva and Zurich
- the Alpine climate – good snowfall but also crisp, clear days for winter sports, and summers that are warm with showers.

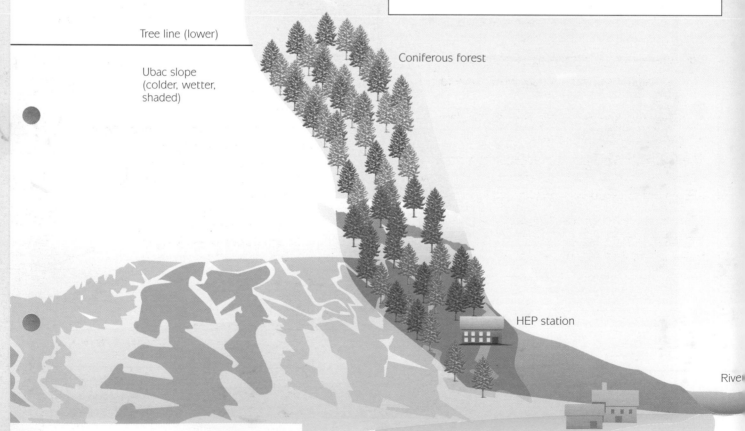

SOUTH

Snowfields and glaciers

Tree line (lower)

Ubac slope
(colder, wetter, shaded)

Coniferous forest

HEP station

River

Hay

▲ **Figure 1** Human activity in an Alpine valley.

Problems of fold mountain areas

Fold mountain areas, such as the Alps, have low population densities. It is difficult to build roads, railways and houses and there are few industries or other types of jobs. Most of the problems are due to the difficult physical conditions, such as:

- the high altitude and steep slopes
- avalanches and rock falls that may block roads and mean avalanche shelters are needed
- the cold, wet climate with winter snowfall
- the short growing season that limits farming.

Farming

The valley floor is the ideal location for farming because:

- the land here is flatter
- the soils are deeper and more fertile
- there is shelter from wind
- there are better communications here.

Most farms are on the warmer and drier south-facing slope. Many farms are dairy farms although some hay, cereals, sugar beet and vines may be grown in warmer areas.

Hydro-electric power (HEP) and industry

The Alps are ideal for making HEP because:

- high rainfall and summer snowmelt give fast-flowing rivers
- steep and narrow valleys are easy to dam
- natural lakes store water.

The HEP is quite cheap to produce. It attracts industries that need a lot of electricity, e.g. sawmills, aluminium smelters and fertilizer making.

Up to about 1800m the slopes are forested. The trees are conifers and they are felled and used as fuel or for building and making pulp and paper.

NORTH

Snow line

High alp (saeter)

Tree line

Adrêt slope (sunnier, warmer, drier)

Ski station

Village

Main roads and railway

Sawmill

Activities

1 Draw a simple cross-section of an Alpine valley. Add the following labels:
   - Farming in the valley floor
   - Summer pasture on the High Alp
   - Ski stations
   - HEP and industry
   - Roads and railways
   - Snow-capped peaks and glaciers
   - Coniferous forests.

2 a Give three advantages of the Alps for tourism.
   b Give three reasons why the Alps is a good area for generating HEP.
   c Give three reasons why farming is mostly located on the valley floors.

3 Why do the Alps have such low population densities?

Volcanoes

Etna, Vesuvius and Mount St Helens are all well-known volcanoes. Each volcano has erupted many times building up layer after layer of lava to form the typical cone shape. The magma that erupts at the surface is called **lava**. The lava is just one product from a volcano. A volcano may also throw out ash, cinders, steam, gases and lava bombs.

There are two main types of lava:

- **acid lava** – with a high silica content is thick or viscous and does not flow very far before cooling. It builds up steep-sided volcanoes that erupt violently.

- **basic lava** – with a low silica content is runny or fluid and flows long distances before cooling. It builds up volcanoes with more gentle slopes and eruptions are non-violent.

How are volcanoes formed?

Volcanoes form where magma escapes through a **vent**, which is a fracture or crack in the Earth's crust. This often happens at plate boundaries, as shown by the distribution of the major volcanoes on **Figure 1** on page 8.

Figure 1 on this page shows how a volcano forms. When the plates collide, the denser oceanic plate is pushed down into the mantle. Here the plate melts and is destroyed in the subduction zone. This is a compressional or destructive boundary. In the subduction zone the plate melts to form a pool of magma. The great heat and pressure may force the magma along a crack where it erupts at the surface. After many eruptions the layers build up to form a volcano.

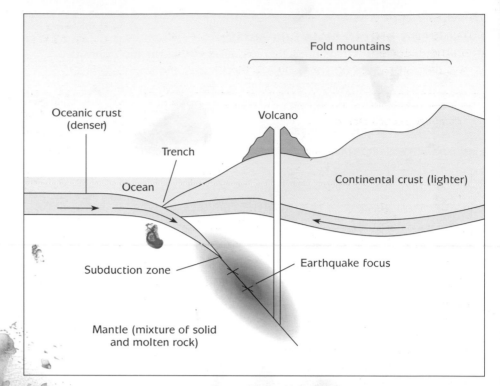

Figure 1 How a volcano is formed at a compressional plate boundary.

Figure 2 Mount Etna, Italy.

Different types of volcanoes

Volcanoes are divided into two main types depending upon the material thrown out in an eruption. **Figure 3** shows the two types and their characteristics.

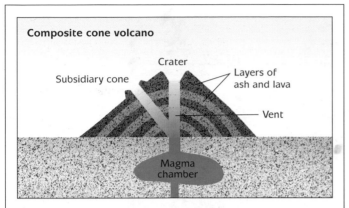

Composite cone volcano

Examples: Mount Etna, Vesuvius, Mount St Helens
Characteristics:

- Steep-sided symmetrical cone shape
- High with narrow base
- Alternate layers of acid lava and ash
- Lava may cool inside the vent – the next eruption is very explosive to remove the plug
- Subsidiary cones and vents form.

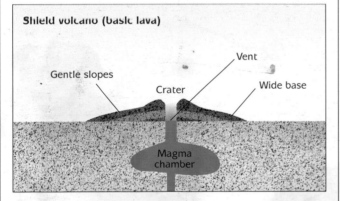

Shield volcano (basic lava)

Examples: Mauna Loa and Kilauea, both on the Hawaiian Islands
Characteristics:

- Gentle slopes and wide base
- Frequent eruptions of basic lava
- Lava flows more easily, travels longer distances before cooling
- Usually non-violent.

▲ **Figure 3** Different types of volcano.

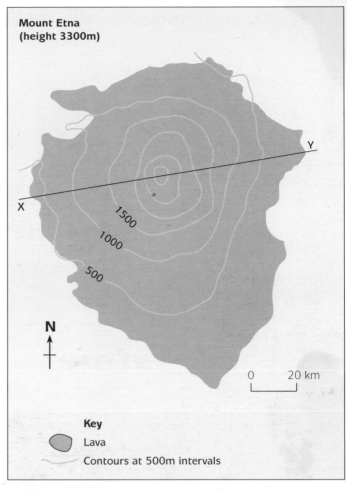

▲ **Figure 4** Map of Mount Etna.

Activities

1 Which type of lava is associated with:
   a violent eruptions   b gentle eruptions?

2 Explain why basic lava results in wide-based and gently sloping volcanoes.

3 With the aid of a diagram explain how a volcano is formed.

4 *Mauna Loa in the Hawaiian islands is 10 000m high, of which 4000m are above sea level. The base of the volcano has a diameter of 400km. In an eruption lava can flow 50km down its gentle slopes (2–10 degrees).*
   a Draw a cross section through Mauna Loa. (Horizontal scale 1cm: 20km, so you will need a 20cm horizontal axis; vertical scale 1cm: 8000m)
   b Using **Figure 4** draw a cross-section through Mount Etna from X to Y.
   c Give two differences between the two cross-sections.

A volcanic eruption on Montserrat in the Caribbean

Figure 1 The location of Montserrat.

Figure 2 Plymouth, a ghost town.

Montserrat is a small island in the Caribbean. It is a British colony and many wealthy British people, including Paul McCartney and Sting, own exclusive villas that line the coast. The population of the island before the volcanic eruption was 12 000. Half of the population lived in the capital city of Plymouth. Many of the people were quite poor and worked as subsistence farmers living in small villages.

Figure 3 The impact of the eruptions on Montserrat.

In July 1995 the Soufrière Hills volcano erupted for the first time in 350 years. The eruptions continued for over a year and they were explosive throwing out millions of tonnes of ash and lava.

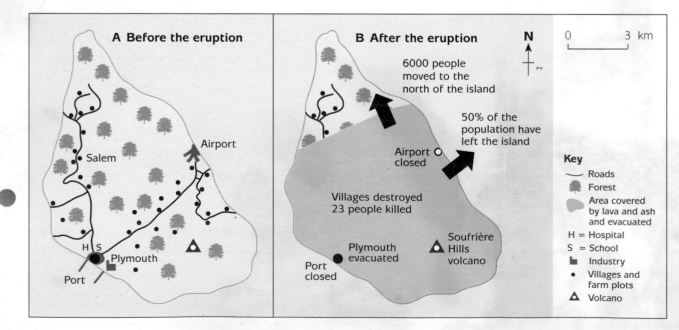

A Before the eruption

Salem

Airport

H S
Plymouth

Port

B After the eruption

N

0   3 km

6000 people moved to the north of the island

50% of the population have left the island

Airport closed

Villages destroyed 23 people killed

Plymouth evacuated

Port closed

Soufrière Hills volcano

Key

— Roads

Forest

Area covered by lava and ash and evacuated

H = Hospital

S = School

Industry

• Villages and farm plots

△ Volcano

> ### ℹ️ Information box
>
> **Primary effects** – the immediate impact of the volcanic eruption, e.g. loss of life, loss of homes, animals and crops.
>
> **Secondary effects** – the after-effects of the eruption, such as the loss of trade including tourism, the need to rebuild, the stress for people.
>
> **The short-, medium- and long-term response to a volcanic eruption** – evacuation of people is an immediate or short-term response, whereas rebuilding settlements is a medium- or long-term response.

The impact of the eruptions

- In August 1995, 50 per cent of the population were evacuated to the north of the island
- Plymouth was covered by several metres of ash and became a ghost town (**Figure 2**)
- Villages were destroyed and 23 people killed
- Over 5000 people left the island, most to settle on the neighbouring island of Antigua but some came to Britain
- The port and airport closed
- Forests and farmland were destroyed
- The people who moved to the north lived in makeshift camps with little food, sanitation or other services
- The tourist industry was destroyed during the eruptions
- The country had to rely on aid from Britain.

After the eruptions, the local people of Montserrat called for compensation from the British Government and money to rebuild the island. The British Government has given over £50 million in aid to redevelop the north of the island and to pay for people to leave the country. But the local people wanted £20 000 per person and there were riots in protest.

Should the island be rebuilt? The population is now below 5000 and the volcano may erupt again – would the investment be worth it?

Activities

1 Describe the location of Montserrat.

2 Montserrat lies close to the Caribbean plate boundary. What happened to cause the eruption?

3 a Describe the primary effects of the eruption.
  b Describe the secondary effects.

4 Describe the short-, medium- and long-term responses to the eruption on Montserrat.

5 In pairs or small groups discuss the following points of view and contribute to a class discussion:
  - The island should be rebuilt and the British Government should pay
  - The island should be abandoned and the British Government should pay for the evacuation and give compensation to those affected.

6 Give three advantages and three disadvantages of living near to a volcano.

Advantages	Disadvantages

• Fertile soil when the lava weathers
• Tourist attractions, e.g. trips to the rim of the crater, hotel accommodation, souvenir shops
• Minerals, e.g. sulphur, borax, pumice
• Lava flows build new land, e.g. Iceland, Hawaii
• Hot springs for bathing, heating
• Heat used to generate electricity.
	• Explosions and eruptions leading to:
	  – dangerous gases
	  – loss of life
	  – loss of homes, animals and crops
	  – disease and fires
	  – avalanches, mudflows and floods
	  – loss of wildlife, trees and plants.

▲ **Figure 4** The advantages and disadvantages of living near volcanoes.

The earthquake hazard

What is an earthquake?

An earthquake is a shaking of the Earth's crust. Earthquakes cannot be predicted; they happen without warning and, as a result, they are often lethal. Since 1900 1.5 million people have died as a result of earthquakes. **Figure 1** gives some examples of earthquakes and the numbers killed.

How are earthquakes measured?

The magnitude or size of an earthquake is measured by an instrument called a **seismograph**. The earthquake is given a value between 1 and 10 on the **Richter scale**. The scale is logarithmic – an earthquake measuring 6 is ten times more powerful than one measuring 5.

Why do earthquakes happen?

Most earthquakes occur when there is movement along plate boundaries. Over 90 per cent occur at compressional boundaries where the plates are pushing together.

At a plate boundary the plates move as a result of convection currents but the movement is not steady or smooth. The plates tend to become jammed together. The pressure then builds up until one plate jerks past the other. This sudden movement causes the earthquake.

The point at which the earthquake happens below the ground surface is called the **focus** (**Figure 2**). The point on the ground surface directly above the focus is called the **epicentre**. If the epicentre is in, or close to, an urban area the effects can be devastating. This was the case in Kobe, Japan, in 1995.

Year	Magnitude on the Richter scale	Location	Approximate number of deaths
1556	8.3	Shansi, China	830 000
1755	9.0	Lisbon, Portugal	100 000
1857	8.3	Fort Tejon, California, USA	1
1906	8.25	San Francisco, USA	700
1920	8.6	Kansu, China	200 000
1923	8.3	Tokyo, Japan	143 000
1960	9.5	Chile	5 700
1964	8.4	Anchorage, Alaska	131
1970	7.8	Ancash, Peru	66 000
1988	7.1	Armenia	25 000
1995	7.2	Kobe, Japan	5 500
1997	7.1	Eastern Iran	1 560

▲ **Figure 1** Some important earthquakes.

The effects of earthquakes

An earthquake causes both primary and secondary effects.

Primary effects (the immediate damage)

- Collapsing buildings and bridges
- Cracked and twisted roads and railways
- Loss of life
- Shock and panic of people affected.

Secondary effects (the after effects of the earthquake)

- Fires caused by fractured gas mains and broken electricity cables. Broken water pipes often mean there are no water supplies to put fires out
- Tidal waves or **tsunamis** often result from an earthquake under the seabed, e.g. in 1960 a tsunami killed 165 people in Japan
- **Landslides** in steep-sided valleys where the rocks are weak sands and clays
- Disease and famine due to lack of clean water and medical facilities.

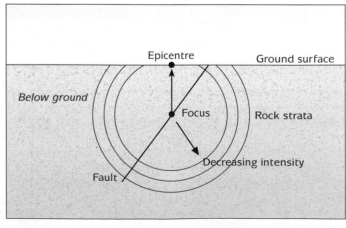

▲ **Figure 2** The features of an earthquake.

Kobe, 17 January 1995 – disaster strikes

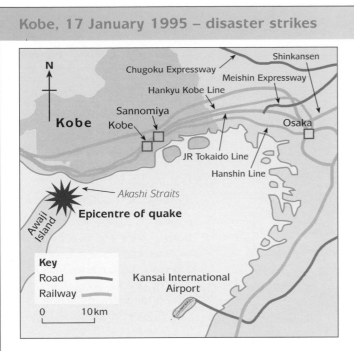

▲ **Figure 3** Kobe and the surrounding area.

▲ **Figure 4** The devastation in Kobe.

- 30 000 people injured
- 300 000 were made homeless
- After two weeks a flu epidemic broke out due to the cold weather and unhygienic conditions in the makeshift camps
- No emergency services were available
- I million homes were without water and power for over a week
- Fires started and burned for well over a week.

Kobe lies close to a plate boundary. In January 1995 the plates jerked past each other along a 50km stretch of the fault. The movement caused an earthquake with the epicentre between Kobe and Awaji Island (**Figure 3**).

The effects of the earthquake

- Landslides were caused
- The port of Kobe was destroyed
- Over 100 000 houses collapsed
- 10 per cent of roads and railways were destroyed
- Electricity, gas and sewage systems were destroyed
- 10 per cent of schools were destroyed
- 5500 people killed

The response to the quake

Emergency action was the first response to help those trapped and injured, to put out fires and to provide food and shelter. Within a week bulldozers were used to clear streets and unsafe buildings. Some electricity supplies and telephones were restored. After two weeks more roads and railways were opened. People were given help to cope with the stress and shock. Three years later parts of the city were still being rebuilt. A modern monitoring system has been put in place in the hope that in the future some warning may be possible. However, no one can predict with any accuracy when an earthquake will happen or how strong it will be.

The impact of tectonic activity

Earthquakes and volcanoes often cause much greater damage and loss of life in:

- LEDCs rather than MEDCs
- urban areas (towns and cities) rather than rural areas (countryside).

Many LEDCs cannot afford early warning systems and monitoring equipment. Housing is often overcrowded and poorly built. Transport routes are often poor so that emergency services take a long time to reach a disaster area.

In urban areas there are higher population densities and more housing, industry and transport routes that may be destroyed. The dense network of power lines and gas mains make fires more likely and increase the number of casualties. Diseases may also spread more rapidly.

Activities

1 What is an earthquake?

2 How is an earthquake measured and what scale is used?

3 Copy **Figure 2**. Using the words below write some sentences to explain how an earthquake happens:
plate boundary   heat and pressure
jammed together   jerks past

4 Where is the focus of an earthquake and how is the epicentre different?

5 Using the Kobe case study answer these questions:
   a Write two lists – one for the primary effects of the earthquake and one for the secondary effects.
   b Describe two short-term responses to the earthquake and two longer-term responses.

Vesuvius and the surrounding plain

Vesuvius is located in Southern Italy close to the major city of Naples (**Figure 1**). Vesuvius is a composite cone volcano. It is dormant at present but it has been very destructive in the past. The largest eruption was in AD79 when the towns of Pompeii and Herculaneum were destroyed. Thousands of people were killed and the towns were buried under metres of ash. So why do so many people choose to live so close to the volcano?

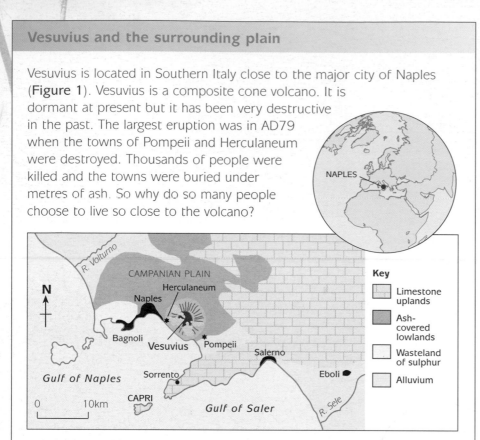

▲ **Figure 1** Map of Campania.

Tourism is a thriving industry. People take trips to the rim of the crater and visit the excavated remains of Pompeii. There are hot springs as well as the attractions of local beaches, the city of Naples and the Mediterranean climate. After several hundred years the ash and lava have formed fertile soils. People farm the land growing peaches, vines, tomatoes and cereals. Yields are very high and some products are exported.

The land around the plain is much less fertile. There are limestone hills that are dry and have only thin soils that cannot be used for crop growing. Another area is a wasteland with a high sulphur content.

So, despite the threat of an eruption in the future, people choose to live and work in the area around Vesuvius. Perhaps they believe or want to believe that an eruption will not happen in their lifetime.

◀ **Figure 2** Naples and Mount Vesuvius.

Activities

1 Match the letters on **Figure 3** with the correct words in the list below:
   magma chamber
   cone   crater   vent
   layers of ash and lava

2 a Does **Figure 3** show a composite or shield volcano?
   b Give two reasons for your answer.

3 a Describe the location of the volcano Vesuvius.
   b Give three advantages for people living close to the volcano.
   c Suggest one reason why living close to Vesuvius may be hazardous.

4 Draw a sketch of the photograph in **Figure 2**. Add a title and the following labels in the correct places:
   crater   steep sides
   Naples   old lava flows
   forested lower slopes

5 **ICT investigation**
   (using CD-ROMs or Internet)
   Produce a newspaper report of either a volcanic eruption or an earthquake. Your report should include a snappy headline, the causes and effects of the eruption or earthquake, some comments from survivors, and the responses to the earthquake or eruption.

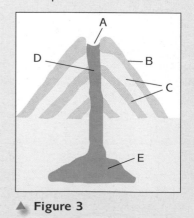

▲ **Figure 3**

Chapter 2

Rocks and landscape

Limestone pavement near Malham in the Yorkshire Dales National Park. This landscape feature forms only in areas of Carboniferous limestone rocks.

Key Ideas

The Earth's crust is composed of different rock types:
- the three rock groups are igneous, sedimentary and metamorphic
- rock types such as granite, Carboniferous limestone, chalk and clay form distinctive landscapes
- each rock type has economic uses, although quarrying rocks is often a local issue.

The Earth's crust is modified by weathering:
- physical weathering processes include freeze–thaw and exfoliation
- chemical weathering leads to limestone solution and distinctive landscape features.

Types of rocks and their distribution within the UK

There are three groups of rocks:

* igneous   • sedimentary   • metamorphic.

Igneous rocks are formed by 'fire' from volcanic activity. They begin as magma in the interior of the Earth. One type is basalt, which can be seen at the Giant's Causeway in Northern Ireland (**Figure 1**). Basalt forms at constructive plate margins. Another type of igneous rock is granite, which forms the famous cliffs at Land's End in Cornwall (**Figure 2**). Granite is formed by magma that cools underground, not on the surface. It often intrudes (in other words is forced into) into other types of rock during the building of fold mountains (page 8). This happens along destructive plate boundaries. After the rocks above have been eroded away, the granite outcrops on the surface, for example in south-west England (**Figure 4**).

Sedimentary rocks are made of sediments. Sediments are small particles of rock transported by rivers into the sea. Most fall to the sea bed, where over millions of years they build up thick layers. The weight of all the new sediment on top compresses the old sediments at the bottom into sedimentary rocks. These form horizontal layers of rock known as beds of rock (**Figure 3A**). The lines of weakness between the layers of rock are called bedding planes. Examples of types of sedimentary rocks include:

* sandstone, formed when sand is compressed

* clay, formed when mud is compressed

* limestone and chalk, formed from the remains of dead plants and animals (e.g. the shells of sea creatures) that collect on the sea floor.

▲ **Figure 1** The Giant's Causeway is made of basalt. It has been eroded into hexagonal (six-sided) blocks.

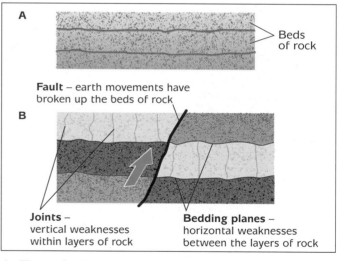

▲ **Figure 3**   **A** Beds of sedimentary rocks.
B Rock weaknesses – bedding planes, joints and faults. These are the first places to be attacked by weathering and erosion.

Metamorphic rocks are those rocks that have been changed. They begin as igneous or sedimentary rocks, but are then changed by heat and pressure. This happens, for example, along destructive plate boundaries and faults. Limestone is changed by heat and pressure into *marble*, which is one type of metamorphic rock. Marble is harder than limestone, which makes it a good building stone. It is used a lot in public buildings in Mediterranean countries such as Italy. Clay is changed into *slate* by heat and pressure. Slate splits easily into sheets; it used to be the main roofing material in the UK. The Lake District and North Wales are famous for their slate.

▲ **Figure 2** Land's End is made of granite. Notice the many vertical weaknesses in the rock, known as joints.

Distribution of rock types within the UK

We often divide the British Isles into Highland Britain and Lowland Britain (**Figure 4**). The dividing line is the Tees–Exe line, which runs from the mouth of the River Tees in north-east England to the mouth of the River Exe in south-west England. Old hard rocks, such as granite, are found north and west of this line in Highland Britain. Younger and softer rocks, such as chalk and clay, are found south and east of the line in Lowland Britain.

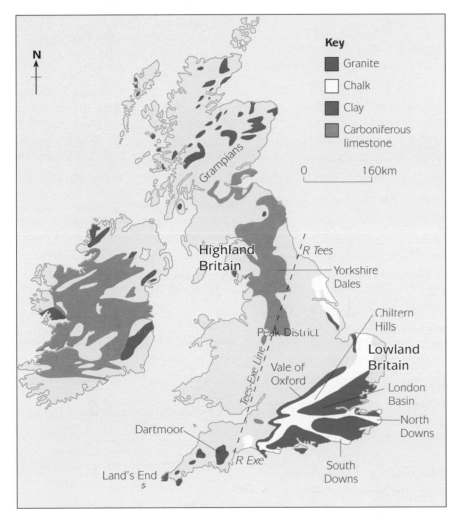

Key

- ■ Granite
- □ Chalk
- ■ Clay
- ■ Carboniferous limestone

0 ——— 160km

N

Grampians

Highland Britain

R Tees

Yorkshire Dales

Chiltern Hills

Peak District

Lowland Britain

Tees–Exe Line

Vale of Oxford

London Basin

North Downs

Dartmoor

R Exe

South Downs

Land's End

▲ **Figure 4** The distribution of four types of rock in the British Isles.

Activities

1 Use **Figure 4** and an outline map of the British Isles. On the outline map of the British Isles, shade and name two areas covered by each of the following rock types:
- granite
- Carboniferous limestone
- chalk
- clay.

Add a key for the shading used for the rock types.

2 Make a table like the one at the bottom of the page. Fill it in for igneous and sedimentary using information from pages 20 and 21.

3 a With the help of **Figure 3B**, draw a diagram to show the three types of rock weaknesses.

  b Write out the sentences below. Fill the gaps using either **vertical** or **horizontal**.

Bedding planes are .... weaknesses between layers of sedimentary rocks. Joints are .... weaknesses within layers of sedimentary rock. The main difference between them is that bedding planes are .... weaknesses and joints are .... weaknesses. Faults are .... weaknesses between different layers of rock. Faults cause the layers of rock to move up or down in a .... direction.

For Activity 2	Metamorphic	Igneous	Sedimentary
Definition	Rocks that have been changed		
Examples of types of rock	Marble and slate		
Where they were formed	Along destructive plate boundaries and faults		
How they were formed	By heat and pressure changing igneous and sedimentary rocks		
Main areas where rocks occur in the UK	In Highland Britain, e.g. slate outcrops in the Lake District and North Wales		

Granite

Landscape features

In south-west England, upland areas such as Dartmoor are formed by outcrops of granite rocks. Granite also forms rocky coastlines, such as at Land's End.

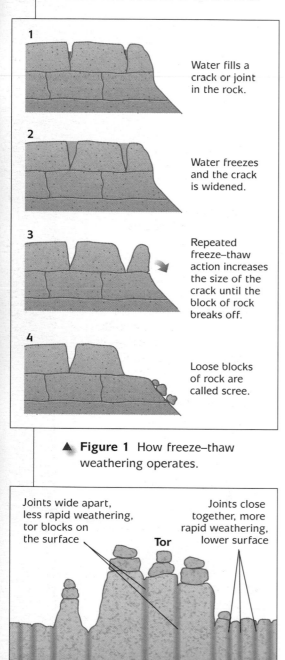

1 Water fills a crack or joint in the rock.

2 Water freezes and the crack is widened.

3 Repeated freeze–thaw action increases the size of the crack until the block of rock breaks off.

4 Loose blocks of rock are called scree.

▲ **Figure 1** How freeze–thaw weathering operates.

Joints wide apart, less rapid weathering, tor blocks on the surface

Tor

Joints close together, more rapid weathering, lower surface

▲ **Figure 2** Effects of joints upon tor formation.

The main features of granite scenery include:

- flat-topped moorlands with frequent rock outcrops
- blocks of rock called **tors** (**Figure 3**) – tors are from five to ten metres high and surrounded by smaller pieces of rock
- many marshes and bogs on the moorlands
- deep and steep sided V-shaped valleys cut by rivers, e.g. the River Dart
- steep coastal cliffs, e.g. at Land's End (**Figure 2** on page 20).

Granite is a hard rock, which resists erosion. This is why it forms upland areas inland and high cliffs along the coast. It is also an impermeable rock; it does not allow water to pass through it easily. This explains why there are so many rivers and areas of standing water on the surface.

Formation of tors

The blocks of rock that form tors are higher than the rocks around them. They have not been weathered and worn away as quickly. The reason for this is shown in **Figure 2**. Where tors occur, the joints in the granite are wider apart. **Freeze–thaw** weathering (**Figure 1**) is most rapid where joints are close together, because there are more cracks in the rock that can be filled with water. Each time the water freezes and expands within a joint, more pressure is put on the surrounding rock and the crack widens. On the tor, where there are fewer joints, it takes longer for the blocks of rock to be broken off. The tors are left as higher blocks of rock when the rocks around them are worn away.

Land uses

Land uses change as you go from upland to lowland. On the uplands a lot of the land is useless because it is bog, marsh and moorland. In some places there are reservoirs for water storage. Often there is nothing better than poor grazing land suitable only for sheep and cattle, and, on Dartmoor, for ponies as well. This is because the soils are acid and infertile. Towards the lowlands pastures improve to allow grazing by dairy cattle and more trees grow on the valley sides.

Economic uses

Granite makes a fine building stone. Aberdeen is known as 'the granite city' since so many of its older buildings are made from local supplies of stone. Granite is often used for headstones in graveyards because it weathers slowly. When chemical weathering attacks granite rock, china clay is formed. There are large deposits in Cornwall, such as near St Austell. Although china clay is best known for making pottery, it is also used in the manufacture of paper and it is an ingredient in paint, toothpaste, skin creams and many other products. Therefore it has many economic uses.

Activities

1 a Draw labelled diagrams to show what happens in freeze–thaw weathering.
b Why does it take place more quickly in rocks with many weaknesses?

2 a What is a tor?
b Name one example.
c Using **Figure 2**, explain why tors form where joints are wide apart.

▲ **Figure 3** Bowerman's Nose, a tor on Dartmoor.

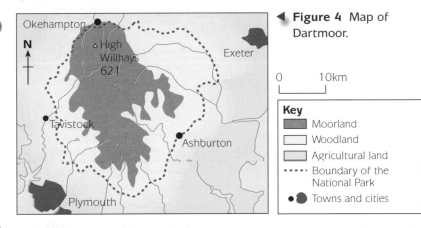

◄ **Figure 4** Map of Dartmoor.

0   10km

Key
- Moorland
- Woodland
- Agricultural land
- - - - - Boundary of the National Park
- ● ◖ Towns and cities

ℹ Dartmoor

- Dartmoor has a high rainfall and is known for its mists and fogs
- Much of the land is covered by heather
- The many boggy areas contain a rich variety of plant life
- Dartmoor ponies live here
- The central upland block was enclosed within a National Park in 1951
- The Park covers almost 100 000 hectares and over 30 000 people live inside it
- Up to 8 million people visit or pass through the Park each year
- Most of the towns, such as Tavistock, Okehampton and Ashburton, are located around the edges of the central block
- Places popular with visitors include Buckfast Abbey, Hay Tor, Becky Falls and Lydford Gorge
- Some of the remains of old woodlands have been preserved as natural nature reserves.

Activities

1 Draw a frame the same size as **Figure 3**. Draw a sketch from the photograph. On your sketch:
   - name and label the tor
   - label the different land uses between the top of the upland and the lower land.

2 Answer the questions below using information from **Figure 4**.
   a Name the highest point on Dartmoor and give its height.
   b (i) State the two main land uses within the Dartmoor National Park.
   (ii) What is different about the locations of these two land uses?
   (iii) State the main land use found outside the National Park.

3 On one side of A4 paper put the title 'Tourism on Dartmoor'. Design an information sheet that can be used as a short case study. Make it look as interesting as possible by using a mixture of maps, sketches, diagrams and written information.
   a Put a sub-heading 'Information about Dartmoor'. Give information about Dartmoor, such as
      - when it became a National Park
      - how large it is
      - how many people visit it each year
      - where it is located (e.g. draw a simple sketch map).
   b Put a new heading 'What visitors go to see'. Make a list of what visitors go to see. Show some of the attractions on sketches and diagrams (tourist brochures of Dartmoor might help).

Case Study – A granite landscape: Dartmoor

Carboniferous limestone

You can see limestone landforms best in two of the English National Parks:

- the Yorkshire Dales around Malham and Ingleton
- the Peak District near Castleton in Derbyshire.

Landscape features

Carboniferous limestone is affected by chemical weathering to produce distinctive landforms both above and below ground. When many landforms are found together they form **karst scenery** (Figure 2).

Above the ground

Limestone pavements are flat surfaces of bare rock broken up into separate blocks. Look back at the photograph on page 19. The flat surfaces of the blocks on which the people are walking are **clints**. The gaps between the blocks that can be seen in the middle and front of the photograph are **grykes**. **Swallow holes** (**Figure 1**) are places where surface rivers disappear underground. **Gorges** are narrow, steep-sided valleys where cave and cavern roofs have fallen in (**Figure 3**).

Below the ground

Caves are common as also are **caverns**. Caves are narrow passageways through the rock, whereas caverns are large chambers. **Stalactites** hang down from the roofs like long icicles. **Stalagmites** are thicker columns that build up from the floor. Sometimes they meet to form **pillars** of limestone. They all form fantastic shapes that visitors go to see in caves that are open to the public.

▲ **Figure 1** The swallow hole at Gaping Gill.

Fell Beck is the surface stream (bottom right) seen disappearing underground down the swallow hole. It drops 110m as a waterfall into a giant chamber more than 150m long and 30m high (i.e. large enough to fit several cathedrals into it). The stream flows several kilometres underground through a complex system of caves before it re-appears on the surface through Ingleton Cave and forms Clapham Beck.

Limestone solution

This is a type of chemical weathering. It leads to the formation of all these limestone landforms. Rain water is slightly acidic, because it combines with carbon dioxide in the atmosphere to form carbonic acid. This acid slowly dissolves the limestone. The limestone is changed from calcium carbonate into calcium bicarbonate, which can be washed away by water flowing through the limestone. Limestone rocks have many lines of weakness (both bedding planes and joints) which speed up the rate of chemical weathering. As rivers flow underground, they widen the lines of weakness making swallow holes, caves and caverns wider and deeper. Lime water drips from the roofs of caves and caverns to form the stalactites, stalagmites and pillars that make caves such weird and wonderful places to visit.

Sometimes the holes, formed by solution and by water flowing underground, become so large that the roof collapses. When the roof of a big cavern falls in, a limestone gorge is formed. An example is Gordale near Malham, where the blocks which formed the cavern roof can be seen left in a pile on the floor (**Figure 3**).

Land uses

In most places limestone soils are too dry and too thin to be used for crop growing. Keeping sheep is the main type of farming. Sheep like the short, turf-like grass which covers limestone rocks. Only on surrounding lowlands, where soils are deeper, does cattle farming become more

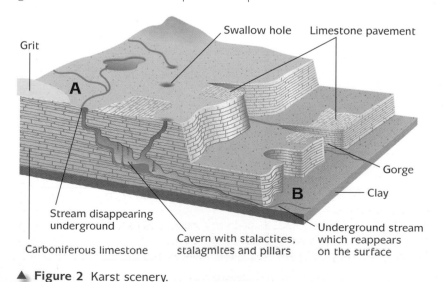

Grit

Swallow hole   Limestone pavement

A

Stream disappearing underground

Carboniferous limestone

Cavern with stalactites, stalagmites and pillars

B

Gorge

Clay

Underground stream which reappears on the surface

▲ **Figure 2** Karst scenery.

◀ **Figure 3** The gorge at Gordale, where the roof of a cavern has fallen in. Notice the narrow top which overhangs and the pile of rocks on the floor.

important. Limestone landforms, especially the underground ones, attract many visitors. Tourism increases the number of jobs in the villages, such as working in shops, running bed and breakfast places or making craft goods for tourists to buy. Some farmers make extra money by using fields as camping and caravan sites (**Figure 1** on page 28).

Economic uses

Limestone is of great economic importance. It is widely used as building stone. It is easier to work than a hard rock like granite. Limestone has been used in many well known buildings, such as St Paul's Cathedral, the Houses of Parliament and the front of Buckingham Palace. It is also used for making cement. Farmers spread lime on their fields as a fertilizer. Limestone is used as a cleanser in the steel industry; it is also used to absorb harmful sulphur dioxide fumes from coal-fired power stations. With so many uses, it is not surprising that there are many quarries in limestone areas. Some visitors feel that these quarries ruin the scenery and natural beauty of the National Parks (pages 28–29).

Activities

1 a Draw a diagram to show karst scenery.
Label the following four landforms on your diagram:
- limestone pavement
- swallow hole
- cavern
- gorge.

b Make a large table like the one below and fill it in.

	Limestone pavement	Swallow hole	Cavern	Gorge
Name of an example				
Describe what it looks like				
Explain how it was formed				

2 a Look at **Figure 2**. Write out the passage below about the course of the stream from A to B.
Use each of the following terms once to fill in the gaps.
clay   grit   joints and bedding planes   limestone   stalactites   stalagmites   swallow hole   water through it

At first near A the stream flows on the surface above the rock called .... This is an impermeable rock, which will not allow ....; this is why the stream flows on the surface. When the stream reaches the .... rock, it disappears underground because this is a permeable rock, full of holes and lines of weakness such as .... The stream goes underground down a .... It flows through caves and caverns, in which there are .... hanging from the roof, ... growing up from the ground and pillars of lime. When the stream reaches the .... rock, which is impermeable, it flows on the surface again towards point B.

b Draw a diagram to show a larger version of the cavern on **Figure 2**. Label its main features.

3 a What is limestone solution?
b How does it lead to the formation of landforms of Carboniferous limestone?

4 a Make a table like the one below using about half a page.

	Carboniferous limestone	Granite
Main landscape features		
Types of weathering which forms them		
Main land uses		
Main economic uses		

b **(i)** State one way in which the land uses for limestone and granite are the same.
(ii) Why are they the same? Explain as fully as you can.
(iii) State one way in which they are different.
(iv) Why are they different? Explain as fully as you can.

Chalk and clay

Landscape features

The **chalk escarpment** is the main landform. It has two parts – the scarp slope, which is steep, and the dip slope, which is more gentle. The other landscape features include:

- gently rolling hills and rounded summits
- few (if any) surface rivers
- steep sided, V-shaped **dry valleys** cut into the dip slope (**Figure 2**).

Chalk outcrops along the coast often lead to high cliffs such as the famous 'white cliffs of Dover' and prominent headlands, such as Beachy Head in Sussex and Flamborough Head in Yorkshire. Erosion around headlands leads to the formation of caves, arches and stacks (look at **Figure 5** on page 65).

The **clay vale** is quite different. It is a wide and often totally flat area of land. There are plenty of rivers and streams, which meander across the flat floors of the clay vales. Along the coast clay forms weak cliffs. These soon collapse, because they are eroded quickly by the waves.

▲ **Figure 1** Chalk and clay meet at the foot of the South Downs near Fulking. *In many places in England chalk (on the right) and clay (on the left) outcrop next to one another. Together they form a distinctive but contrasting landscape of chalk escarpment and clay vale. Chalk and clay are both sedimentary rocks and only outcrop in Lowland Britain; they have little else in common.*

▲ **Figure 2** Devil's Dyke dry valley east of Fulking.

Formation of the chalk escarpment

Look at **Figure 3A**.

- Both chalk and clay rocks outcrop on the surface.
- The beds of rock lie at an angle to the surface.

Look at **Figure 3B**.

- The clay is softer than the chalk and is eroded more quickly.
- A clay vale is formed.
- The chalk resists erosion better than the clay.
- A high escarpment is left standing up above the clay vale.

Land uses

The main land use on the chalk escarpment is pasture. The short but rich turf is good for sheep grazing and training racehorses. On the chalk Downs there are famous racecourses, such as Epsom and Goodwood. The main land use on clay vale is pasture also. The soils are too wet and heavy to plough and grow crops. The grass grows longer than that on the chalk and is more likely to be grazed by cattle, especially dairy cattle.

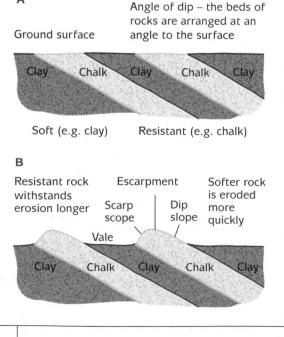

▲ **Figure 3 A:** Rock arrangement needed for the formation of an escarpment. **B:** Formation of an escarpment.

Some of the earliest humans to reach the British Isles settled on the chalk escarpments. Names and symbols showing historical sites are common on OS maps of chalk areas.

Look at **Figure 4**. On the chalk south of the village of Fulking, 'Tumulus' (which is a burial mound) is written on the map in the old style of writing. 'Motte & Bailey' and 'Fort' show old defences. Where grid lines 21 and 10 meet 'Cultivation Terraces' are named. The chalk escarpments were drier and easier for people to travel across than the clay vales, which were marshy. You could see a long way, which was useful for defence. The chalk contained flint, which was used for tools and weapons by early settlers.

The main problem for settlement in areas of chalk was shortage of water. **Springs** form at the junction of the chalk and clay; water seeping down through the spaces in the porous chalk meets the impermeable clay (which does not allow water through) and reappears on the surface as a flow of water. Notice that in square 2411 on **Figure 4** a stream begins. Settlements grew along the spring line and Fulking is a classic example.

Economic uses

Chalk with flint provides an attractive and strong building material. Chalk has many of the same economic uses as the limestone, such as in the manufacture of cement. The underground stores of water, known as **aquifers**, are widely used for water supply in south-east England. Clay, taken from pits, is a raw material for making bricks.

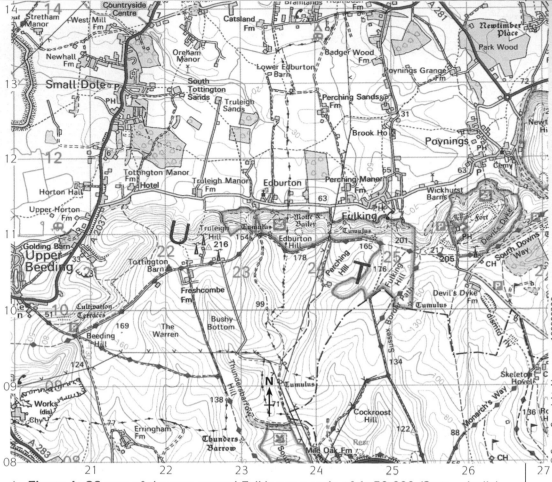

▲ **Figure 4** OS map of the area around Fulking at a scale of 1: 50 000 (2cm = 1mile).

© Crown Copyright. Licence no. 100000230

Activities

1 a Draw a frame the same size as **Figure 1**.
      (i) Make a sketch based on what can be seen on **Figure 1**.
      (ii) Add the following labels to your sketch.
      flat clay vale   steep scarp slope   dip slope
   b (i) Draw a labelled cross-section of the valley shown in **Figure 2**.
      (ii) Why does a road run along the bottom instead of a river?
   c Explain why (i) clay forms low vales   (ii) chalk forms high escarpments.

2 Look at the OS map in **Figure 4**. The are many differences between the clay vale north of Fulking and the chalk escarpment south of Fulking. Make a table like the one below (covering about half a page). Fill it in using information from the map.

	Clay vale north of Fulking	Chalk escarpment south of Fulking
Relief: heights, shape of land		
Drainage: surface streams present? number and density?		
Land uses: woodland, farms, settlements and their size		
Economic uses: quarries for building materials		

Quarrying

Quarrying is an old activity. Early settlers quarried stone for building shelters, defensive works and burial mounds. Dry-stone walls in the Yorkshire Dales National Park show that quarrying limestone has been an important activity for hundreds of years (**Figure 1**).

What happens in quarrying?

There are several stages:

A **Preparing the site** After being given planning permission, giant earth-moving equipment is brought in. All the topsoil is scraped off and piled up.

B **Extracting the rock** Explosives are placed in holes drilled into the rock face. Thousands of tonnes of rock come crashing down. This is cleared by giant diggers.

C **Treating the rock** Giant crushers break down the rock into smaller pieces. Rocks are sorted into pieces of different sizes before being sent away to be used. In some quarries the rock is processed into a manufactured product on site; for example, chalk and limestone are often made into cement on site to avoid costs of transport for what are bulky raw materials. Waste materials are dumped.

D **Transporting the rock** For most quarry owners, the rock is transported by road.

E **Cleaning up the site** After quarrying has finished there are various options:

- The quarry may be used as a landfill site for rubbish from urban areas.
- Other quarries are landscaped and used for recreation as in the Eden Centre near St Austell in Cornwall.
- Some are abandoned and left as scars on the landscape.

Some of the advantages associated with quarrying rocks are given in **Figure 2**.

Problems caused by quarrying

These are shown in **Figure 3**. Planners and Local Authorities have an important role to play in preventing the companies that operate the quarries from thinking only of how to make the largest profits.

▲ **Figure 1** Dry-stone walls, made of limestone, on a farm in the Yorkshire Dales.

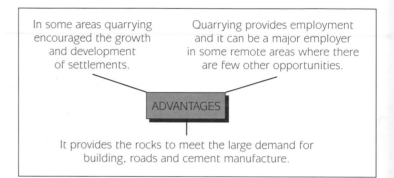

In some areas quarrying encouraged the growth and development of settlements.

Quarrying provides employment and it can be a major employer in some remote areas where there are few other opportunities.

ADVANTAGES

It provides the rocks to meet the large demand for building, roads and cement manufacture.

▲ **Figure 2** Positive impacts of quarrying.

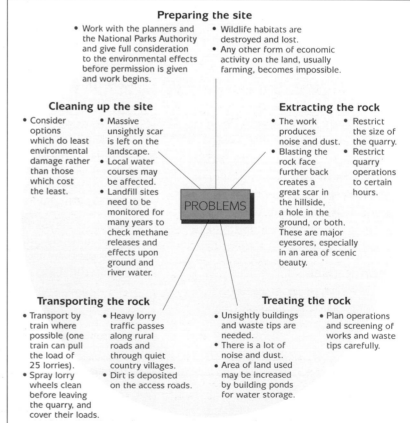

Preparing the site
- Work with the planners and the National Parks Authority and give full consideration to the environmental effects before permission is given and work begins.
- Wildlife habitats are destroyed and lost.
- Any other form of economic activity on the land, usually farming, becomes impossible.

Cleaning up the site
- Consider options which do least environmental damage rather than those which cost the least.
- Massive unsightly scar is left on the landscape.
- Local water courses may be affected.
- Landfill sites need to be monitored for many years to check methane releases and effects upon ground and river water.

PROBLEMS

Extracting the rock
- The work produces noise and dust.
- Blasting the rock face further back creates a great scar in the hillside, a hole in the ground, or both. These are major eyesores, especially in an area of scenic beauty.
- Restrict the size of the quarry.
- Restrict quarry operations to certain hours.

Transporting the rock
- Transport by train where possible (one train can pull the load of 25 lorries).
- Spray lorry wheels clean before leaving the quarry, and cover their loads.
- Heavy lorry traffic passes along rural roads and through quiet country villages.
- Dirt is deposited on the access roads.

Treating the rock
- Unsightly buildings and waste tips are needed.
- There is a lot of noise and dust.
- Area of land used may be increased by building ponds for water storage.
- Plan operations and screening of works and waste tips carefully.

▲ **Figure 3** Negative impacts (the problems) are given in red. Ways of reducing the problems are given in blue.

Limestone quarrying and Hope cement works in the Peak District

The Hope quarry and cement works is the largest single employer of workers in the Castleton area (**Figures 4** and **5**). Some 300 people are employed, nearly all of whom live locally. Without the works, many more people would be forced to commute by road to towns outside the National Park, particularly Manchester and Sheffield. The quarry covers a large area and smoke pours out of its chimney. This means that there is a problem, because thousands of tourists visit the Castleton area every year. The limestone caverns are a big attraction.

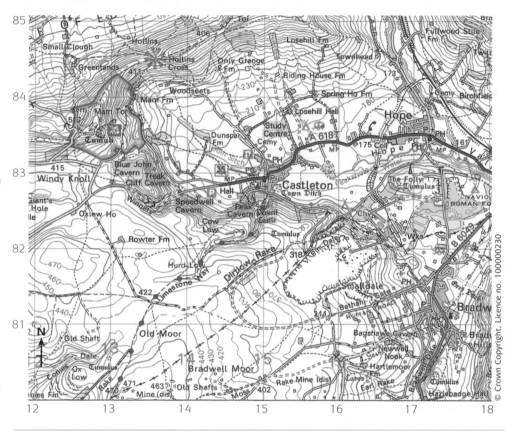

© Crown Copyright, Licence no. 100000230

▲ **Figure 5** Hope quarry and cement works.

◀ **Figure 4** OS map of Castleton at a scale of 1: 50 000 (2cm = 1km).

Case Study – Peak District National Park near Castleton

Activities

1 At the top of a page put a heading 'Quarrying'. Complete the table below to show what happens in quarrying and the problems caused by quarrying. Use the headings A-E on page 28. A has been filled in to show you what to do.

2 Look at the OS map in **Figure 4**.
  a Name three places for tourists to visit near Castleton.
  b State map evidence which suggests that many tourists travel here by car.
  c In square 1581 there is a limestone quarry.
  (i) Measure the length and width of the quarry.
  (ii) Why is the quarry badly affecting the landscape?

3 People living in Castleton have differing views about both the quarry and tourist visitors.
  a Suggest why some people in Castleton like the quarry and cement works while others do not.
  b Suggest why some like the tourist visitors and some do not.

	Type of work	Problems	Reducing the problem
A Preparing the site	Topsoil scraped off by giant earth-moving machines	Wildlife habitats and farmland destroyed	Think about the effects on the environment before starting the work
B Extracting the rock			

Weathering

Weathering is the breakdown of rock at or near the surface caused by the weather, such as by changes in temperature. The rocks are broken down where they lie, without any movement.

There are two main types of weathering:

1 Physical weathering. The rock is broken up without any change in the minerals that form the rock. In cold climates the most widespread type is freeze–thaw (**Figure 1** on page 22). Temperatures must change above and below freezing point many times for this to happen. The pieces of rock that are broken off have sharp edges and form scree. Scree slopes can be seen below rock outcrops in all upland areas (**Figure 1**).

▲ **Figure 1**   Scree slopes on the side of Wast Water in the Lake District.

2 Chemical weathering. The rock is broken up after the minerals that form the rock have been changed. Granite is one example of a rock that can be broken up by chemical weathering. After heating and cooling, feldspar, one of the minerals which make up granite, is changed into clay minerals such as kaolin (china clay). China clay has many economic uses (page 22).

Another example of a rock affected by chemical weathering is limestone. The distinctive landforms in areas of Carboniferous limestone, both above and below the ground, are formed by **limestone solution** (pages 24–25).

ℹ **Limestone solution**

Rain water mixes with carbon dioxide in the atmosphere

↓

Carbonic acid is formed

↓

Carbonic acid attacks the limestone (calcium carbonate)

↓

The limestone (calcium carbonate) is changed into calcium bicarbonate

↓

Calcium bicarbonate is soluble – it dissolves in water and is washed away

---

Activities

1a Define 'weathering'.
  b State one similarity and one difference between physical and chemical weathering.

2a Draw a labelled sketch of **Figure 1** to show the scree slopes.
  b Using this page and page 22, explain how scree is formed.

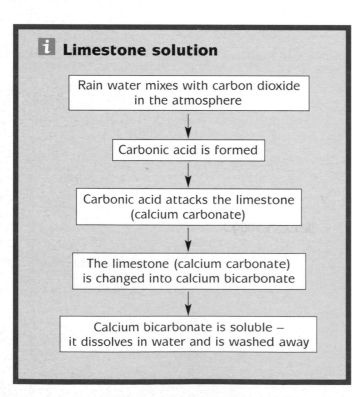

Chapter 3

River landscapes and processes

The Iguaçu Falls on the border between Brazil and Argentina are a stunning example of the erosive power of rivers.

Key Ideas

The Earth's crust is modified by river processes:
- the processes of erosion help to create waterfalls and gorges
- rivers transport and deposit material, helping to form flood plains, deltas and leveés
- meanders and ox-bow lakes are formed by both erosion and deposition.

Causes and effects of flooding:
- river flooding has different causes
- the effects of flooding in LEDCs and MEDCs can be devastating
- there are different ways of preventing and reducing flood damage.

River basins

Rivers begin in upland areas and flow downhill, becoming wider and deeper, until they enter the sea. Where a river begins is called the **source** and where it ends is the **mouth**. Along a river's journey to the sea other smaller rivers called **tributaries** may join the main river at a **confluence**. A river and its tributaries obtain their water from the surrounding land. The area drained by a river and its tributaries is called the **drainage basin** (**Figure 1**). The boundary of the drainage basin is called the **watershed** and it is usually a ridge of high land.

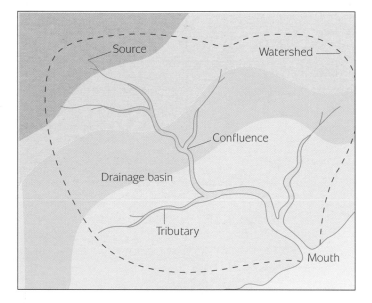

▲ **Figure 1** The drainage basin of a river.

Activity

Match the terms in **Figure 1** to the following definitions:

Where a river begins is called the _upper course_ .

A small river joining a larger river is called a _____ .

Where the two rivers join is called the _____ .

Where a river flows into the sea is called the _____ .

The area drained by a river is called the _____ .

The 'line' that separates two drainage basins is called the _____ .

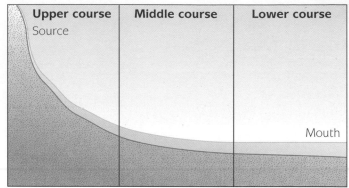

Upper course Source	Middle course	Lower course
		Mouth

▲ **Figure 2** The long profile of a river.

A river flows downhill from its source in a highland area to its mouth, where it enters the sea. As you move downstream there are changes in:

- the gradient (slope) of the long profile
- the river channel
- the valley cross-section.

The long profile of a river is the shape of the land from its source to its mouth. In the upper course (**Figure 2**) the river has a steeper gradient. The gradient becomes less through the middle and lower courses. In the lower course the valley is almost flat.

The river flows in a **channel** unless it floods and spills onto the land either side. The size and shape of the river channel also changes as the water flows downstream (**Figure 3**). The channel becomes deeper and wider.

A river flows in a valley and the shape of the cross-section of the valley changes downstream. A cross-section shows the valley as if it has been cut in half. Look at the cross sections in **Figure 3**. Notice how the cross-section in the upper course has a V shape. In the middle course there is more of a flat valley floor and in the lower course the valley is very wide with gentle valley sides.

Erosion

The changes in a river and its valley as it flows towards the sea are caused by changes in a river's energy. In the upper course the river has a lot of energy and it uses this to erode downwards – vertical erosion. This causes the valley to be V shaped. Lower down the river erodes more sideways – lateral erosion. This makes the valley wider.

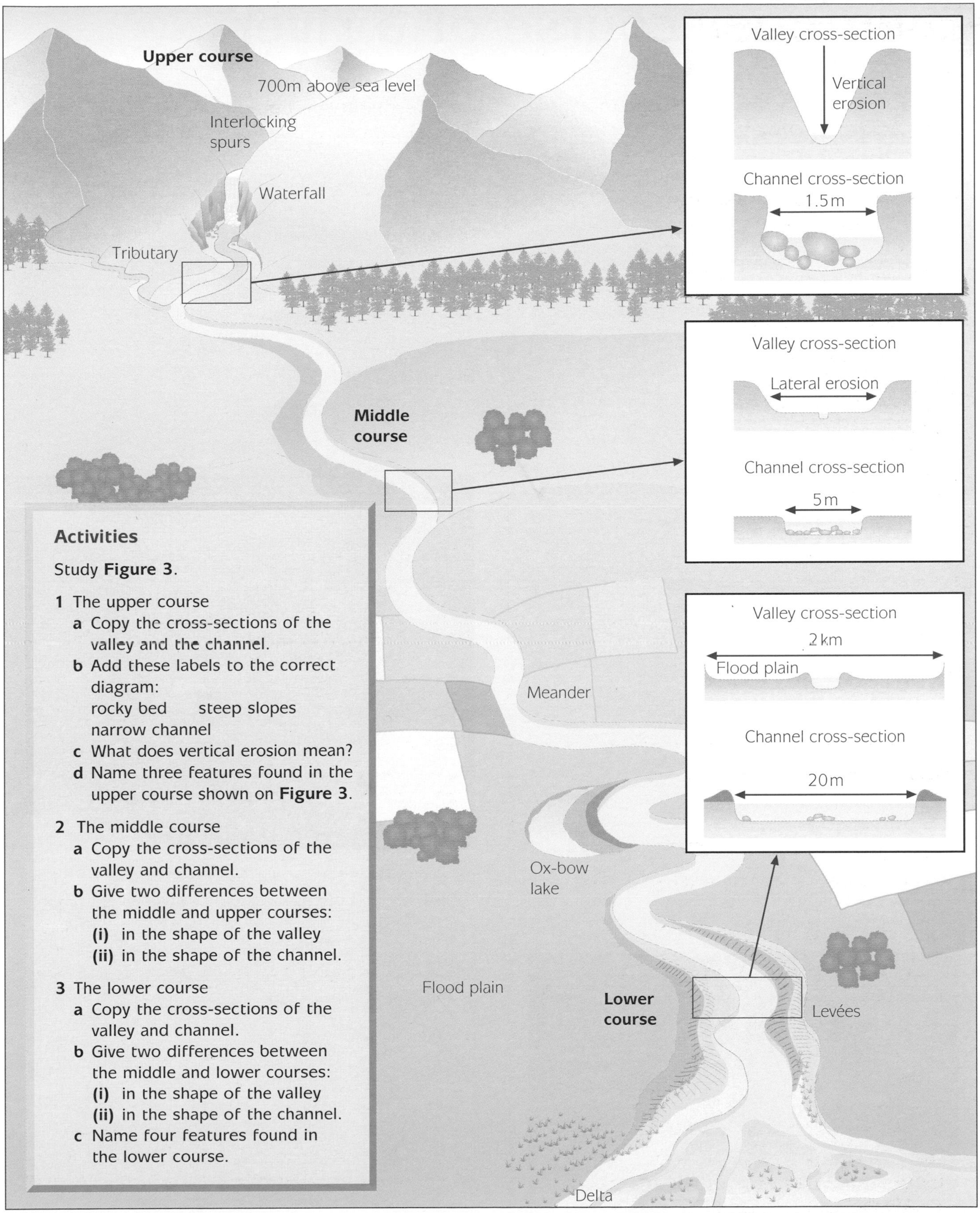
Upper course
700m above sea level
Interlocking spurs
Waterfall
Tributary
Valley cross-section
Vertical erosion
Channel cross-section
1.5m
Middle course
Valley cross-section
Lateral erosion
Channel cross-section
5m
Meander
Valley cross-section
2km
Flood plain
Channel cross-section
20m
Ox-bow lake
Flood plain
Lower course
Levées
Delta

Activities

Study **Figure 3**.

1 The upper course
  a Copy the cross-sections of the valley and the channel.
  b Add these labels to the correct diagram:
  rocky bed   steep slopes
  narrow channel
  c What does vertical erosion mean?
  d Name three features found in the upper course shown on **Figure 3**.

2 The middle course
  a Copy the cross-sections of the valley and channel.
  b Give two differences between the middle and upper courses:
  (i) in the shape of the valley
  (ii) in the shape of the channel.

3 The lower course
  a Copy the cross-sections of the valley and channel.
  b Give two differences between the middle and lower courses:
  (i) in the shape of the valley
  (ii) in the shape of the channel.
  c Name four features found in the lower course.

▲ **Figure 3** The changes downstream in a river valley.

The upper course of a river

In the upper course of a river, erosion is the dominant process. A river may erode by one of the four processes in **Figure 1**.

Hydraulic power

This is the force of the water on the bed and banks of the river. It is particularly powerful when the river is in flood. The force of the water removes material from the bed and banks of the river.

Corrasion

When the river is particularly full pebbles and boulders are carried along by the water. These rub against the bed and banks of the river and wear them away. This process is also called abrasion. ✓

Corrosion

River water sometimes causes some rocks to slowly dissolve (for example, limestone dissolves in slightly acid water and is carried away in solution (as a liquid) as calcium hydrogen carbonate).

Attrition

The pebbles and small rocks being carried by the river – the load – collide and rub against each other, breaking up into smaller and smaller pieces. The rough edges become smooth, forming smaller, rounded material. Eventually the particles are reduced to sand and silt-sized particles. ✓

▲ **Figure 1** Processes of erosion.

Landforms in the upper course

Typical features of a river valley in the upper course include:

- a steep-sided and narrow valley – **V-shaped valley** – formed by the river cutting downwards in the upper course (vertical erosion)
- **interlocking spurs** where the river winds around areas of hard rock (not to be confused with meanders)
- narrow and shallow river channel
- rocky river bed with large boulders
- steep valley gradient
- **waterfalls and rapids**
- clear water.

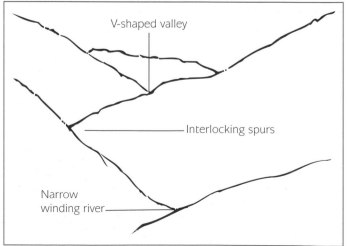

V-shaped valley

Interlocking spurs

Narrow winding river

▲ **Figure 2** A V-shaped valley with interlocking spurs.

▲ **Figure 3** Niagara Falls, on the border between Canada and the USA.

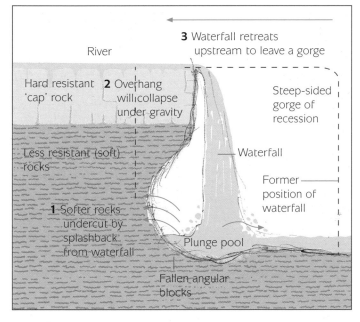

▲ **Figure 4** The formation of a waterfall.

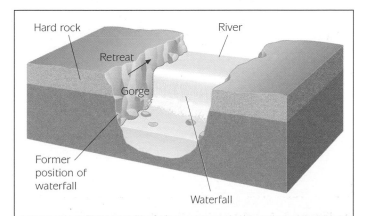

◄ **Figure 5** Formation of a gorge of recession.

Waterfalls and gorges

The main features of a waterfall are:

- a steep drop in the river called a high head of water
- a plunge pool at the base
- hard, resistant rocks at the top – the cap rock
- softer rocks below that are undercut.

Waterfalls and gorges are formed over a very long time in the following way:

1 A band of hard rock lies on top of softer rocks.

2 The softer rock is eroded more quickly, undercutting the hard rock.

3 The hard rock overhangs until eventually it collapses.

4 The collapse adds large blocks of rock to the base of the waterfall.

5 The base of the waterfall is eroded to form a plunge pool.

6 The softer rock continues to be eroded and the overhanging rock collapses again causing the waterfall to retreat.

7 The process is repeated again and again and the gradual retreat of the waterfall forms a steep-sided gorge of recession.

Activities

1 Use the photographs on these pages to draw labelled sketches.
  a Draw a frame about the same size as each photograph.
  b Sketch in the main features shown.
  c Label your diagram as fully as you can.
  d Colour in your sketch and give it a title.

2 Give three features of a waterfall.

3 Draw a cross-section of a waterfall and label the features.

4 Rearrange the following statements to explain how a waterfall is formed:
  - The hard rock overhangs until eventually it collapses
  - The retreat forms a steep-sided gorge of recession
  - A band of hard rock lies on top of softer rocks
  - The repeated collapse causes the waterfall to retreat
  - The base of the waterfall is eroded to form a plunge pool
  - The collapse adds large blocks of rock to the base of the waterfall
  - The softer rock is eroded more quickly, undercutting the hard rock.

The middle course of a river

As the river flows downstream it leaves the steep upper course. The gradient becomes less steep as it enters the middle course. Here the river:

- begins to erode sideways (or laterally) rather than downwards
- forms meanders
- creates a wider valley
- begins to transport more material.

The river transports material in four ways that are shown in **Figure 1**. How much material a river transports depends upon:

- the volume of water – the greater the volume the more it can carry
- the velocity or speed – the greater the velocity the more load it can carry
- the rock type – the softer the rock the more easily it can be eroded.

Traction – large boulders roll along the river bed

Saltation – smaller pebbles are bounced along the river bed, picked up and then dropped as the flow of the river changes

Suspension – the finer sand and silt-sized particles are carried along in the flow, giving the river a brown appearance

Solution – minerals, such as limestone and chalk, are dissolved in the water and carried along in the flow, although they cannot be seen

▲ **Figure 1** Transporting the river's load.

Meanders

A meander is a bend in the river (**Figure 2**). The water is deeper and flows faster on the outside bend of a meander. The force of the water erodes the outside bend forming a **river cliff**. The water is shallower and flows more slowly on the inside bend. Sand and gravel are deposited on the inside bend to form a **slip-off slope** (**Figure 3**).

As the meander erodes the outside bend the bends get wider. This lateral or sideways erosion widens the valley floor. The meanders also slowly migrate (spread out) downstream creating a line of river cliffs at the edge of the valley floor.

▲ **Figure 2** The features of a meander.

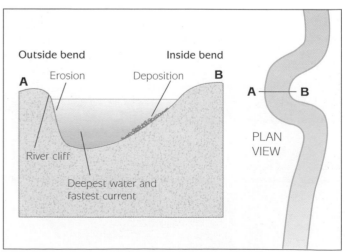

▲ **Figure 3** A cross-section through a meander.

The lower course of a river

In the lower course the river channel is wider and deeper. The river flows more quickly in this smoother channel than in the upper course. The valley floor, called the flood plain, is wide and flat. The river in the lower course often looks brown because it is carrying a large amount of sand and silt in suspension. Deposition of the sand and silt, called **alluvium**, occurs when:

*   the river slows down, e.g. on the inside bend of a meander
*   there are obstacles to the flow, e.g. a bridge parapet or where the river meets the sea
*   the river level falls, e.g. in the summer during a drought

Ox-bow lakes

Figure 5 shows how an **ox-bow lake** is formed. Hydraulic power and corrasion erode the outside bends of the meander. This makes the neck of the meander narrower. Eventually, often when the river is in flood, the neck is broken through.

This creates a new straight channel. As the river level falls sand and silt are deposited sealing off the ends of the old meander. This forms the ox-bow lake. Eventually the ox-bow lake will dry up to leave a **meander scar**.

The flood plain

The flood plain is the wide, flat area of land either side of a river in its lower course. It is formed by both erosion and deposition.

As a meander migrates and erodes sideways the flood plain is made wider.

When the river floods sand and silt are deposited on the flood plain. Over many years this builds up as a thick layer of alluvium. Deposition on the slip-off slopes of meanders also helps to build up the valley floor.

Activities

1. **a** What do we call the material carried by a river?
    b Draw diagrams and describe the four ways in which a river transports its load.

2. **a** Draw and label a cross-section through a meander.
    b How does the river erode the outside bend of a meander?
    c Explain why a river deposits material on the inside bend of a meander.

3. Copy **Figure 5** and write some notes to explain how an ox-bow lake is formed.

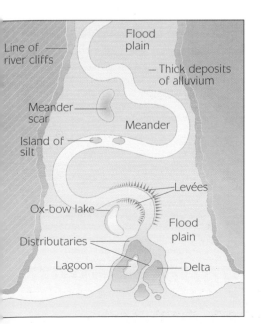

◄ **Figure 4** Features of the flood plain.

Line of river cliffs
Flood plain
Thick deposits of alluvium
Meander scar
Island of silt
Meander
Levées
Ox-bow lake
Flood plain
Distributaries
Lagoon
Delta

▶ **Figure 5** Formation of an ox-bow lake.

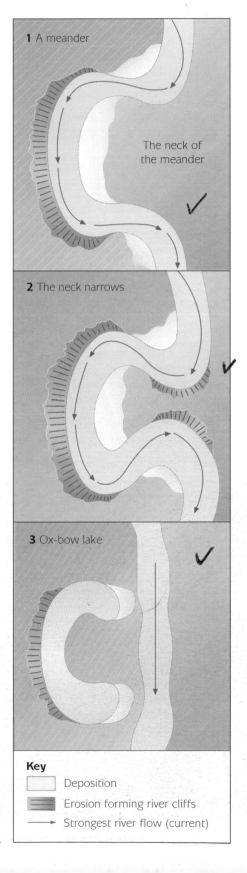

1 A meander

The neck of the meander ✓

2 The neck narrows ✓

3 Ox-bow lake ✓

Key

☐ Deposition

▦ Erosion forming river cliffs

→ Strongest river flow (current)

Levées

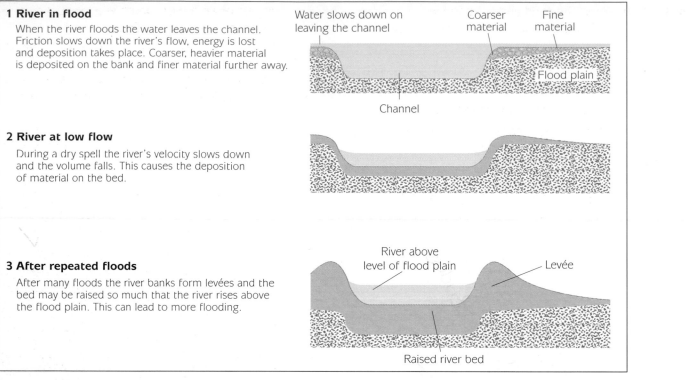

1 River in flood

When the river floods the water leaves the channel. Friction slows down the river's flow, energy is lost and deposition takes place. Coarser, heavier material is deposited on the bank and finer material further away.

Water slows down on leaving the channel

Coarser material

Fine material

Flood plain

Channel

2 River at low flow

During a dry spell the river's velocity slows down and the volume falls. This causes the deposition of material on the bed.

3 After repeated floods

After many floods the river banks form levées and the bed may be raised so much that the river rises above the flood plain. This can lead to more flooding.

River above level of flood plain

Levée

Raised river bed

▲ **Figure 1** The formation of levées.

Levées are high banks of sand and silt along the side of a river (**Figure 1**). They can be several metres higher than the level of the flood plain. They are formed along rivers that:

*   flow slowly

*   carry a large load of sand and silt

*   flood quite frequently.

Along some rivers, such as the Mississippi in the USA, people have raised the height of levées to try to prevent flooding.

The mouth of a river

As a river meets the sea it may flow into a **delta** or an **estuary**.

Deltas

A delta is a flat area of sand and silt built out into the sea. They are often fan-shaped. The delta is formed by river deposition (**Figure 2**). When the river

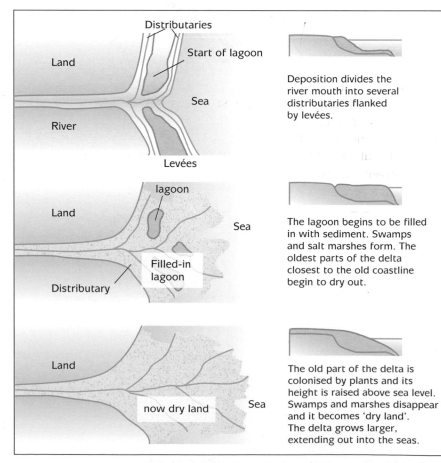

Distributaries

Start of lagoon

Land

Sea

River

Levées

Deposition divides the river mouth into several distributaries flanked by levées.

lagoon

Land

Sea

Filled-in lagoon

Distributary

The lagoon begins to be filled in with sediment. Swamps and salt marshes form. The oldest parts of the delta closest to the old coastline begin to dry out.

Land

now dry land

Sea

The old part of the delta is colonised by plants and its height is raised above sea level. Swamps and marshes disappear and it becomes 'dry land'. The delta grows larger, extending out into the seas.

▲ **Figure 2** The formation of a delta.

meets the sea the sea acts as a break and the river slows down. The salt also causes the sand and silt particles to 'stick together' and they sink more quickly to the seabed.

All rivers are slowed down when entering the sea, which causes some deposition, but deltas do not form at the mouth of all rivers. Special conditions are needed for them to form:

- the river needs to be carrying a large load
- the sea needs to be sheltered without strong tides and currents.

▶ **Figure 3** Satellite photo of the Nile delta.

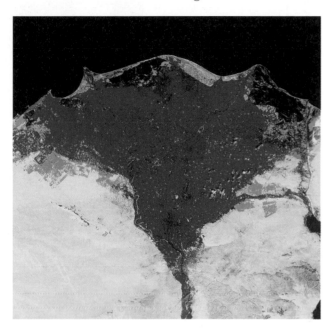

The Rhône Delta

The River Rhône flows into the Mediterranean Sea in southern France. Where it enters the sea the river has created a large delta called the Rhône delta. The river has split into two smaller channels called **distributaries**. There are many islands of silt called **eyots** in the river channels. The river channels have levées along their banks and there are several large lakes called *étangs* with spits and bars.

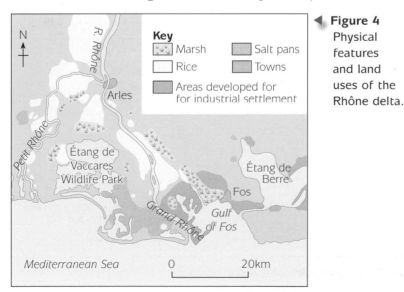

Key
- Marsh
- Rice
- Areas developed for for industrial settlement
- Salt pans
- Towns

R. Rhône
N
Arles
Petit Rhône
Étang de Vaccares Wildlife Park
Grand Rhône
Étang de Berre
Fos
Gulf of Fos
Mediterranean Sea   0   20km

◀ **Figure 4** Physical features and land uses of the Rhône delta.

Estuaries

An estuary is a river mouth in a lowland area where the valley has been drowned by a rise in sea level. The river channel is wide with mud flats and salt marshes. The valley is also wide and quite flat. In Britain examples of estuaries include the rivers Thames, Mersey, Humber and Tees.

▲ **Figure 5** The estuary at Keyhaven and Solent Way.

Activities

1 What is a levée?

2 Draw and label diagrams to show how levées are formed.

3 What is a delta?

4 Give three reasons why a delta has formed at the mouth of the River Rhône.

5 On a sketch map of the Rhône delta:
   a Name the two main distributaries of the River Rhône.
   b Name an example of a lake.
   c Add these labels – spit, salt pan, islands of silt.

6 Draw a sketch of the estuary in **Figure 5**. Label the sketch to show the physical features of the estuary.

The drainage basin of the River Tees

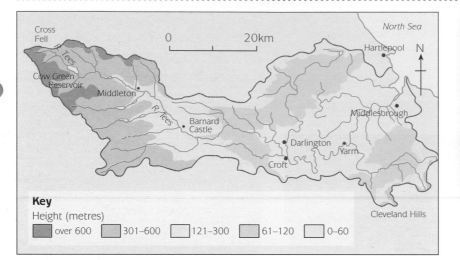

Figure 1 The drainage basin of the River Tees.

Key
Height (metres)
over 600   301–600   121–300   61–120   0–60

Figure 3 High Force on the River Tees.

The River Tees (**Figure 1**) is located in north-east England. Its source area is high in the Pennines in the west. The river flows eastwards into the North Sea.

In the uplands

The source of the River Tees lies on Cross Fell (893m) in the Pennines. Over 2000mm of rain falls in the Pennines each year. Run-off is high because of the impermeable rocks and the steep slopes. **Figure 2** shows the steep-sided V-shaped river valley of the Tees in its upper course. The long profile has a steep gradient. The river bed is rocky and the flow is turbulent. There are many rapids such as those at Low Force and a waterfall at High Force (**Figure 3**).

High Force in grid square 8828 is the highest waterfall in England and has a very deep plunge pool at its base. The cap rock is a very hard resistant rock called **whinstone**. Below the whinstone are softer sandstones and shales. Over hundreds of years the waterfall has retreated to form a gorge.

Figure 2 OS map of part of the upper course of the River Tees at a scale of 1: 50 000 (2cm = 1km).

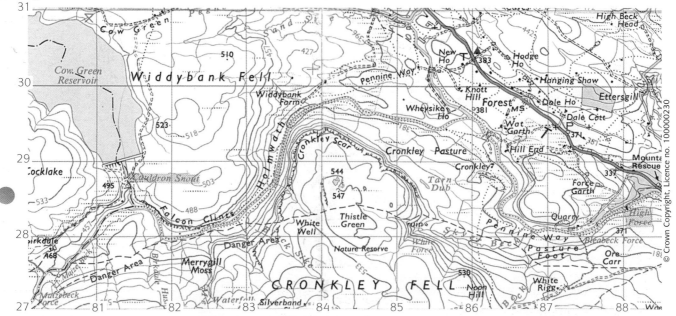

© Crown Copyright. Licence no. 100000230

The River Tees in the lowlands

Moving downstream the valley begins to widen and the river starts to meander (**Figure 4**). There are more bridging points and larger villages and towns, such as Yarm. Nearing the river mouth the river meanders in large loops across its flat flood plain. It is 30km as the crow flies from Darlington to Teesmouth but the river travels 75km. It used to be longer but several of the meanders were cut off in the 19th century to shorten the journey for boats navigating the river up to Stockton and Yarm.

At Teesmouth the river flows into an estuary where there are huge areas of mud flats such as Seal Sands. These are important wildlife areas for migratory birds and seals (see **Figure 2**, page 173).

River basin management

The River Tees needs to be managed because:

- the river has a long history of flooding
- there is a large demand for water for homes, industry and farming
- there is a growing demand for developments linked to recreation and tourism.

Cow Green Reservoir was built in 1970. It is a regulating reservoir, releasing water when demand from industry is high and storing water when there is high rainfall. This helps to prevent flooding. The reservoir is also connected by a tunnel to the River Tyne and Kielder Reservoir. During a summer drought water can be added to the River Tees so that water is always available for people and industries.

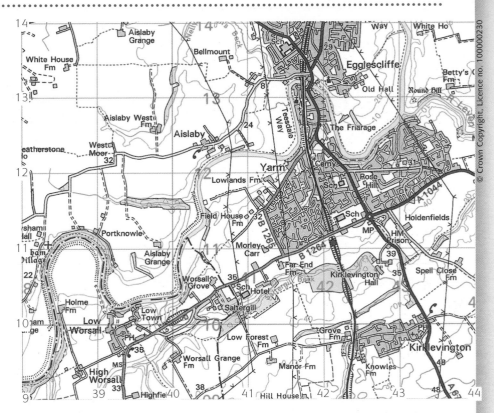

© Crown Copyright, Licence no. 100000230

▲ **Figure 4** The River Tees meandering through Yarm. Scale 1: 50 000 (2cm = 1km).

Activities

1 Study **Figure 2**.
  a What is the highest altitude shown on the map? Give the four-figure grid reference for the spot height.
  b Name and locate by a six-figure grid reference one place where visitors could stay in this part of Upper Teesdale.
  c Describe the shape of the Tees valley at Holmwath named in grid squares 8328 and 8329.

2 Complete a table like the one below to compare the River Tees and its valley in the upper and lower courses. The first row has been done for you.

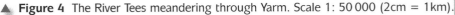

	Upper Course (Figure 2)	Lower Course (Figure 4)
River features:		
Straight or meandering?	*Quite straight; bends round areas of hard rock*	*Meandering in wide loops*
Width of river channel		
Gradient		
Valley features:		
Shape		
Width of valley floor		
Steepness of valley sides		
Other features:		
Land uses in the valley		

Management in the lower Tees valley

Schemes:

1 The Tees Barrage

The barrage was completed in 1995 and cost £54 million. The 22km stretch of river between Yarm and Stockton is now kept permanently at high tide. The water is fresher and cleaner as it does not mix with the tidal salt water in the lower estuary. The barrage also reduces the risk of flooding at very high tides. The barrage has led to £500 million of investment in offices, housing, educational, leisure and shopping facilities.

2 Dredging

The lower stretches of the Tees estuary are dredged periodically. This improves navigation by maintaining a deep-water channel.

3 Cutting of meanders

In 1810, the Tees Navigation Company cut across the neck of the Mandale Loop, a large meander near Stockton. The new route shortened the river by 4km. Other stretches of the river have been artificially straightened. This allows the water to move faster along the channel, reducing the flood risk.

4 Yarm's flood defence scheme

Yarm, a historic market town and once an inland port, is located on the inside bend of a large meander. Yarm is particularly prone to flooding. The most recent serious flood was in January 1995. Since then a new flood defence scheme costing £2.1 million has been built with:

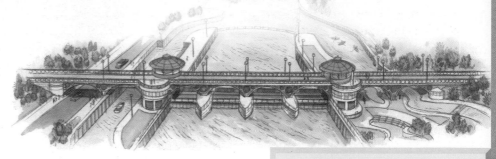

▲ **Figure 1** The Tees Barrage.

> ### ℹ River basin management schemes
>
> 'Hard' management schemes involve large-scale engineering works and are usually expensive. 'Soft' schemes cost less, do not have a major impact on the environment, and are thought to be more sustainable.

- reinforced concrete walls with flood gates for access by people and vehicles
- earth embankments
- gabions (baskets filled with stones) to protect the walls and embankments from erosion
- fishing platforms, street lighting and replanting to improve the environment
- building materials approved by English Heritage to be in keeping with existing architecture.

5 Improved flood warning systems

There is better communication with the Meteorological Office, police and other emergency services.

6 New development discouraged

Building on low-lying and flood-prone land is discouraged.

Activities

1 River basin management aims to:
- stop flooding
- provide a permanent, clean water supply
- conserve or improve the environment for wildlife and recreation.

   Which of the River Tees schemes achieve each of the three aims above?

2 Choose one of the schemes and describe how it works.

3 Complete a table like the one below by listing the schemes for the River Tees under the correct heading.

Hard management schemes	Soft management schemes

4 Put an S beside the schemes above that you think contribute to sustainable development. Choose one that is sustainable and one that is not and explain why you chose them.

5 In small groups choose one of the schemes and discuss what the views would be of:
- a local resident
- a conservation group
- the Environment Agency who pay for the scheme.

   Contribute your ideas to a class discussion.

River flooding

At certain times of the year the discharge or amount of water may increase so much that the river channel cannot hold all of the water, and flooding occurs.

Flooding is a normal occurrence in the lower course of a river, and is why a flood plain is created by a river. A flood occurs when the water in a river overtops its banks and leaves the channel (**Figure 1**). Most floods occur because of the weather, for example:

- long, continuous periods of rainfall, as happened in continental Europe in the winter of 1992–93
- a cloudburst in a thunderstorm which causes large amounts of run-off
- a sudden increase in temperature that rapidly melts snow and ice. In winter the water often cannot soak into the ground because it is still frozen.

Sometimes human activities can make the flooding worse:

- building new towns or increasing an urban area makes surfaces impermeable (water cannot soak through) – the result is more water runs off the surface
- deforestation reduces interception (water collects on the trees) – the result is more water runs off more quickly
- occasional disasters occur, such as a burst dam.

In many countries people have tried to control rivers to stop them flooding. **Figure 2** shows several different ways of dealing with floods.

▲ **Figure 1** River in flood.

Activities

1 Give three natural causes of flooding and three human causes of flooding.

2 Make a copy of the table below and complete it for the options shown in **Figure 2**. The first one has been done for you.

Option	Impact	Advantages	Disadvantages
Do nothing	None, may discourage people from settling. Floods occur	• Cheap • River naturally floods • Fertile silt/ water supply for farming	• Floods homes, fields, roads, services, etc. • Costly to clean up and repair damage

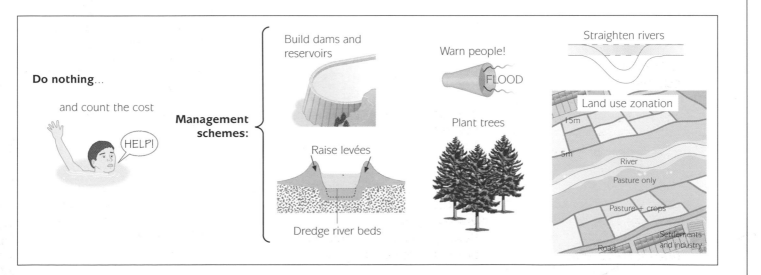

▲ **Figure 2** Dealing with floods: what are the options?

The 1998 floods in Bangladesh

Bangladesh suffers from flooding almost every year. The floodwaters bring with them fertile silt, which make the delta and flood plains ideal for farming. But when the flooding is severe it causes loss of life and brings great suffering to the population. The physical causes of the floods are summarized in **Figure 1**.

The human causes of the floods

In Nepal and Tibet the populations have grown rapidly. Large areas of forest have been cut down to provide fuel, timber and grazing land. This is called deforestation. In Nepal 50 per cent of the forest cover that existed in the 1950s has been cut down. The forests are important because:

- roots absorb water from the ground
- the roots bind the soil particles together
- trees reduce the impact of rain droplets on the ground surface
- the forest cover slows the journey of the water to the river channels.

The removal of the forest cover has increased landslides, soil erosion and overland flow. The soil is deposited in the river channels causing the raising of the riverbeds. This means the channels cannot carry as much water and so flooding is made worse.

Some people blame global warming for the increased flooding. A rise in sea level is blamed for the long duration of 56 days of the 1998 floods and the warmer global temperature is blamed for the especially high rainfall in the Himalayas in 1998.

The effects of the flooding in 1998

- Over 57 per cent of the land area was flooded.
- In Assam 1 million people lost their homes.
- In Nalbari district 240 villages were submerged.
- Large amounts of land used for housing and farming were eroded away.
- Over 1000 people were killed and millions made homeless.
- Supplies of drinking water and dry food ran low.
- Diseases spread such as bronchitis and diarrhoea.
- As the waters drained away, brown fields of rotting crops, villages buried in sand and wrecked roads and bridges were left behind.
- The floods of 1998 cost the country almost $1 billion.

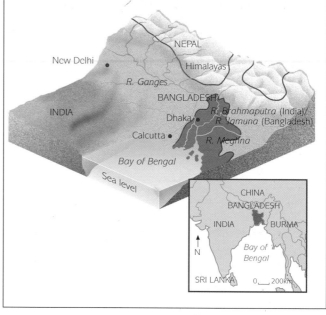

Physical causes of the floods

- Most of the country is the huge flood plain and delta of the rivers Ganges and Brahmaputra
- 70 per cent of the total area is less than 1 metre above sea level
- Rivers, lakes and swamps cover 10 per cent of the land area
- Tropical cyclones and storm waves cause heavy rain and coastal floods
- The snow melts in the Himalayas in the late spring and summer
- Heavy monsoon rain falls, especially over the uplands, including the Himalayas

▲ **Figure 1** The physical causes of flooding in Bangladesh.

▲ **Figure 2** Human misery caused by the 1998 flooding.

Managing the floods: in the short term
The **Bangladesh government**
- distributed money and 400 tonnes of rice
- provided relief supplies of fresh water, water tablets and sanitation services.

The **aid agencies**
- provided boats to rescue people
- supplied medicines to treat and prevent the spread of diseases
- supplied clean drinking water by digging and repairing wells
- set up a medical treatment centre
- distributed fodder for livestock
- distributed food, plastic sheeting and water tablets
- planned a programme to repair and construct housing and sanitation.

The **governments of other countries also** gave aid including millions of tonnes of wheat, and money for medicines, water tablets, house repair, sanitation and to help farming and fishing.

Managing the floods: in the long term
In July 1987 the World Bank prepared an Action Plan for Flood Control (**Figure 3**). Flood control measures include:
- 3500km of embankments
- seven huge dams
- twelve to fifteen floodwater storage basins to hold floodwater diverted from the main rivers
- replanting of forest cover in Nepal and Tibet.

Some people suggest that no 'hard' engineering works should take place and no costly flood prevention schemes. They oppose the scheme because raised levées and embankments along the Mississippi are thought to have made the flooding worse. The scheme would also cut off wetland areas valuable for water supply and fishing, a major source of protein in Bangladesh. In their place they believe that there should be flood forecasting and warning schemes, and improved flood shelters and emergency services to help the victims of flooding.

Such schemes would:
- be much cheaper than the building of extensive embankments or huge dams
- use more appropriate technology, in keeping with the knowledge, skills and finances of the communities

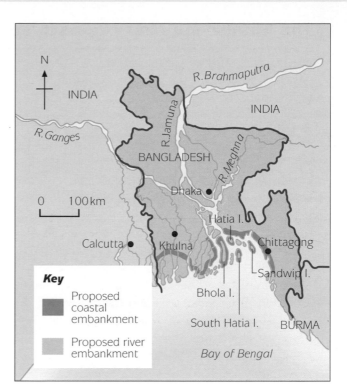

▲ **Figure 3** Action Plan for Flood Control.

- be less likely to damage delicate ecosystems so contributing to sustainable development
- avoid political difficulties with neighbouring countries.

In Bangladesh both hard and soft engineering have been used. Embankments have been built to protect densely populated and intensively farmed areas. Low-lying, less densely populated areas are used for floodwater storage. This is a soft approach that allows the flood plain to be used to hold floodwater – just as nature intended. It also benefits the soil, fishing and local ecosystems.

Activities
1 Using **Figure 1** and the text produce a table to show the physical and human causes of the flooding in Bangladesh.

2 List the ways the local people, the economy and the environment were affected by the floods.

3 Write two lists of the hard and soft flood prevention strategies used in Bangladesh. Which flood prevention techniques contribute most to sustainable development and why?

Case Study – Flooding in Bangladesh, an LEDC

The Mississippi river floods in spring and summer 1993

The floods in 1993 were the worst since records began (**Figure 1**). At the peak of the flood the Mississippi river was up to 18m deep, 25km wide and flowing at a speed of 96km an hour.

The effects of the flood

- Lives lost: 28.
- Homes lost: 36 000 people affected.
- Many more people were evacuated.
- Roads and railway lines were under water.
- Electricity lines collapsed, leaving towns without power.
- Six million acres of farmland were flooded, ruining maize crops.
- Millions of tonnes of silt and sand were deposited in the flood zone. This needed to be cleared after the flood.
- Estimated US $10 billion were needed to repair the flood damage.

The causes of the flood

The floods began when snow melting in the spring was followed by 50 days of very heavy rain and thunderstorms across the American mid-West. The area of the USA affected by the flooding was larger than the whole of Britain (**Figure 2**).

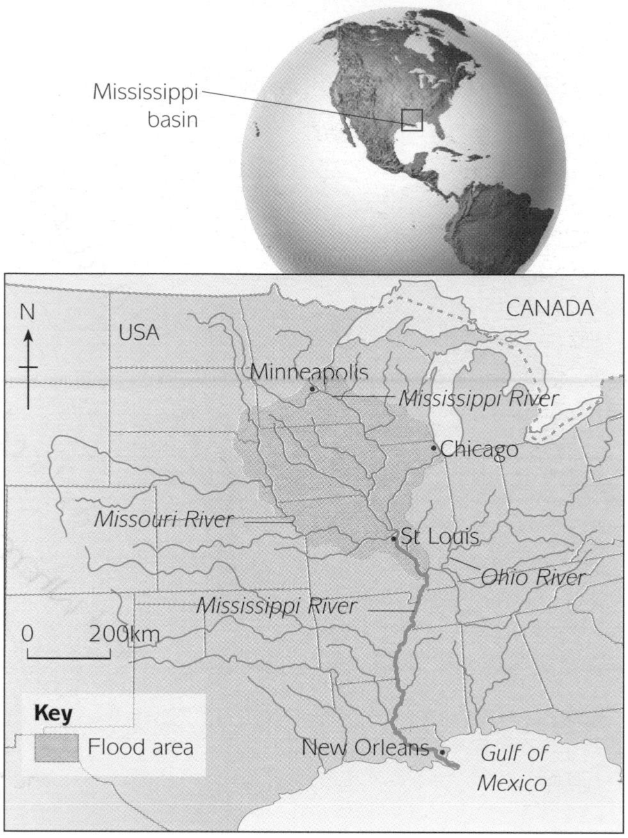

Mississippi basin

▲ **Figure 2** The extent of the flooding in 1993 in the USA.

Flood protection

▲ **Figure 1** The 1993 Mississippi river floods.

For many years the US Corps of Engineers have tried to reduce the flood risk and prevent serious floods affecting land and property. They have raised and strengthened levées (**Figure 3**), straightened out meanders, dredged the river bed and built revetments (protective walls).

The levées were meant to prevent flood water from spilling out of the river onto the surrounding land. In 1993 the floods were just too great and the water rose over the tops of the levées. In some places massive quantities of boulders were piled on top of the levées to make them higher, in the hope of keeping the river in its channel. Houses in danger of being flooded were protected by sandbags. In just one town, Sainte Genevieve, 750 000 sandbags were used.

▲ **Figure 3** A raised and strengthened levée on the Mississippi.

After the floods some people began to question the flood prevention schemes. They argued that less damage would have been done if the flood water had been allowed to spill out over farmland rather than the catastrophic flooding that occurred when levées failed. The water would have been absorbed by the land and would have flowed back into the channel once the floods began to recede. Others argue that people have no right to settle on the flood plains and to cover large areas with concrete and tarmac which makes them impermeable. They believe that the function of the flood plain is as a place for excess water when the river floods.

Notice how extensive the hard engineering schemes are on the Mississippi River, while in Bangladesh there has been much greater use of soft schemes such as flood basins and early warning systems, which are cheaper to build and maintain.

Activities

1 Produce a newspaper article with illustrations for the 1993 Mississippi floods. Your article should contain the following:
   • an eye-catching headline
   • the dates of the floods
   • the causes of the floods
   • the long-term and short-term effects of the floods
   • the response to the floods.

2 Suggest possible reasons why the Mississippi floods killed relatively few people but the cost of repairs was high.

3 Describe how you think the US Corps of Engineers should respond to the flood threat – build protection schemes, do nothing, or some other solution? Explain your ideas.

4 If you were responsible for designing a flood protection strategy in your local area, what schemes would you consider and why?

Summary: How a river changes as it flows downstream

How much can you remember? This summary does not describe or explain the formation of the landforms created by rivers. You will need to look back into the chapter for this information.

	Upper course	Middle course	Lower course
Valley long profile			
Valley cross-section and features	Shape of valley: V-shaped with interlocking spurs and a steep gradient	A more open V-shape with a flatter valley floor and sloping valley sides.	The valley is now wide and flat – there is a flood plain with levées.
Valley cross-section			
Processes at work	Mainly vertical erosion, cutting downwards.	Still some vertical erosion but lateral or sideways erosion is becoming more important, widening the valley.	Some lateral erosion on the outside bends of meanders. Deposition increases in importance on the river bed in times of low flow and on the flood plain when floods occur.
Features of the river	Pools, potholes and boulders in river bed: river narrow and turbulent with rapids and waterfalls; water often clear.	The river begins to meander with river cliffs and slip-off slopes. The river channel is broader and flatter.	Meanders may become cut off to form ox-bow lakes, islands of silt may braid the river and levées may form. At the mouth a delta is a possibility or mud flats and salt marshes in estuaries.

▲ **Figure 1** Summary of the changes along the course of a river.

Activities

1 Make a copy of the table below. Place the following eight features into the correct column to show which are formed by processes of erosion, by deposition or by a mixture of the two:

- Ox-bow lake
- Levée
- Waterfall
- Meander
- Delta
- Gorge of recession
- Flood plain
- V-shaped valley

Erosional features	Depositional features	Formed by both erosion and deposition

2 Explain the differences between the following pairs of terms:
 a Lateral erosion and vertical erosion
 b Slip-off slope and river cliff
 c Corrasion and corrosion.

3 Select any two of the following landforms. With the help of labelled diagrams explain their formation:
 a Waterfall
 b V-shaped valley
 c Ox-bow lake
 d Delta
 e Levée.

Chapter 4

Glacial landscapes and processes

The Andes in southern Chile, where the effects of frost shattering, glacial erosion and glacial deposition upon the landscape can be seen.

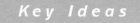

Key Ideas

The Earth's crust is modified by glacial processes which result in distinctive landforms:

- glacial processes (abrasion and plucking) combine with freeze–thaw weathering to produce landforms of erosion
- in upland areas valley glaciers form landforms of erosion such as corries, glacial troughs and ribbon lakes
- in lowland areas valley glaciers and ice sheets form landforms of deposition such as moraines and drumlins.

Landscape features affect human activities:

- upland areas offer opportunities for farming and tourism, but they need to be managed.

Valley glaciers and ice sheets

Snow consists of ice crystals with many air spaces between them. When you make a snowball, you compress the snow and remove the air spaces. The same happens naturally when snow is compressed into ice by the weight of new snow that falls on top of it. A moving mass of ice is known as a **glacier**.

Types of glaciers
There are two main types:

1 **Valley glacier** – a moving mass of ice which moves down a valley. It begins in the mountains and follows a river valley down to the lower ground. Most are found near the tops of ranges of young fold mountains. One example is the Rhône glacier in the Swiss Alps.

2 **Ice sheet** – a moving mass of ice which covers all the land over a big area. The world's largest ice sheet is in Antarctica. The ice is so thick that only a few rocky outcrops stick out above the ice (**Figure 2**).

▲ **Figure 1** A valley glacier reaching the sea in southern Chile.

◀ **Figure 2** Antarctica covered by its ice sheet. There is just enough bare rock next to the coast for the location of a base for Chilean scientists.

Processes of glacial erosion
There are two ways (processes) by which glaciers erode the land:

1 **Abrasion** – rocks in the bottom of the glacier wear away the rocks over which the glacier moves. The rocks carried in the bottom of the glacier have sharp edges. Because of the great weight and pressure of the ice above, they act like a giant file to make deep grooves, called **striations**, into the rocks below (**Figure 3**).

2 **Plucking** – blocks of rock are pulled away by the movement of the glacier. Blocks of rocks between joints in the rock freeze to the bottom of the glacier. They are pulled out sharply by the glacier as it moves, which is called plucking.

▲ **Figure 3** Striations (grooves and scratches) on the hard rocks which outcrop in Central Park in New York.

High rates of glacial erosion
Erosion is greatest with the following:

• fast-moving valley glaciers

• frost-shattered rocks from freeze–thaw weathering (see page 22)

• rocks which have weaknesses, such as many joints.

Distribution of landforms of glaciation in the British Isles

During the Ice Age, most of the British Isles was covered by ice and snow. The Ice Age lasted for about two million years. Heavy snowfall in the mountains led to the formation of valley glaciers in the Lake District, Snowdonia and Scottish Highlands. Ice sheets invaded from Scandinavia and made the British Isles a wilderness of snow and ice as far south as London and Bristol. It is only 10 000 years ago that the great Ice Age ended. This is why it is possible to see so many glacial landforms in the British Isles today (**Figure 5**).

Ice flow

Sharp-edged rocks embedded in the bottom of the ice

Blocks of rock pulled away by the ice flow

Rock surface scratched and polished

Joints in rock into which melt-water, created by pressure, enters

|—— ABRASION ——| |— PLUCKING —|

▼ **Figure 5** Distribution of glacial landforms from the Ice Age. *(Landforms of erosion are explained on pages 52–55. Landforms of deposition are dealt with on pages 56–57.)*

▲ **Figure 4** How rocks below ice are eroded by glacial processes (abrasion and plucking).

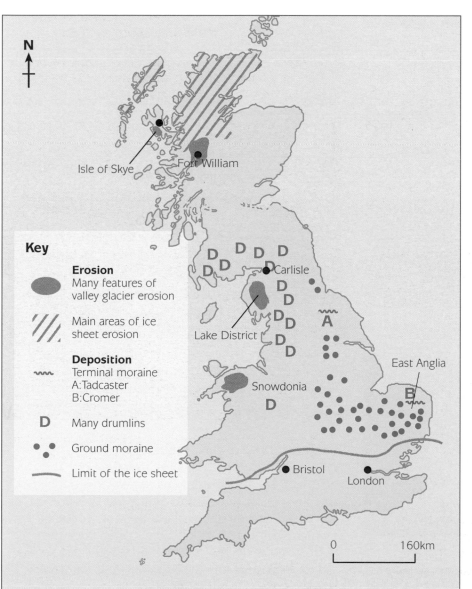

N

Key

Erosion

Many features of valley glacier erosion

Main areas of ice sheet erosion

Deposition

Terminal moraine
A: Tadcaster
B: Cromer

D Many drumlins

Ground moraine

Limit of the ice sheet

Isle of Skye

Fort William

Carlisle

Lake District

Snowdonia

East Anglia

Bristol

London

0   160km

Activities

1 a How is ice different from snow?
  b What is a glacier?
  c Name the two types of glaciers.
  d What are the main differences between the two types?

2 a (i) Draw and label the part of **Figure 4** which shows how abrasion works.
    (ii) What are striations?
    (iii) Explain how abrasion forms striations.
  b (i) Draw and label the part of **Figure 4** which shows how plucking works.
    (ii) Explain what is meant by plucking.

3 Look at **Figures 2** and **3**.
  a Describe as fully as possible what you can see on **Figure 2**.
  b How do we know that New York used to look like Antarctica does today?

4 Look at **Figure 5**. State where each of the following are located:
  a areas of ice sheet erosion
  b areas of valley glacier erosion
  c areas with many drumlins
  d areas of ground moraine.

5 During the Ice Age, how different would the area around Carlisle have looked compared to the area south of London?

Glacial erosion: corries and mountain peaks

Eiger (3970m)   Monch (4099m)   Jungfrau (4166m)

Valley glaciers make the greatest changes to landscapes in the mountains, where the ice is deepest. They make the slopes steeper, and the peaks sharper and more pointed, as is shown in **Figure 1**.

Corrie (cirque)

The first landform formed by a glacier is the **corrie**. The corrie is a circular rock hollow, located high in the mountains. The back wall of the corrie is especially steep and high. Although steep rock outcrops and sharp ridges are found on three sides, the fourth side at the front is open with only a low rock lip. The bottom is often filled by a small round lake known as a **tarn**. **Figure 2** shows a corrie, which matches this general description.

▲ **Figure 2** Corrie hollow occupied by Red Tarn in the Lake District. The rocky back wall is on the left; the rock lip is beyond the edge of the lake on the right.

Figure 1 View of the Swiss Alps. After studying these two pages, you should be able to pick out corries, arêtes and pyramidal peaks. How many visitors to Switzerland can do this?

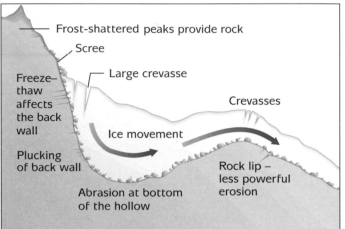

Frost-shattered peaks provide rock

Scree

Large crevasse

Freeze–thaw affects the back wall

Crevasses

Ice movement

Plucking of back wall

Rock lip – less powerful erosion

Abrasion at bottom of the hollow

▲ **Figure 3** The formation of a corrie.

How is a corrie formed?

This is shown in **Figure 3**.

* *Freeze–thaw weathering* affects the back wall and loose rocks (scree) are broken off.

* *Plucking* occurs on the back wall; at first ice sticks to the back wall and then it pulls away blocks of rock as it moves.

* *Abrasion* takes place in the bottom of the hollow; the glacier uses the loose rocks like a giant file to scrape away the rocks below.

Erosion is greatest at the bottom of the back wall, where the ice is thickest. As the glacier leaves the hollow, there is less weight and pressure from the ice. This means that erosion is less powerful here, which is why the rock lip forms.

Formation of a tarn lake

When all the ice melts, a corrie hollow is left. This is an obvious place for water to collect. Water is trapped by steep slopes on three sides; on the fourth side the rock lip forms a natural dam to hold the water back. In mountainous areas precipitation is often high; the bottom of the hollow soon fills up with water, because the steep slopes around it form a natural catchment area for collecting rain water.

Arête and pyramidal peak

Look at **Figure 1**. Notice how pointed the peaks of the mountains are. A long and narrow knife-edged ridge links the Eiger, Monch and Jungfrau. This is a called an **arête**; it is a two sided sharp-edged ridge along a mountain top. Next look at **Figure 4**. The Matterhorn is a three-sided slab of rock. One of its sides can be seen very clearly. There is a part view of a second side on the right. The third side is out of view behind the rock. The Matterhorn is an example of a **pyramidal peak** because it has three sides.

Both landforms are formed in the same way. When the back walls of corries are worn away by freeze–thaw, plucking and abrasion, only a narrow piece of rock is left along the ridge top.

- For an arête, two corries cut back – one on either side.
- For a pyramidal peak, there are three corries – one on each side. The peaks are kept sharp by frost action.

▲ **Figure 4** The Matterhorn near Zermatt in Switzerland, a pyramidal peak.

Activities

1 Look at **Figure 1**.
  a Describe what the tops of the mountains look like.
  b (i) Draw a sketch of all or part of **Figure 1**.
  (ii) On your sketch, mark A for an arête, C for a corrie and P for a pyramidal peak.
  c Suggest why the peaks on **Figure 1** are sharper than those around the corrie in **Figure 2**.

2 Write out the following statements about corries so that the tops and tails match. Start with the tops.

Tops	Tails
A corrie can be described as	the ice is thickest here so that there is more weight and pressure.
The ways (processes) that form corries are	arêtes and pyramidal peaks are formed.
A corrie's back is steeper than its front because	rain falls into a hollow with steep sides and a rock lip as a dam.
As the back walls of corries are worn away	a circular hollow with steep rocky sides on three of its sides.
The corrie is a great place for a lake to form after the ice melts because	freeze–thaw weathering and plucking.

3 Look at **Figure 5**.
  a Give the four-figure grid reference for the square in which most of Red Tarn lies.
  b State the direction in which the river that leaves Red Tarn flows for most of the time.
  c Describe what the land around the sides of Red Tarn is like. (Look closely at the contour lines – are they close to each other or far apart? What does this tell you? Can you see the different heights marked on the contour lines? They will tell you whether the land is getting lower or higher.)
  d How high is the highest peak on the map?
  e Striding Edge is an arête. What is the map evidence that suggests this?
  f Brown Cove (a little further north) is a corrie. State two pieces of map evidence for this.
  g Draw a labelled sketch map to show what corries and arêtes look like on OS maps.

▼ **Figure 5** OS map of Helvellyn in the Lake District at a scale of 1: 50 000 (2cm=1km)

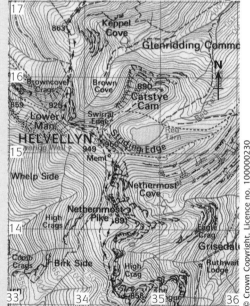

© Crown Copyright. Licence no. 100000230

4 From anywhere on these two pages, give one named example of each of the following landforms:
  arête   **corrie**   **tarn lake**   **pyramidal peak**.

Glacial erosion: valley landforms

Figure 1 The Lauterbrunnen valley in Switzerland was formed by glacial erosion. The valley is too big to have been eroded by the small stream that flows in the valley bottom today.

Figure 3 Waterfall from a hanging valley along the sides of the Lauterbrunnen valley. This is a close up view of one of the several waterfalls that can be seen in Figure 1.

The U-shaped valley is an impressive landscape feature (**Figure 1**). It can be hundreds of metres deep with vertical rock walls, down which waterfalls cascade from **hanging valleys**. Above the steep valley sides the land becomes flatter and forms a **high-level bench**. This is known as an 'alp' in the Alps of Switzerland (you can see an example in the front part of the photograph in **Figure 1**). Notice also the great difference between the flat floor and the steep sides of the Lauterbrunnen valley. The river, which flows down the middle of the valley, is known as a **misfit stream**, because it is so small compared with the size of the valley. Lakes fill parts of the valley floor in many U-shaped valleys. These are **ribbon lakes**, so called because of their long and thin shape. In the lower parts of the valley **terminal moraines** (see pages 56–57) are found. The main feature of the *long profile* of a valley that has been formed by a glacier is its irregular shape, shown by the black line in **Figure 2**.

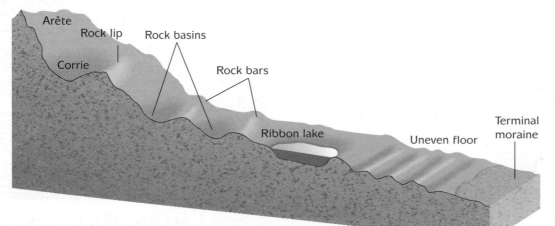

Arête
Rock lip
Rock basins
Corrie
Rock bars
Ribbon lake
Uneven floor
Terminal moraine

Figure 2 Long profile of a glaciated valley.

Formation of valley landforms

All the features of a U-shaped valley show how the powers of erosion of a glacier are much greater than those of a river.

Before a glacier moves down a valley	After the glacier moves down a valley
V-shaped river valley	It is widened, deepened and straightened into a U-shaped valley.
River erosion confined to that part of the valley where the river flowed, mainly in the middle of the valley.	Glacial erosion takes place in all the valley, because ice fills the valley, making direct contact with all the floor and both sides.
Rivers go around obstacles in their path and form interlocking spurs (page 34).	Glaciers flow straight down the valley because of their great power. Edges of interlocking spurs are cut off to form truncated spurs and straight valley sides.
Tributary rivers join the main river at the same level.	Glacial erosion is so great in the main valley that tributary rivers are left to join above the level of the main valley. The tributaries are left hanging and form waterfalls or hanging valleys.
Except for waterfalls that are mainly in its upper course, the long profile of a river valley is smooth.	Glaciers erode soft rock outcrops by abrasion and plucking to form hollows known as rock basins, while hard rock outcrops resist erosion and form rock bars. This makes the long profile uneven. After the ice melts, the rock basins are filled up by rivers and form ribbon lakes.

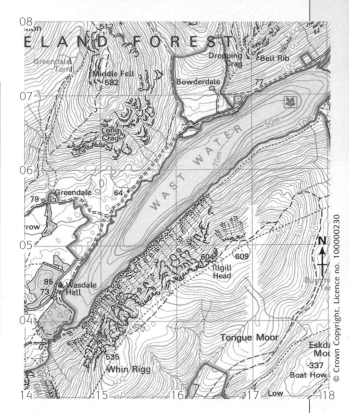

© Crown Copyright. Licence no. 100000230

▲ **Figure 4** OS map showing Wast Water, the deepest of the English Lakes, at a scale of 1: 50 000 (2cm = 1km).

Activities

1 Write down each landform and match it up with the correct definition.

Landform	Definition
U- shaped valley	long and narrow area of water in a glaciated valley
Hanging valley	hollow on a valley floor eroded by abrasion and plucking
Truncated spur	tributary valley with a river cascading down as a waterfall
Rock basin	a projection in a river valley that has later been eroded away by a glacier so that the valley sides are vertical
Ribbon lake	a valley with a flat floor and steep sides

2 Draw a frame the same size as **Figure 1**.
  Draw a sketch of the following landforms and label it.

  U-shaped valley   hanging valleys   high-level bench truncated spurs

3 a Where can screes be seen in **Figure 5**?
  b Where are screes named and how are they shown in **Figure 4**?
  c Look back at pages 22 and 30. Explain how the screes are formed.

4 Look at **Figure 4**. Imagine that you had been told to walk from the north-west corner (1408) to the south-east corner (1803).
  a Describe why you would find this difficult (if not impossible).
  b Name the features of glaciation you would cross or see on the way.

▲ **Figure 5** Wast Water and its scree slopes in the Lake District.

Landforms of glacial deposition

Ice behaves in the same way as all the other agents of erosion, such as rivers and the sea.

1 It wears away the land surface – *erosion*.

2 It carries away the eroded materials – *transportation*.

3 It dumps the materials it is carrying elsewhere – *deposition*.

Glaciers erode with so much power that great amounts of loose rock are transported. Look at **Figure 1** which shows an **erratic**. This big boulder, made of grit, has been dumped on top of the white limestone rock below. There are hundreds of these boulders in the area. Think of the power of glaciers that allows them to carry boulders of this size for long distances.

▲ **Figure 1** Erratic block of grit left perched on the top of limestone in the Yorkshire Dales National Park after the ice melted.

Not even a glacier can keep on growing and moving for ever. It reaches a point where more ice is melting in the lowlands than is being formed in the mountains. When this happens, the glacier must begin to deposit its load.

◀ **Figure 3** Boulder clay.

▲ **Figure 2** A glacier with lateral and medial moraines on the ice surface.

Therefore, glacial deposition takes place:

- when glaciers melt as they reach lower ground
- when temperatures increase and melt the ice
- where the glacier has become too thin to carry all of its load any further.

All materials transported and deposited by glaciers are included under the heading **moraine**. They are dumped on the ground when the ice melts. Four types of moraine can be distinguished:

1 **Lateral moraine** – line of deposits along the side of a glacier or a valley. These show up as the dark lines of loose rock and stone on top of the glacier shown in **Figure 2**. They can be seen along both sides. The material that forms these moraines is broken off from rocky peaks above by frost action before falling down the valley sides onto the ice.

2 **Medial moraine** – line of deposits in the middle of a glacier or a valley. In **Figure 2** boulders and stones can be seen on the ice at different places, but with a more obvious line of deposits down the middle. These moraines are formed by valley glaciers joining together. Two separate lateral moraines combine to form one medial moraine.

3 **Ground moraine** – deposits carried in the base of a glacier. Most come from the erosion of the rocks as the glacier moves over them. They are deposited and spread all over the ground when the ice melts. The general name given for all materials deposited by ice is boulder clay. As its name suggests, this is usually clay that contains boulders of many different sizes. Look at **Figure 3**. Nothing has been sorted; large and soft rocks are all mixed together with clay, sand and soil. The big boulders have sharp edges.

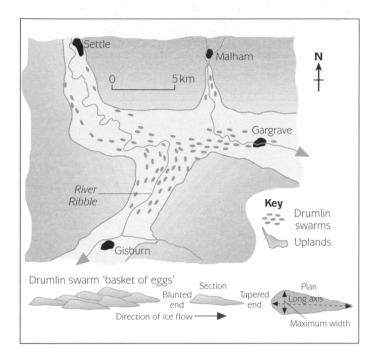

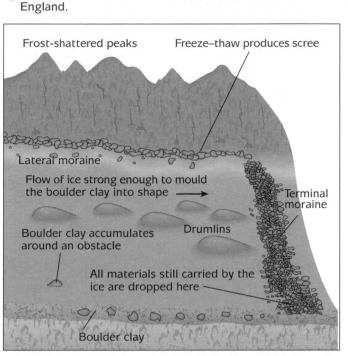

Figure 4 Drumlins in the Ribble Valley in north-west England.

Figure 5 Location and formation of drumlins and terminal moraines.

The 'ingredients' of boulder clay vary greatly according to what the glacier had eroded before it reached the area and what it was carrying. As the glacier melts, it leaves behind a trail of ground moraine, which forms a hummocky surface (meaning that the land goes up and down without any pattern to it).

4 **Terminal moraine** – deposits at the end of a glacier. All the remaining load is dropped and dumped at the furthest point reached by the ice. This point is marked by a ridge of boulder clay, running parallel to the front of the ice, known as the terminal (or last) moraine. Terminal moraines that cross valleys form natural dams. Behind these dams river water can pile up and form lakes. These lakes are also called ribbon lakes because of their shape, which is long and thin.

Drumlins

In the lowlands of south-west Scotland and north-west England there are many **drumlins**. Drumlins are easy to recognise because:

- there are many low hills
- each hill is about 30–40 metres high and 300–400 metres long
- all the hills lie in the same direction
- all have similar shapes (blunt at one end and tapered at the other)
- each hill looks like an egg.

Drumlins occur in swarms and are said to form a 'basket of eggs' type of landscape. This is because of the lumpy shape of the landscape (**Figure 4**).

Drumlins form in this way:

- a melting glacier is over-loaded with stones and boulders
- it meets a small obstacle which is enough to encourage deposition
- on first meeting the obstacle, more deposition of boulder clay takes place, which forms the blunt end
- the moving ice moulds the boulder clay into shape around the obstacle, which forms the tapered end.

Activities

1 State three factors which encourage glacial deposition to take place.

2 a What is boulder clay?
   b What type of moraine is boulder clay?
   c (i) Name one landform which is made of boulder clay.
   (ii) Draw a diagram to show what this landform looks like.
   (iii) Explain the formation of this landform.

3 a Name a type of moraine shown in both **Figures 2** and **5**.
   b Explain why it can be seen both in areas with ice and in areas where the ice has melted.

Human activities in upland glaciated areas

Difficulties

Many upland areas are not easy places for people to settle in, even before the effects of glaciers on the landscape are taken into account. The higher you go, the colder it becomes, which reduces the length of the growing season and restricts what farmers can do. There is more precipitation; this also means more cloud and less sunshine. There is more chance of the precipitation falling as snow, which brings other problems for farmers.

Many of the changes caused by glaciers do not help. Glaciers are so powerful that the land can be scraped bare of all its soil by glacial erosion. Valley glaciers increase the steepness of the land and the height of the valley sides, making access more difficult, if not impossible.

Possibilities for settlement and use in the UK

Although glacial erosion creates problems for farmers in upland areas, there are three main benefits from glacial erosion and deposition:

1 On the valley floors and in the lowlands, opportunities for farming are improved.

2 Upland areas are more attractive to tourists.

3 The number of good sites for generating HEP (hydro-electric power) is increased. Mountainous areas with high totals of precipitation offer opportunities for setting up HEP stations, but glacial erosion improves these opportunities. After an upland area has been glaciated, there are more waterfalls and they are higher for faster flowing water; large ribbon lakes provide areas of natural water storage.

Farming and forestry

Valley glaciers make valley floors wider and flatter. In upland areas, such as the Lake District, land on the valley floor is precious for farmers because there is:

- more space for buildings and fields
- better shelter from cold winds
- deeper and more fertile soils from glacial deposition.

Many farms in the Lake District are split up into three parts (**Figure 1**):

1 **Inbye** – land on the valley floor around the farm. For the reasons given above, this is the best land, which is why farmers use it intensively for growing crops and making hay and silage. The high clay

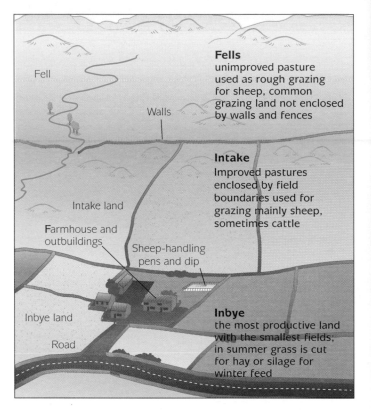

▲ **Figure 1** Layout and land uses on a Lake District farm. A typical farm can be split up into three parts.

content of the boulder clay soils favours good grass growth and dairy cattle are often kept here as well.

2 **Intake** – improved land on the lower slopes. The land can only be used for pastoral farming (keeping livestock), sometimes beef cattle, but more often sheep. Some farmers have planted coniferous trees on land that is too steep for farming to be profitable.

3 **Fells** – rough grazing land on the steep upper slopes and moorland tops. Only sheep can feed on the poor grasses and withstand the difficult weather conditions. There are also many areas of useless rocky or boggy land.

Tourism

Some farmers, faced with the great problems of trying to make a good living in glaciated upland areas, also cater for tourists. There is money to be made from charging people for camping or for parking caravans in fields next to the farm. Some rooms in the farmhouse may be let for bed and breakfast; many B&B boards can be seen along the sides of roads in the Lake District and Snowdonia. The farm may be some distance from the nearest shop, which means that the farmer can also sell farm produce such as milk and eggs.

Without the effects of glaciation, the landscape in the Lake District would be much less attractive to visitors. Glaciation formed the sharp knife-edged peaks and valleys were deepened. The scenery was made more spectacular for visitors and fell walkers. There are also more bare rock outcrops, which are attractive to mountaineers and rock climbers. After the glaciers melted, large ribbon lakes were left in the valleys, without which Cumbria could not be called 'The Lake District'. Water always attracts tourists. Visitors come for walks around the edges of the lake, or for picnics, to take boat rides or go sailing. Without the effects of glaciation on its landscape, the Lake District would not be the great magnet for visitors that it is today. Lake Windermere is the largest and most visited lake (**Figure 3**).

▲ **Figure 2** Lake District farm. Notice how much greener the improved pastures are on the valley floor.

Activities

1 a State three ways in which the weather is worse in mountain areas than in the surrounding valleys.
 b Describe two ways in which glacial erosion makes farming more difficult.
 c **(i)** What is HEP?
  (ii) Why are the opportunities for generating HEP greater in areas that have been glaciated?

2 a Explain why the farming is different on the valley floor to that on the Fells.
 b **(i)** Make a frame and draw a sketch of **Figure 2**. On it, name and label the following:
  Inbye   Intake   Land impossible to farm
  (ii) Suggest reasons why the farmers living in the area shown in **Figure 2** should be able to make extra money from tourists.

3 Lake Windermere as a case study – Part 1
 a **(i)** Lake Windermere fills a rock basin. Look back at pages 54–55 and explain how it may have been formed by glacial erosion.
  (ii) There is a terminal moraine at the southern end of Lake Windermere. Look back at pages 56–57 and explain how it may also have been formed by glacial deposition.
 b From **Figure 3**,
  (i) State the ways in which tourists use Lake Windermere.
  (ii) Name and locate the facilities provided for tourists.
 c Research from tourist information brochures or web sites on the Internet. Find out more information about Lake Windermere as a tourist centre.

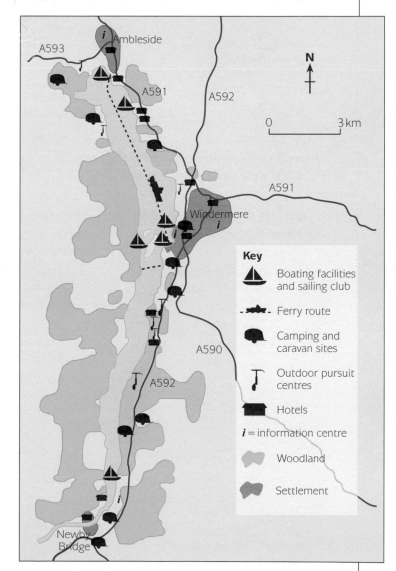

▲ **Figure 3** Windermere – places of interest and facilities for visitors.

The need for management

Some places receive large numbers of visitors. The most popular areas are referred to as '**honeypots**'. In these areas management is needed most:

1 to reduce damage to the environment
2 to lessen the conflicts which may arise
   • between local residents and visitors
   • between different groups of visitors with varied interests.

Reducing the damage to the environment

Large number of walkers following the same paths cause footpath erosion. This can lead to scars on the landscape (**Figure 1**). It is more likely to happen in glaciated upland areas where slopes are steep and soils are thin, as along the top of the arête ridge in **Figure 1**.

What can management do about footpath erosion?
• Divert the course of the footpath.
• Fence off the old footpath to give the grass time to recover.
• Lay down artificial footpaths, e.g. placing stones over soft surfaces and making steps on steep slopes.

▲ **Figure 1** Footpath on Striding Edge on Helvellyn in the Lake District.

Lessening conflicts between users

In the table (right), there are some examples of conflicts in tourist areas such as the Lake District as well as possible methods of management to reduce (if not solve) the conflicts.

Conflicts	Management methods
Between farmer and visitor	
• Visitors clambering over and knocking down the old walls between fields	• Making and maintaining stiles
• Letting dogs off the lead that may worry lambs and sheep	• Educating people about the country code
• Walking through the hay fields	• Warning notices to keep to the paths
• Dropping litter	• 'Take your litter home' campaigns
Between different groups of visitors	
• Noise and speed of boats and water-skiers compared with quiet and peaceful activities such as sailing and fishing	• Speed boats not allowed on some lakes, while large lakes such as Windermere are divided up into zones for different activities

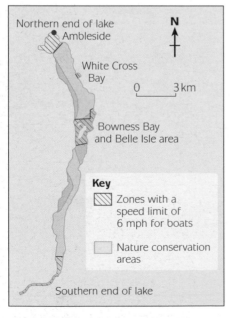

▲ **Figure 2** Lake Windermere: attempts at management to conserve areas that are important for wildlife and to keep parts of the lake free from speed boats.

Activities

1 a What is a honeypot?
  b State two reasons why honeypots need management.

2 a Look at **Figure 1**. Why is footpath erosion a problem on Striding Edge?
  b Name three methods of footpath management.
  c Choose one of the methods of footpath management. Do you think this method would be easy to use on Striding Edge? Explain your answer.

3 Lake Windermere as a case study – Part 2
  a Look at **Figure 2**. Draw your own sketch map of Lake Windermere and shade in the areas that are managed. Finish it off with a key for the different types of managed areas.
  b Explain why management of tourist activities is needed on Lake Windermere.

Chapter 5

Coastal landscapes and processes

*On the brink ...
in 1996 a farmer
in Holderness
(Yorkshire) next to
her farmhouse after
coastal erosion had
already destroyed a
garage and dairy unit.
Is it still there now?*

Key Ideas

**The Earth's crust is modified
by coastal processes, resulting
in distinctive landforms:**
- destructive waves are
  responsible for coastal erosion
- processes of erosion form
  distinctive landforms such
  as cliffs, wave-cut platforms,
  caves, stacks and arches
- longshore drift transports
  eroded materials along the
  coast which are deposited
  elsewhere by constructive waves
- beaches and spits are examples
  of landforms of deposition.

**Landscape features affect
human activities:**
- coastal management is needed
  for sea defences and tourism.

How is the coast eroded?

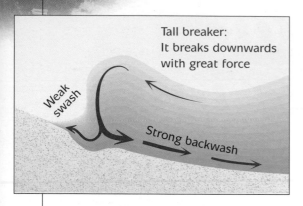

▲ **Figure 1** A destructive wave.

▲ **Figure 2** Chalk cliffs at Beachy Head formed by destructive waves.

▶ **Figure 3** 'Waves lash the sea front at Porthleven in west Cornwall' – photograph from *The Guardian*, 5 January 1998.

Waves do most of the work of erosion along coasts. As a wave reaches the coast, its lower part is slowed by friction with the sea bed, but its top keeps moving forwards and topples over. The wave breaks against the cliff or surges up the beach. Waves that do most erosion are called **destructive waves** (Figure 1).

The power of destructive waves

Destructive waves have three main features:

1 They are high in proportion to their length.

2 Their backwash is stronger than their swash, so that loose rocks, pebbles and sand are carried back out to sea.

3 They are frequent waves, breaking at an average rate of between eleven and fifteen per minute.

Waves that have travelled over a large area of ocean release their energy when they break against the coastline. The length of water over which the wind has blown the wave is called the **fetch**. There are two simple rules to remember:

1 The longer the fetch and the stronger the wind, the more powerful the wave.

2 The more powerful the wave, the greater the amount of erosion caused.

From time to time around the coasts of the British Isles, weather conditions are ideal for huge destructive waves to form. One time was on 4 January 1998 in Cornwall (**Figure 3**). Notice how angry the sea is and how big the waves are. Imagine the weight and force of the water crashing against the pier and buildings during this storm. These huge waves were caused by:

• onshore south westerly winds

• strong winds with many gusts over 160 km/h

• winds with a long fetch over the Atlantic Ocean.

The newspapers were mainly interested in telling their readers about the damage caused. Can you suggest a caption for **Figure 3** that a geographer would be more likely to write?

Insurance companies face £500 million payout for storm damage

We don't like to be beside the quayside

Worst storms since 1987 hurricane

Processes of coastal erosion

These are the ways by which waves erode rocks that outcrop along the coastline.

> **A** **Hydraulic power:** This is the weight of water against the coastline. Hundreds of tonnes of water may hit the rock face in a storm. Any air trapped in cracks in the rock is compressed by the waves; this increases the pressure on the rock.
>
> **B** **Corrasion:** This is another name for abrasion. Waves throw sand and pebbles against the rock face as they break; in storms boulders are also flung against the cliffs. These break off pieces of rock. Cliffs are undercut (cut away at the bottom) by corrasion.
>
> **C** **Attrition:** Boulders and pebbles are broken down into sand-sized particles when they hit rock faces, or when they collide with one another. Sand is easier for the waves to carry away.
>
> **D** **Corrosion:** This is the chemical action of sea water on rocks. It happens most on limestone rocks, which will dissolve in sea water.

The speed of erosion

Out of the four processes of erosion listed above, hydraulic power and corrasion are the most important. The highest rates of erosion are recorded in storms, like the one shown in **Figure 3**. Other factors that lead to high rates of coastal erosion are the type of rock or the way they are positioned.

These include:

- rock outcrops with many weaknesses such as joints, bedding planes or faults (shown in **Figure 3B** on page 20)
- cliffs made of soft rocks such as boulder clay
- the arrangement of the rocks, e.g. at Barton on Sea east of Bournemouth (**Figure 4**) with clay rock below sand.

Sand

Clay

▲ **Figure 4** Cliff erosion at Barton on Sea. Clay is a soft rock easily eroded by the waves. When it rains, water seeps down through the sand above the layer of clay. The bottom of the layer of sand becomes saturated and moves, causing landslides and slumping.

Activities

1 a (i) Draw a large labelled diagram to show the main features of a destructive wave.
(ii) State one feature of a destructive wave which you cannot show on your diagram.
(iii) State one feature of the destructive waves shown in **Figure 3**.
(iv) Explain why destructive waves hit the coast of Cornwall on 4 January 1998.
b Look carefully at **Figure 2**. What can you see on the photograph that suggests that more of the cliffs at Beachy Head will soon collapse?
c Destructive waves erode by hydraulic power and corrasion. State what is meant by
(i) hydraulic action and **(ii)** corrasion.

2 a What is the weather like in a storm?
b Name the people who lose money as a result of storm damage along the coastline.
c Why is there more coastal erosion during a storm than at other times?
d The cliffs at Barton on Sea are eroded during storms.
(i) Where in the UK is Barton on Sea?
(ii) Draw **Figure 4**. Add labels to your diagram to explain why cliff erosion is fast at Barton on Sea.

Landforms of coastal erosion

Landforms of coastal erosion are named and described in **Figure 1**.

Cliffs and wave-cut platforms

The sea cliff is the main landform of coastal erosion. It is formed in the following way:

- Destructive waves attack the bottom of the rock face between the high and low water marks.

- Waves erode by the processes (ways) already described on the previous page, such as hydraulic power and corrasion.

- A wave-cut notch is formed at the bottom of the cliff so that the rock above overhangs.

- The notch increases in size with continued wave attack.

- After a time the weight of the overhanging rock is so great that it collapses.

- The cliff retreats inland.

- Once waves have removed all the loose rocks and stones from the bottom of the collapsed cliff, erosion begins again.

The 'White Cliffs of Dover', made of chalk, are one of the best known examples of cliffs.

As the cliff retreats inland, a wave-cut platform is formed at the bottom of the cliff. This is a gently sloping rocky area between the high and low water marks. It is only covered by the sea at high tide.

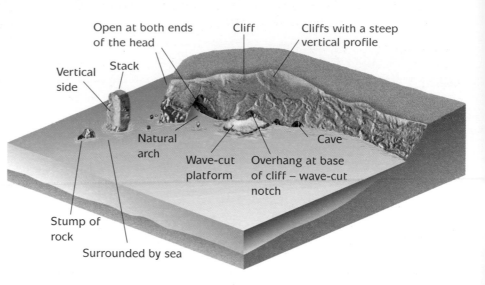

Open at both ends of the head — Cliff — Cliffs with a steep vertical profile — Vertical side — Stack — Natural arch — Wave-cut platform — Overhang at base of cliff – wave-cut notch — Cave — Stump of rock — Surrounded by sea

▲ **Figure 1** Main features of landforms of coastal erosion.

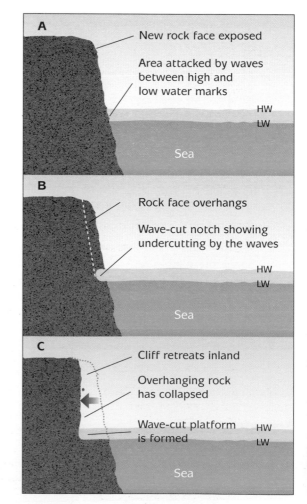

A — New rock face exposed — Area attacked by waves between high and low water marks — HW — LW — Sea

B — Rock face overhangs — Wave-cut notch showing undercutting by the waves — HW — LW — Sea

C — Cliff retreats inland — Overhanging rock has collapsed — Wave-cut platform is formed — HW — LW — Sea

▲ **Figure 3** Marsden Rocks – stacks near Sunderland. Notice in particular the amount of undercutting around the base of the rocks.

▲ **Figure 2** Formation of cliff and wave-cut platform.

As the tide goes out, surface rock that is broken by ridges and grooves is exposed. This is the area of flat rocks that holidaymakers can walk onto at low tide, sometimes looking for crabs. It is also where some get trapped as the tide races back in! The wave-cut platform is the rock left behind as the cliff retreats inland.

Caves, arches and stacks

Waves are good at opening up weaknesses in rocks. A vertical line of weakness, such as a joint or a fault (page 20) can be increased in size to form a cave. The gap in the rock is widened into a cave by hydraulic action and corrasion.

If the cave has formed on a narrow headland the pressure of the waves can erode the back of the cave as well. After a long time, this leads to the formation of a natural arch (**Figure 4**).

The rock at the bottom of the arch continues to be attacked by waves. This puts more and more pressure on the top of the arch, especially if a vertical line of weakness exists. After continued erosion, the arch collapses and becomes a stack. The stack is a piece of rock, surrounded by sea that is isolated from the main coastline. Marsden Rocks are examples of stacks (**Figure 3**). The bottom of the stack is eroded by waves on all sides until it eventually collapses.

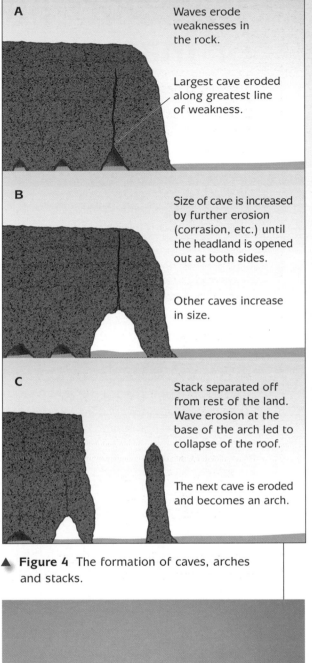

A — Waves erode weaknesses in the rock.

Largest cave eroded along greatest line of weakness.

B — Size of cave is increased by further erosion (corrasion, etc.) until the headland is opened out at both sides.

Other caves increase in size.

C — Stack separated off from rest of the land. Wave erosion at the base of the arch led to collapse of the roof.

The next cave is eroded and becomes an arch.

▲ **Figure 4** The formation of caves, arches and stacks.

Activities

1 a Mix and match.
Write out the definitions so that they match the landform.

Landform of coastal erosion	Definition
Cliff	Rocky opening so that you can see through a headland
Wave-cut platform	Hollow area at the bottom of a cliff
Cave	Area of flat rocks only seen at low tide
Natural arch	Piece of rock separated from the coastline
Stack	Steep rock outcrops along the coastline

b Choose either **Figure 3** or **Figure 5**.
   (i) Draw a sketch.
   (ii) Add labels for as many of the landforms named in **a** that you can see.

2 a Explain with the help of labelled diagrams how cliffs form.
   b Name an example of cliffs in the UK.

3 a If an examination question is 'Explain the formation of a stack', why do you have to explain the formation of a cave and a natural arch as well?
   b What do you think will happen to the stacks shown in **Figure 3** during the next 50 years? Explain as fully as you can.
   c Suggest why the cliffs in **Figure 5** are being eroded less quickly than those at Barton on Sea a few kilometres east of Bournemouth (page 63)?

▲ **Figure 5** Part of the coastline a few kilometres west of Bournemouth.

Transport and deposition of material along the coast

Transport

Materials of all sizes are transported by the waves further along the coast before being deposited. The transport of sand and pebbles along the coast by waves is called longshore drift. This is shown in **Figure 1A**. Waves often approach at an angle to the coastline, but the backwash is always at right-angles. Pebbles keep on being pushed up the beach by the waves at an angle, but they roll back down the beach at right angles to the coastline because this is the steepest gradient. The pebbles are then caught by the next wave. In this way pebbles and other materials are transported along the coastline.

Figure 1B shows the direction of the longshore drift around the British Isles. It is controlled by the direction of the dominant wind. Prevailing south-westerly winds cause the drift from west to east along the Channel coast and from south to north along the west coast. Along the east coast the dominant wind blows from the north, which causes the longshore drift to move from north to south.

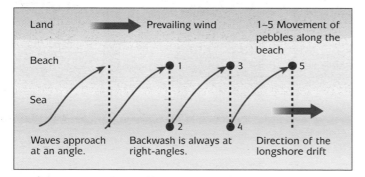

▲ **Figure 1A** Explanation of longshore drift.

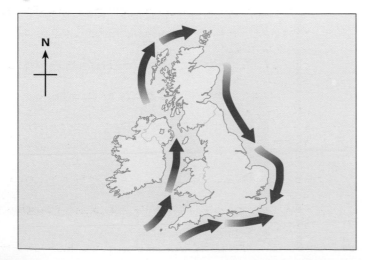

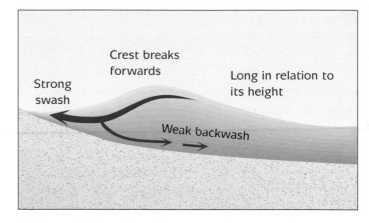

▲ **Figure 2** Features of a constructive wave.

Deposition

Waves carry sand, shingle and pebbles. These are deposited by **constructive waves** (**Figure 2**). Constructive waves have three main features:

1 They are long in relation to their height.

2 They break gently on the beach, so that the swash carrying materials up the beach is stronger than the backwash carrying them away.

3 They break gently with only between six and nine waves per minute.

They are most likely to occur:

• when sea conditions are calm

• when winds are light and are not blowing directly onshore

• during summer when there are fewer storms

• in sheltered places such as in a bay.

Beaches and their formation

Everyone who has been to the coast knows what a beach is. Without a good beach, holiday resorts cannot attract large numbers of visitors. The beach is the area of sand (**Figure 3A**) or shingle (**Figure 3B**) along the coast that is not covered by the sea. It becomes a lot narrower at high tide. Beaches slope gently down to the sea. Some extend for several kilometres along the coastline. Others, located in bays, are shorter and more curved in shape.

◄ **Figure 1B** Direction of longshore drift around the British Isles.

Beaches are formed from the materials carried and deposited by the longshore drift. One of the most likely places for a beach to be formed is at a bend in the coastline, where it is more sheltered. Constructive waves deposit material, which accumulates over time and builds up the beach.

How do spits form?

A spit is a long and narrow ridge of sand or shingle (**Figure 4**). One end is attached to the land while the other end lies in the open sea. It is like a beach that goes out into the sea instead of hugging the coastline. Some spits have a hooked end, especially those found in the English Channel, such as Hurst Castle spit. Others run in the same direction as the coast, sometimes extending for several kilometres across an estuary. Spurn Point (**Figures 1** and **4** page 70) is an example of this type.

A spit is formed in the following way. Follow the formation by looking at **Figure 4** as well.

1 The waves pick up eroded materials, which are carried along the coast by the longshore drift.

2 At a bend in the coastline deposition begins.

3 Sediment accumulates and a long ridge is built out to sea.

4 Mud and marsh are trapped in the sheltered water behind the spit.

5 As the end of the spit reaches deeper water, it is more affected by strong winds and sea currents, which curve the end of the spit into a hook.

▲ **Figure 3** ▼
Two different beaches: A is made of sand; B is made of shingle.

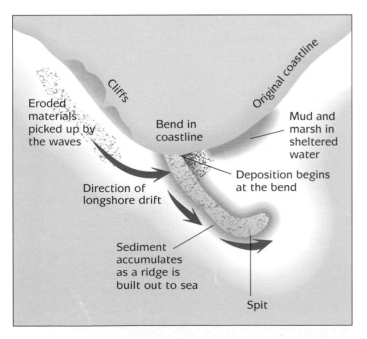

▲ **Figure 4** Formation of a spit.

Activities

1 a Draw a labelled diagram to show how longshore drift works.
  b (i) Name the seaside resort closest to where you live or the one which you visit most.
    (ii) Look at **Figure 1B**. In which direction is the longshore drift at your resort?
    (iii) What makes the longshore drift go in that direction?

2 a (i) Draw a large labelled diagram to show the main features of a constructive wave.
    (ii) Why is it called a constructive wave (rather than a destructive wave)?
  b (i) State two differences between the beaches in **Figures 3A** and **3B**.
    (ii) Which one would be better for a seaside resort? Explain your answer.
    (iii) Explain how a beach forms.

3 a Describe two ways in which a spit is different from a beach.
  b Describe two ways in which the formation of beaches and spits are similar.

Human activities and coasts

▲ **Figure 1** Sea wall at Scarborough.

Many people dream of living in a place next to the sea – for sea views, fresh air and plenty of space for exercising the dog. The downside to this dream is the danger from coastal erosion and flooding, unless people choose very carefully the place where they are going to live.

Coastal areas have always attracted people to them. The coasts of the UK are lined with resorts, such as Bournemouth and Brighton in the south of England and Blackpool and Morecambe in the north (all of which grew as resorts in Victorian times during the nineteenth century). Today they attract not only holidaymakers and day trippers, but also retired people and commuters (people who travel to work in the cities, but prefer to live in more pleasant places such as on the coast).

How are coasts managed?

The greater the number of people who live near or who visit the coastline, the greater is the need for coastal management. In UK seaside resorts management is necessary for two reasons:

1 To keep the sea out.
2 To keep the beach there.

1 To keep the sea out

The usual method is to build a sea wall (**Figure 1**). Notice its shape. It has a curved lip at the top to deflect the force of the waves. It also directs any sediment the waves may be carrying away from the promenade along the sea front. Walls are expensive to build and costly to maintain, because at certain times they do take quite a battering from the waves (**Figure 3** page 62). The costs can only be justified if many people live there and there is a lot of property to be defended.

2 To keep the beach there

The usual method is to build groynes. Often made of wood, these are built out into the sea at right angles to the coastline. Four groynes can be seen in **Figure 2**. They are a simple and effective way of keeping a beach, because they trap sediment as it is transported along the coast by the longshore drift. They also reduce the energy of the waves making it less likely for the beach and cliffs behind it to be eroded.

Problems of coastal management

Most councils manage their own stretch of coastline without considering the likely consequences for places further along the coast. By trapping sand behind groynes, waves are deprived of their load of sediment. Beaches rely on new supplies of sediment to survive, and without the beaches the cliffs are more quickly eroded. This means that further down the coast beyond the groynes, the erosion is made much worse. The groynes you can see in **Figure 2** are doing a great job of keeping the beach and protecting the soft cliffs at Bournemouth; but they are helping to speed up the already rapid rates of erosion of the cliffs at Barton on Sea, which is located to the east of Bournemouth (page 63). Despite spending more than £1 million and using a variety of methods, the cliffs at Barton on Sea are still being eroded back. Holiday villages and housing estates are in danger.

▲ **Figure 2** Groynes at Bournemouth.

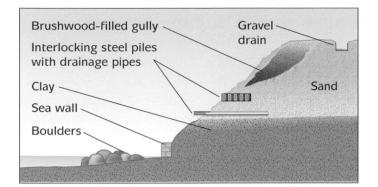

Good management of the coastline takes all relevant factors into account. One way to do this is to make a full cost benefit analysis before any money is spent, like the one in the table below.

Costs	Benefits
• What will it cost to complete?	• What are the advantages which justify the cost?
• How much will it cost to maintain?	• For how long will the benefits last?
• Who will be badly affected by it?	• Who will gain from it?
• Which areas will be badly affected by it?	• How large an area will gain from it?
• Will there be environmental damage?	• Will it improve the environment?

Some people now say that the cost of protecting parts of the British coastline is too great. They argue that it would be cheaper to pay compensation to those affected by erosion and flooding.

Activities

1 Look at **Figures 1** and **2**. For each one in turn:
   a name the method of coastal protection shown
   b draw a labelled diagram to show how it works
   c explain its advantages and disadvantages for coastal management.

2 a Name the methods of coastal protection used at Barton on Sea:
   (i) to protect the clay from erosion by the waves
   (ii) to stop further slumping at the top of the cliffs.
   b Suggest a reason why more than one method is being used.
   c Give two reasons why it is difficult to stop cliffs at Barton on Sea from eroding more.
   d Who are most worried about the danger of more cliff collapses at Barton on Sea?

◀ **Figure 3** Methods of protection for the cliffs at Barton on Sea.

Coastal management in the Netherlands

The Dutch are the world experts in coastal management. They need to be. The western half of the country, which contains all the large cities, most of the industries and the best farm land, lies up to 8m below the present sea level. No one thinks about the cost of coastal protection; without it half the country would be covered by the sea. The great cost is paid for by money raised by taxes, so that everyone pays.

Types of coastal protection in the Netherlands

A Natural
   • Sand dunes line the west coast.

B Human
   • Groynes have been built the full length of the coast.
   • The Great Dyke is a dam blocking off the Zuider Zee from the sea.
   • Many dams seal off the large inlets in the Delta region in the south.

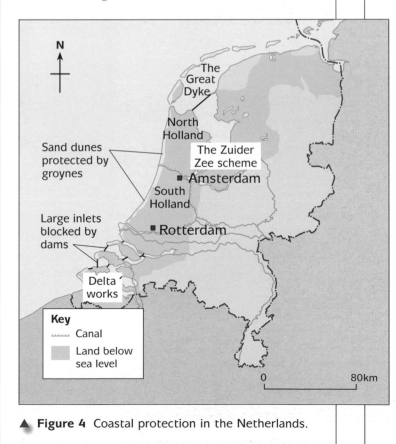

▲ **Figure 4** Coastal protection in the Netherlands.

The Yorkshire coastline from Scarborough to the Humber estuary

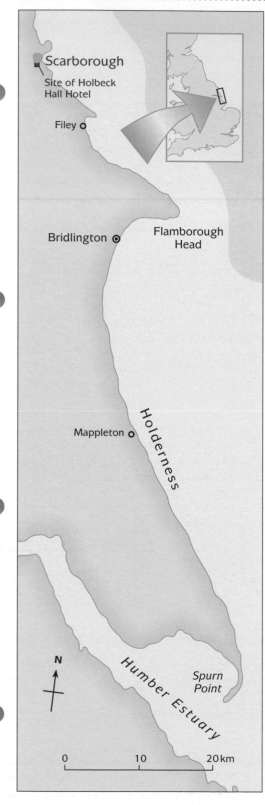

▲ **Figure 1** Map of the Yorkshire coast from Scarborough to the Humber estuary.

◀ **Figure 2** The beach at Scarborough.

▼ **Figure 3** Flamborough Head – note the cliffs, caves and arches.

▲ **Figure 4** The spit at Spurn Point.

Scarborough – the number one resort of the Yorkshire coast

Sandy beaches are found on both sides of the castle headland. Most tourists visit the beach on the South Bay which is nearer to the town centre. On a hot summer's day the narrow strip of sandy beach is packed with adults sitting in deckchairs, children playing on the beach and taking donkey rides, and people of all ages bathing in the North Sea (despite water temperatures below 14°C). Behind the beach, on the other side of the promenade and coast road, is a line of amusement arcades, gift shops and cafes, catering almost exclusively for tourist visitors. One street runs up the steep hillside behind the South Bay linking the beach area with the town centre shops and stores. A sea wall runs for the full length of the bay.

However, the collapse of the cliff under the five star Holbeck Hall hotel in 1993, located on the southern side of the bay in what was thought to be a safe position on the cliff top, highlighted the serious problem of coastal erosion along the Yorkshire coast. It has led Local Authorities to think again about what needs to be done for coastal protection.

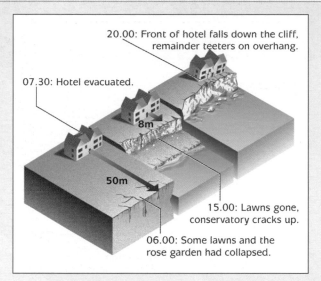

20.00: Front of hotel falls down the cliff, remainder teeters on overhang.

07.30: Hotel evacuated.

8m

50m

15.00: Lawns gone, conservatory cracks up.

06.00: Some lawns and the rose garden had collapsed.

How the Holbeck Hall hotel fell over a cliff on 4 June 1993.

Flamborough Head

A thick bed of chalk outcrops here. Chalk forms impressive cliffs, because it is a harder rock than the boulder clay that covers land to the north and south. Rocky wave-cut platforms can be seen in front of some of the cliffs (**Figure 3**). Notice also that the chalk here has many lines of weakness in it. Wave erosion has been concentrated along these weaknesses. The bottom of the cliffs is full of caves. Along headlands, where there are vertical joints or faults, the caves have grown and been eroded away to form natural arches. Small stacks have been left and have names such as the King and Queen rocks or the Adam and Eve pinnacles.

Spurn Point

This spit is a major feature of coastal deposition (**Figure 4**). The longshore drift of material is from north to south. There is plenty of sand and clay for the waves to collect because of the rapid erosion of the boulder clay cliffs along the coast of Holderness from Bridlington southwards. At the bend in the coastline formed by the Humber estuary, deposition begins. In the last 150 years a ridge of sand some 8km long has built up.

Activities

1 Using **Figure 1** trace or draw an outline of this stretch of coastline. Mark and name on it one example of each of the following coastal landforms:
   • cliff   • wave-cut platform   • cave   • natural arch
   • stack   • beach   • spit

2 a Describe what the beach at Scarborough looks like on a hot summer's day.
   b When the Holbeck Hall hotel fell over the cliff on 4 June 1993, state and explain what happened:
      (i) between 6am and 3pm.
      (ii) between 3pm and 8pm.
   d Why was it such a surprise that the hotel collapsed?

3 Choose one landform of coastal erosion from along this stretch of coastline and one landform of deposition. For each one,
   a show and label its main features on a sketch or diagram
   b explain its formation.

4 Individually or in small groups, put together a leaflet, suitable for visitors to the local tourist office, with the title 'The geographical attractions of the Yorkshire coast'.

Holderness – problems of coastal management

Being top of the European league for coastal erosion is not something which pleases the people of Holderness. Today, waves remove between 7 and 10m of land every year. This does not sound like very much, but over time it adds up to the loss of a lot of land. Today's coastline is three to four kilometres further west than it was in Roman times. In the past thousand years 29 villages have been lost to the sea. All the way along the coast of Holderness farm land and farm houses are at risk (page 61); caravan sites and holiday homes have already been lost to the sea. The rate of erosion is unlikely to be reduced, because of the combination of land sinking on the eastern side of the British Isles and a possible sea level rise as a result of global warming. Sea levels in Holderness are estimated to be rising by 4mm a year.

Why is the coastline being eroded so quickly?

The main reason is rock type. The rock in Holderness is boulder clay, which was left by the ice sheets. It is made up of soft clay and sands that are not cemented together. Waves easily wash away the clay and sands from between the boulders, which increases the rate of erosion.

Also, when it rains, water enters cracks and spaces in the rock. After heavy rains this makes the cliff top unstable and liable to slumping. Most erosion occurs when winds blow from the north or north east. The waves cross a long stretch of open sea and have a long fetch (page 62); this means that the waves are more powerful and capable of greater erosion. It is difficult protecting such a long stretch of coastline of over 50km long.

Coastal defences at Mappleton

Mappleton is a small village. By 1990 it was under a real threat of becoming lost village number 30 along the coast of Holderness. The B1242 is the main coastal road and it would have been expensive to find a new route for it. This helped to justify spending almost £2 million on a coastal protection scheme for a village of about 100 people. Blocks of granite were imported from Norway for sea defences at the bottom of the cliff and for two rock groynes. The purpose of the two rock groynes is to trap beach material, which will protect the sea wall from wave attack.

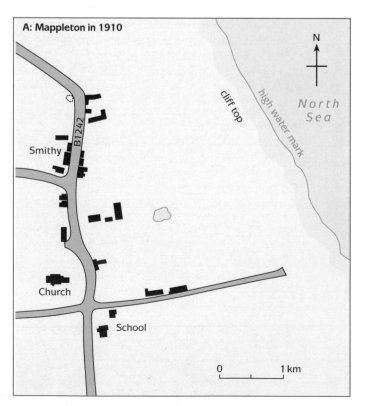

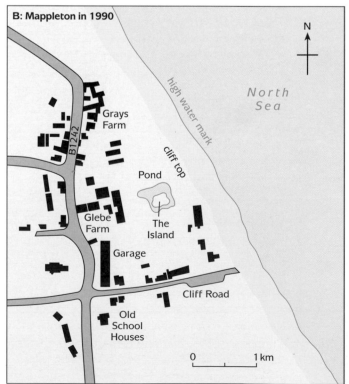

▲ **Figure 1** Mappleton in 1910 and 1990.

▲ **Figure 2** Mappleton and its sea defences.

Some views on coastal protection in Holderness

Holderness Council
We are a small authority with a total annual budget of only £4m. Spending a large amount of money to protect a village is hard to justify. Many people agree that the village should be allowed to disappear ... but it is terribly difficult to say this.

Ministry of Agriculture
We are moving towards a policy of 'managed retreat'. Although towns, villages and roads would be protected, farmland and even isolated houses would be regarded as dispensable and allowed to disappear. There are food surpluses in the EU so that every bit of farmland is no longer needed.

Dr John Pethick
– a top scientist at the University of Hull
Low-lying farmland should be abandoned and cliffs allowed to collapse because they are the main sources of sand and silt that build up to protect other parts of the coast, including towns and cities.

Farmer living just south of Mappleton
My farm is at greater risk from the sea than ever because of the coastal protection works at Mappleton.

Activities

1 Using **Figure 1** page 70, trace or draw a sketch map to show the location of Holderness and the village of Mappleton.

2 a Look at **Figure 2** above. Describe what the cliffs at Mappleton look like.
  b From page 72, state two pieces of evidence that rapid erosion has taken place along the coast of Holderness.
  c Explain why the coastline is being eroded so quickly.
  d Why is the rate of erosion expected to increase rather than decrease in the future?

3 a Use **Figure 1** page 72.
  (i) By how many metres has the coastline at the northern edge of the map moved west between 1910 and 1990?
  (ii) What is the difference in the distance between the B1242 road and the nearest cliff top in 1910 compared with the distance in 1990?
  b With the help of **Figure 2**, describe the methods used to protect Mappleton.
  c Explain why the farmer who owns the land south of the cliff road, which can be seen in **Figure 2**, is complaining about the coastal protection works at Mappleton.

4 a Make two columns. Put headings 'Reasons for protecting the coastline of Holderness' and 'Reasons for not protecting the coastline of Holderness'. List as many reasons as you can under each heading.
  b What do you think would be the best policy for Holderness? Explain your own view.

Case Study – Blackpool

Solving problems in coastal resorts – Blackpool

▶ **Figure 1** Blackpool, the UK's largest seaside resort.

In 1850 Blackpool (**Figure 1**) was a small village. Today it is the UK's largest seaside resort and a town of about 150 000 people. During the nineteenth century the textile towns in Lancashire grew; workers and their families began to visit the coast at Blackpool because it was close by. When the railway line to Blackpool opened in 1846, the number of visitors increased greatly. Today most people arrive by car using the M55 motorway link from the M6. Although more than 8 million people visit Blackpool in a year, the resort still has its problems.

Problems in Blackpool

- Overcrowding, especially at weekends and bank holidays.
- Unemployment during the winter when some facilities close down.
- Keeping the beach and resort clean.
- Land, air and water pollution.
- Coping with coastal erosion.
- Competition with other resorts in Britain and abroad.
- The unpredictable British weather which drives people to the Mediterranean for guaranteed summer sunshine.

Solving Blackpool's problems

- Investment by the local council in beach and street cleaning equipment.
- Providing new facilities to attract visitors, some of them indoor, e.g. Pepsi Max for when the weather is wet.
- Extending the season, e.g. Blackpool illuminations in the autumn and conferences in winter.
- Providing new parking facilities, park and ride and encouraging the use of the trams.
- Gaining the EU Blue Flag award for having good bathing water quality, and facilities for visitors, e.g. toilets, safety belts and lifeguards.
- Building and maintaining groynes and sea walls.
- Reducing the amount of sand extraction that takes place along the coast from Blackpool.

Activities

1 Use an atlas.
a Find Blackpool and draw a sketch map to show its position.
b Add the main motorways and name four large towns or cities near Blackpool.

2 Make a table with the title 'Problems of Blackpool and attempted solutions'. Follow the layout given below. One row has been completed for you. Under A state the problem. Under B state whether the problem is environmental, economic (to do with money and income) or social (to do with people).

Some can be more than one of these. Under C select one or more of the items listed under 'Solving Blackpool's problems'.

3 Take the role of one of the following:
- a local person who owns an amusement arcade on the sea front at Blackpool
- someone from a conservation group
- a member of Blackpool council
- owner of a sand extraction company.

Write a letter to the local paper stating what you would like to see happening in Blackpool in future and how this should be managed.

A Problem	B Type of problem	C Attempted solution
Overcrowding, especially at weekends and bank holidays.	Social	Providing new parking facilities, park and ride and encouraging the use of trams.

Chapter 6

Weather and climate

Winter weather in the Lake District under anticyclonic conditions. Under the settled and calm weather conditions created by an area of high pressure, radiation fog forms in the valleys and frost lingers longer on the shaded slopes.

Key Ideas

Weather and climate are influenced by location:

- the global (world) distribution of climates is affected by factors such as latitude, distance from the sea and prevailing winds
- there are regional differences in climate in the UK based upon factors such as temperature and precipitation
- depressions and anticyclones lead to different and varied weather conditions in the UK.

Weather and climate influence human activity:

- climates affect environments and human activities
- drought and tropical storms affect human activities
- people respond to weather hazards in different ways.

Global distribution of climates

What is meant by the climate of a place?

The climate in the UK is described as having mild, wet winters and warm, wet summers. It is called a **temperate maritime climate**.

- Temperate means that the UK does not feel either the heat of tropics or the coldness of the poles.

- Maritime tells you that the UK feels the influence of the sea.

The sea has two important effects on the climate of the UK:

1 It reduces temperature differences between winter and summer.

2 It increases the amount of precipitation.

The climate of a place is an average of its weather conditions. Temperature and precipitation are averaged out over many years. They show what weather you can normally expect in a place.

Example – Palma in Majorca

Look at the temperature and rainfall figures for Palma in **Figure 1**. Imagine you are going there on holiday in August.

- The top graph shows you the average temperature that you can expect – about 25°C.

- The bottom graph shows you that there is on average about 20mm of rain in August; this means that you can expect it to be dry for most of the holiday.

Hot and dry weather in August helps to explain why so many British people take summer holidays in Spain.

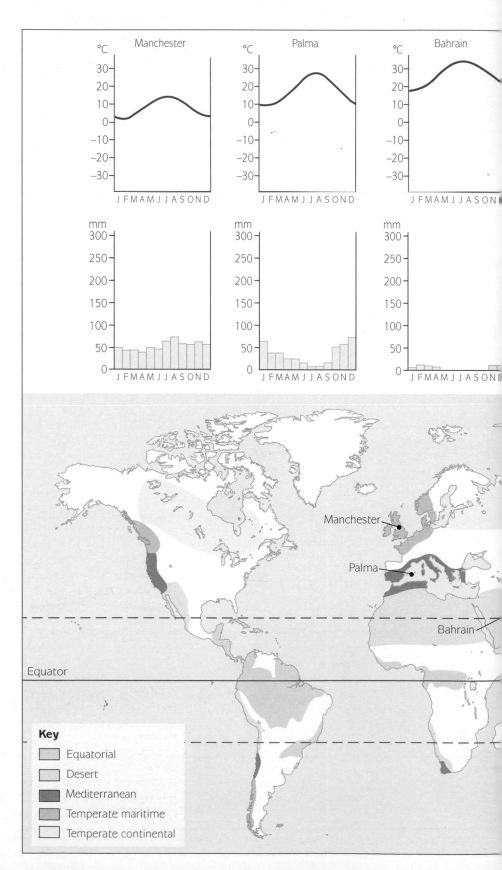

Key
- Equatorial
- Desert
- Mediterranean
- Temperate maritime
- Temperate continental

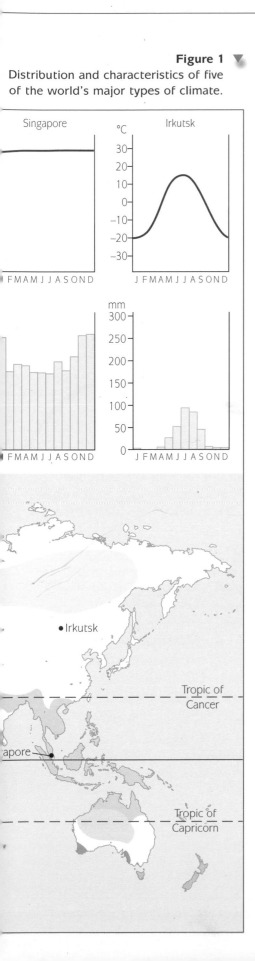

Figure 1 ▼
Distribution and characteristics of five of the world's major types of climate.

ℹ How to describe and use climatic graphs

A Temperature graph
1 State the highest (maximum) temperature and name the month.
2 State the lowest (minimum) temperature and name the month.
3 Work out the annual range of temperature by subtracting the lowest from the highest and stating the difference.
4 Describe the shape (gradient) of the temperature line.
5 Check that you have stated the temperature unit (°C) and that your answers are accurate.

B Precipitation graph
1 Name the month with the highest amount of precipitation and state the amount.
2 Name the season or seasons in which most precipitation falls. (Note that in some places the answer could be 'all year'.)
3 Name the month with the lowest amount of precipitation and state the amount.
4 Name the season or seasons in which little precipitation falls.
5 Give some idea of the total amount of precipitation for the year. (Occasionally you may need to calculate the exact total; usually it is sufficient to use descriptions such as 'little' or 'very low' for under 250mm per year and 'high' for over 1500mm per year.)
6 Check that you have stated the precipitation unit (mm) and that your answers are accurate.

Activities

1 Following the guidance in parts A and B of the Information Box, describe **a** the temperature and **b** the precipitation for Manchester.

2 **a** State two ways in which:
   (i) temperatures in Manchester are different from those in Irkutsk
   (ii) precipitation in Manchester is different from that in Irkutsk.
   b Manchester in the UK has a temperate maritime climate. Irkutsk in Siberia has a climate similar to that of the temperate continental. Which climate would you prefer? Explain your answer.

3 Singapore has an equatorial climate.
   a (i) Describe two ways in which temperatures in Singapore are different from those in the other four places in **Figure 1**.
   (ii) What is the main way in which the precipitation in Singapore is different from that of the others?
   (iii) The normal description for an equatorial climate is hot and wet all year. State the evidence to support this from the graph for Singapore.
   b Look at the world map in **Figure 1**.
   (i) Describe where Singapore is located.
   (ii) Name a continent where large areas have an equatorial climate.
   (iii) Where are the equatorial and temperate continental climates in the world? State two ways in which their distribution is different.

ctors that affect the global
world) distribution of climates

Factors affecting temperature

A Latitude

This is of greatest importance. Highest temperatures occur around the Equator in the tropics. Lowest temperatures occur in polar latitudes north and south of 60°.

Heating is greatest near the Equator because of **insolation** (**Figure 1**). Near the Equator:

- the sun shines from a high angle in the sky all year
- less of the sun's light is lost by reflection
- direct rays mean that there is a smaller area of the Earth's surface for each ray to heat up.

Therefore there are high rates of insolation in the tropics and it is the warmest part of the Earth.

It is the opposite near the Poles. Here,

- the sun shines from a low angle in the sky and there are hardly any sun's rays in winter
- a lot of the sun's light is reflected back and lost
- rays from an oblique angle mean that each ray has a larger area of surface to heat up.

Therefore there are low rates of insolation in polar latitudes.

B Distance from the sea

In summer, the sea heats up less quickly than the land. People swimming in the sea on summer holidays know this. The sea is a lighter surface than the land, so more of the sun's light is reflected and not absorbed. As a result, places close to sea have less hot summers than those inland.

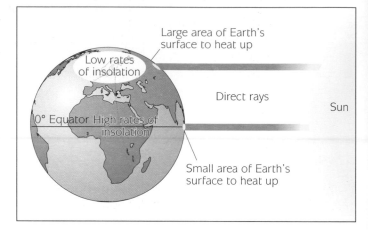

▲ **Figure 1** The effects of latitude on temperature – insolation.

During winter months the opposite happens. The sea keeps its store of summer heat for longer than the land. On cold winter days the temperature of the sea water will be higher than the air on land. The land soon loses heat from its surface in winter. The warmer sea water means that places close to the sea are warmer than those further inland in winter.

C Prevailing winds

A prevailing wind is the direction from which the wind blows most often during the year. Across the British Isles it is south-westerly. As a result the UK is warmer in winter than expected for its latitude in winter. **Figure 2** helps to show you why. Winds blowing from the south-west have crossed large areas of sea, as well as warm ocean currents, before reaching the British Isles. The Gulf Stream and North Atlantic Drift are warm ocean currents; any wind passing over them is warmed up, especially in winter.

D Height above sea level

Mountain and hilly areas are colder. Temperature decreases by about 1°C for every 150m in height. This is because the air becomes thinner, so less of the Earth's heat is trapped and more is lost into space. However, there are great temperature differences within upland areas. In the northern hemisphere, sunny south-facing slopes are warmer than shaded slopes that face north.

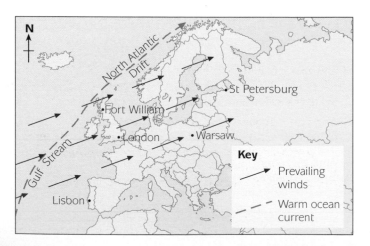

◀ **Figure 2** Why places near to the sea are warmer in winter.

Precipitation

Precipitation is the name for all types of moisture that come from the atmosphere. This includes rain, snow and hail. Precipitation occurs when air rises to high levels in the atmosphere. One type of precipitation is **convectional rainfall** (**Figure 3**) which is formed as follows:

1 Direct rays of the sun heat the surface.
2 Great heating of the surface causes the hot air to rise.
3 Hot air rises and cools.
4 Cooling causes moisture in the air to condense.
5 Tall cumulo-nimbus clouds form.
6 Water droplets increase in size in the cloud.
7 When the droplets grow large, they fall as rain.
8 Heavy downpours occur, often with thunder and lightning (**Figure 4**).

Convectional rain falls all year near the Equator, because rates of insolation are always high. It happens in the middle of the large land masses of North America, Europe and Asia in summer when the land becomes hot.

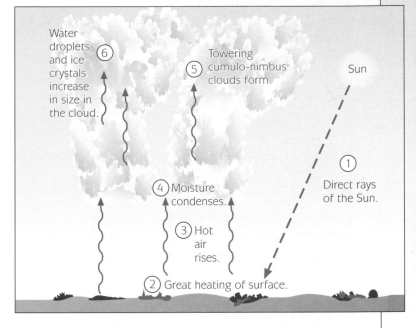

▲ **Figure 3** Formation of convectional rain. The stages in the formation of convectional rainfall are numbered 1–6.

Activities

1 Write out the sentences below. Fill in the gaps using either WARMER or COLDER.
   • Places on the Equator are .... than places near the Poles.
   • In summer places next to the coast are .... than places further inland.
   • It is .... on the tops of mountains than in the valleys.
   • South-facing slopes north of the Equator are .... than those facing north.
   • The North Atlantic Drift makes the UK climate .... than would be expected for its latitude.
   • Because the prevailing wind in the UK is south westerly, winters are .... and summers are .... than if the prevailing wind had blown from the east across large areas of land.

2 Go back to **Figure 1** on pages 76–77.
   a How many degrees warmer is Palma in August than Manchester?
   b How many degrees colder is Irkutsk in January than Manchester?

3 a **(i)** Draw a labelled diagram to show how insolation works.
     (ii) Explain why Palma is warmer than Manchester in August.
   b **(i)** Draw a labelled sketch map to show why the UK has warm winters.
     (ii) Explain why Manchester is warmer than Irkutsk in January.

▲ **Figure 4** Tropical thunderstorm in Malaysia.

4 Draw a large labelled diagram to show the formation of convectional rainfall. Make sure that you add what happens in stages 7 and 8.

5 Give one reason for each of the following.
   a More convectional rain falls in summer than in winter.
   b Convectional rain falls more often in Malaysia than in UK.
   c Convectional rain is heavy rain.
   d Convectional rain falls from high and tall clouds.

The climate of the UK

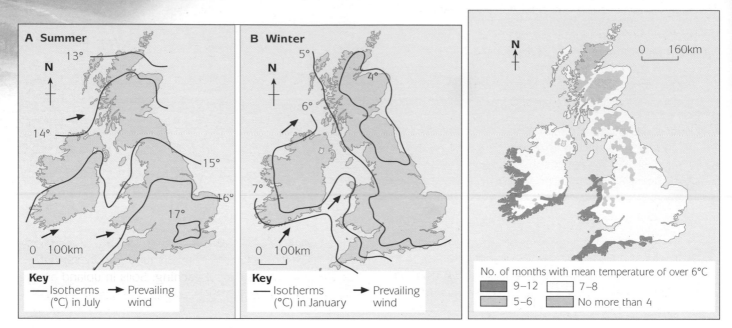

▲ **Figure 1 A:** summer temperatures; **B:** winter temperatures.

▲ **Figure 2** Length of growing season.

The type of climate in the UK is temperate maritime (page 76). However, there are variations in average temperatures and precipitation from one part of the UK to another. These affect human activities.

Temperature variations in the UK

In summer

Look at **Figure 1A**. The general pattern is that the south is warmer than the north. The red lines that show this are called isotherms (lines linking together places with the same average temperature). They run mainly from west to east across the British Isles. Most of the Midlands and the south of England are shown to have summer temperatures above 16°C, whereas in most of northern Scotland summer temperatures are below 14°C.

Why is the south warmer than the north? The sun shines at a higher angle in the sky. This means that rates of insolation are higher in the south; its latitude is lower. London is on average 4°C warmer than northern Scotland in summer.

In winter

Now look at **Figure 1B**. Can you spot how the position of the isotherms has changed? More of the lines run north to south for at least part of their courses. This tells us that the west of the British Isles is warmer than the east in winter. Warmest of all is Land's End in Cornwall where the average temperature is above 7°C. Coldest is eastern Scotland where winter temperatures fall below 4°C in those areas that lie inside the isotherm for 4°C.

Why is the west warmer than the east? The sea is warmer than the land in winter. South-westerly winds pick up warm air from crossing the Atlantic Ocean and North Atlantic Drift. Western parts of the UK feel this warm air first.

Influence of temperature on human activities

Farmers are affected most. The length of the growing season (**Figure 2**) is controlled by temperature. Grass grows when temperatures go above 6°C. It grows all year in coastal regions of Cornwall and Devon. Good grass growth favours dairy farming. Flowers and vegetables (e.g. daffodils and cauliflowers) from south-west England reach the market early, which fetches higher prices for farmers. There are more seaside holiday resorts along the south coast than along any other coast in England because of its high summer temperatures. Old people feel the cold more than the young, which is why so many people retire to the south coast in general and to south-west England in particular.

Activities

1 Trace or sketch a small outline map of the British Isles.
   a Mark and name on it the place where you live.
   b (i) Using **Figure 1A**, state the average summer temperature for your area.
      (ii) Using **Figure 1B** do the same for winter.

Precipitation

Look at **Figure 3**. It shows that precipitation in the UK is highest in the west and lowest in the east. Why?

1 **Direction of the prevailing winds**
   The south-westerly winds have crossed a large area of ocean and have picked up a lot of moisture. They drop their moisture first in the west and become drier as they move across the UK.

2 **Frontal depressions**
   These areas of low pressure with their warm and cold fronts also move from west to east. They also drop their rainfall first in the west.

3 **Relief**
   Most upland areas are located in the west. When winds that are full of moisture are forced to rise over hills and mountains, a lot of precipitation results. Labels 1–4 in **Figure 4** show the formation of relief rainfall. To the east of high ground there is much less rain. This is known as a rain shadow; it is shown by labels 5 and 6 in **Figure 4**.

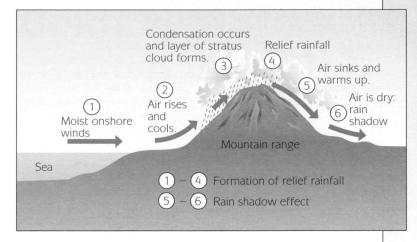

▲ **Figure 4** Relief rainfall and the rain shadow effect.

Influence of precipitation on human activities

High rainfall washes the minerals (and goodness) out of the soil. This is called **leaching**. Soils in upland areas become acid and infertile after heavy leaching. In many upland areas the land is no good for farming. However, it may be good for water storage in reservoirs, especially where there are steep-sided valleys and natural lakes (e.g. North Wales and the Lake District).

High precipitation in lowland areas in the west gives good grass growth; dairy farming is usually the main type of farming (e.g. Devon and Cheshire). Low precipitation in lowland areas in the east favours crop growing. This is usually a mixture of cereals (e.g. wheat and barley) and root crops (e.g. potatoes and sugar beet). East Anglia, with under 625mm per year, is the most important crop-growing region in the UK.

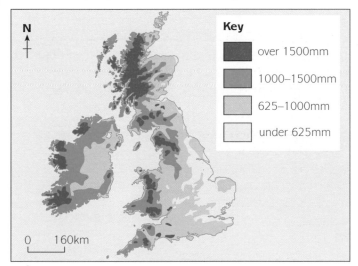

Key
- over 1500mm
- 1000–1500mm
- 625–1000mm
- under 625mm

0   160km

▲ **Figure 3** Average annual precipitation.

---

2 **a** Describe the differences between the course of the 16°C isotherm in summer and that of the 5°C isotherm in winter.
  b Give reasons for one of the differences described in **a**.

3 Overall, south-west England is the warmest part of the UK.
  a Explain why it is the warmest part of the country.
  b **(i)** Name two human activities in south-west England that benefit from this.
  (ii) Explain how and why they benefit.

---

4 Look at **Figure 3**.
  a Name where the largest area with over 1500mm of precipitation is found.
  b Name where the largest area with below 625mm is found.
  c Describe how the map shows that western Britain is wetter than the east.
  d State three reasons why the west is wetter.
  e Give one advantage and one disadvantage of high precipitation for people.

5 Mountain tops in the Highlands of Scotland reach above 1000m.
  a Draw a labelled diagram to show why relief leads to increased amounts of precipitation.
  b Some of the precipitation in the Highlands falls as snow. Suggest ways in which snow **(i)** hinders and **(ii)** gives opportunities for human activities.

Weather in the UK – frontal depressions

Climate is the long-term average, whereas **weather** is the day-to-day variations. A breakfast TV weather forecast for the day usually covers:

- temperatures
- whether it is going to rain or not
- whether it is expected to be cloudy or sunny
- wind speed and direction.

As you know the weather forecasters do not always get it right. The British weather is famous for being changeable and unpredictable. However, the use of new high technology, such as satellite data, radar showing rainfall and computer models, means that weather forecasts are much more accurate than they used to be.

Frontal depressions

Depressions are areas of **low pressure**. Air is rising which leaves low air pressure at the surface. Winds blow in an anti-clockwise direction. They bring spells of unsettled weather with plenty of wind, cloud and rain.

From time to time the UK is hit by depressions with very low pressures. Heavy downpours lead to local flooding; storm force winds cause damage to trees and buildings. One famous example was the 'hurricane' which devastated south-east England in October 1987.

Formation

Frontal depressions form where warm air from the tropics meets cold air from the poles. The warm air is forced to rise, which creates the centre of low pressure. The line between warm and cold air is called a front.

In most depressions there are two fronts:

1. A **warm front**, so called because as it passes over the UK, warm air follows it. The air is warm as it has come from the tropics. This front is shown in red in **Figure 3**.

2. A **cold front**, so called because as it passes over the UK, cold air follows it. The air is cold as it has come from the poles. This front is shown in blue in **Figure 3**.

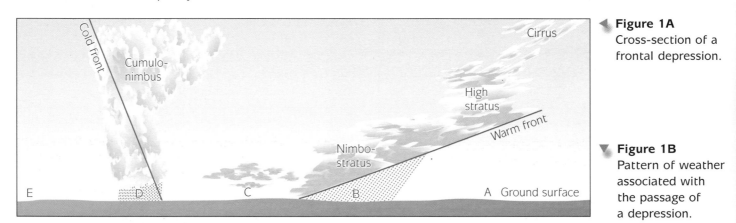

◄ **Figure 1A**
Cross-section of a frontal depression.

▼ **Figure 1B**
Pattern of weather associated with the passage of a depression.

Location	Weather	Reasons
A Well ahead of the warm front	Starts to cloud over. Clouds are high.	Warm air is being forced to rise above the warm front.
B Ahead of the warm front	A thick sheet of cloud. Steady rain is falling.	Moisture in the rising warm air is condensing.
C Between the warm and cold fronts	The temperature increases and the rain stops.	The warm air at ground level is not being forced to rise.
D At the cold front	Tall clouds develop. Heavy rain is falling. There may be thunder and lightning.	The warm air is being forced up high into the sky by the powerful push of the cold air.
E Behind the cold front	Temperatures fall. The weather is a mixture of sunshine and showers.	Any rising air along the front has moved away. There are small areas of rising air giving showers.

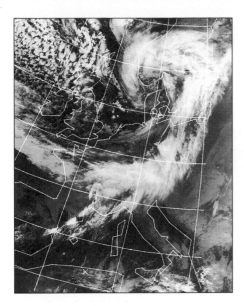

Figure 2 Satellite photograph of a frontal depression.

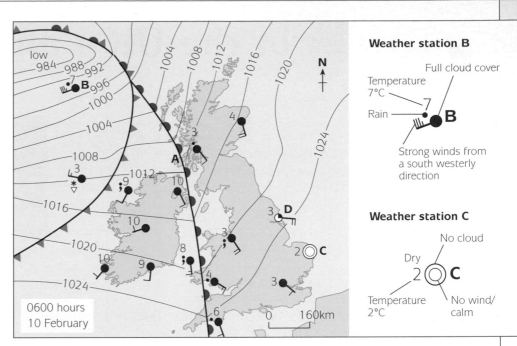

Figure 3 Synoptic chart dominated by a frontal depression.

You will have seen satellite photographs like the one in **Figure 2** on the TV weather forecasts. In **Figure 2**:

- the swirl of cloud shows the centre of the low pressure
- the lines of almost continuous white cloud show the fronts
- the white speckles of cloud in the top north-west corner show shower clouds in the cold air.

Figure 3 shows a weather map. Its proper name is synoptic chart. Each weather station is shown by a circle. The shading in the centre and symbols outside give information about its weather. Stations B and C on the chart are given as examples. A key to some of the symbols used on weather maps is given on page 85.

Activities

1 Mix and match. Write out the following so that the definition matches the term.

Term	Definition
weather	another name for a depression
low pressure	it brings heavy rain and lower temperatures
warm front	daily changes in temperature and precipitation
cold front	it brings steady rain and higher temperatures

2 a Draw a large cross-section of a frontal depression.
  b Add extra labels by using information from **Figure 1B**.

3 a Make a frame the same size as **Figure 2** and sketch the clouds inside it.
  b Add the following labels:
    low pressure   fronts   shower clouds.

4 Answer the following questions from **Figure 3**.
  a State the pressure value in the centre of the low.
  b Name the type of front marked A.
  c Why is it raining in western Scotland, Wales and south-west England?
  d (i) State the evidence from the map that temperatures are higher in Ireland than in England.
    (ii) Give one reason for these higher temperatures in Ireland.
  e (i) In what way is the cloud cover in weather stations C and D different from the others?
    (ii) Where are weather stations C and D located?
    (iii) The weather system is moving eastwards. What kind of weather are C and D likely to record later in the same day?

Weather in the UK – anticyclones

Anticyclones are areas of **high pressure**. Air is sinking which gives high air pressure at the surface. Winds blow in a clockwise direction. They bring spells of dry weather with light winds and calm conditions. Although for most of the time depressions dominate the UK's weather, sometimes a strong anticyclone stays for one week or more. Then it blocks out the frontal depressions.

Anticyclonic weather and the reasons for it

Weather	Reasons for it
Summer weather	
Dry	Sinking air stops air from rising, cooling and forming rain.
Hot and often sunny	The sun is at a high angle in the sky.
A heatwave is possible	Temperatures build up day by day.
Winter weather	
Dry	Sinking air stops air from rising, cooling and forming rain.
Cold but usually sunny by day	The sun is at a low angle in the sky. Days are short. The land doesn't warm up much in the weak winter sun. Low insolation.
Frost and fog at night.	Nights are long. Skies are clear. Heat is lost (or radiated) into space from the ground surface.
A big freeze is possible.	It gets colder day by day.

Fog and frost are more likely to form in valley floors and low-lying areas. **Figure 1** shows that these are the coldest places at night. Cold air is denser than warm air, so it sinks towards the lowest ground. Look back to the photograph on page 75. Mist and fog is only affecting the valleys; the tops of the Lake District hills are clear. Also notice the frost, which can be seen mainly on the shaded sides of the valleys (i.e. those which face north).

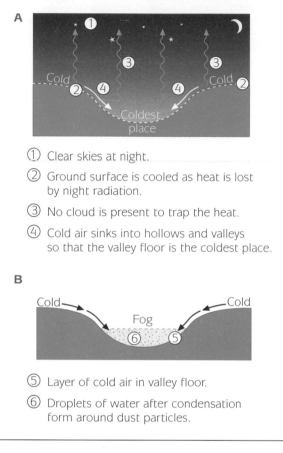

① Clear skies at night.

② Ground surface is cooled as heat is lost by night radiation.

③ No cloud is present to trap the heat.

④ Cold air sinks into hollows and valleys so that the valley floor is the coldest place.

⑤ Layer of cold air in valley floor.

⑥ Droplets of water after condensation form around dust particles.

▲ **Figure 1** Formation of radiation fog.

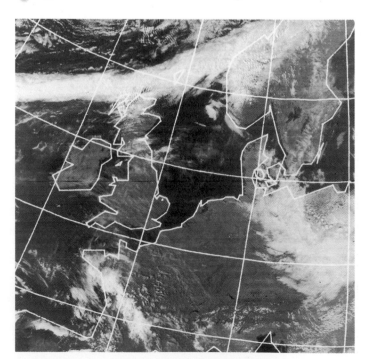

▶ **Figure 2** Satellite photograph of an anticyclone over the British Isles. Skies are mainly cloudless. Only in the north of Scotland is there a band of cloud from a frontal depression. The presence of the anticyclone has stopped these fronts from moving further south over the UK.

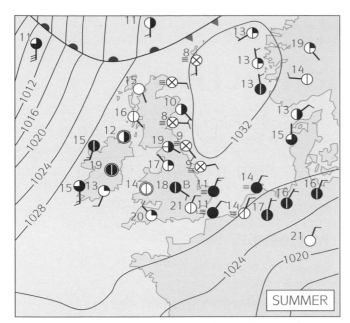

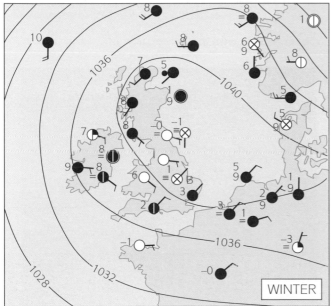

▲ **Figure 3** Synoptic charts showing anticyclonic weather in the UK.

Key to synoptic charts

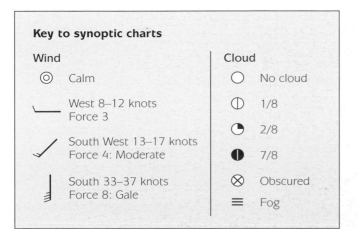

Wind		Cloud	
◎	Calm	○	No cloud
—	West 8–12 knots Force 3	◑	1/8
╱	South West 13–17 knots Force 4: Moderate	◔	2/8
⌇	South 33–37 knots Force 8: Gale	◖	7/8
		⊗	Obscured
		≡	Fog

▲ **Figure 4** A motorway in fog.

The effects of fog on human activities

Fog is the most common hazard of anticyclonic weather in the UK. Thick fog on motorways is dangerous (**Figure 4**). Multiple crashes and pile-ups happen most often when motorists suddenly meet a patch of thick fog, often in valleys or other low areas. Although motorway warning signs and lights along certain sections of motorways have helped to reduce the numbers of accidents, many motorists travel too fast for the conditions. Fog causes delays at airports. Lighthouses have foghorns to warn ships of dangers, such as rocks, when the light cannot be seen.

Activities

1 Write out the sentences filling in the spaces with HIGH or LOW.
  • Air rising leads to areas of .... pressure, whereas air sinking leads to areas of .... pressure.
  • Winds blow clockwise around areas of .... pressure and anti-clockwise around areas of .... pressure.
  • Wet and windy weather can be expected when pressure is ...., whereas dry weather is likely when pressure is ....
  • Heatwaves occur in summer when pressure is ....; big freezes occur in winter when pressure is ....
  • Storms and flooding are associated with deep areas of .... pressure.

2 a Draw diagrams to show how fog forms.
  b Why is fog more likely to form in low-lying areas?
  c (i) Name two types of transport badly affected by fog.
    (ii) For one of these, explain how the fog hazard can be reduced.
  d Look at the weather map for summer in **Figure 3**.
    (i) In which part of England is fog recorded?
    (ii) What temperatures are reported for the weather stations with fog?
    (iii) Suggest why temperatures in other parts of England are higher.

The effects of weather and climate on human activity

We are not used to extreme weather conditions in the UK. There are no daily downpours as in the wet tropics. It is not dry month after month as in hot deserts. There is not a hurricane season as in the Caribbean and Florida. For most of the time the British weather can be described as not very exciting. However, just occasionally the UK weather hits the headlines (Figure 1).

Drought

Water is essential for life. People only live in hot deserts if there is a source of water. Drought is a hazard when rainfall is much lower than average, and a lot less than the amount people had planned for. Droughts in Africa since 1970 have had devastating effects. When crops fail and vegetation is burnt off by the heat so that animals die, people starve. The groups most at risk are the young, the old and the sick. The drought in Ethiopia was at its worst in 1983 and thousands died. Severe drought affected countries in southern Africa in the early 1990s; the maize crop, upon which rural people depended, failed. Many deaths followed. The economies of countries such as Zimbabwe were hit hard by the shortage of crops for export.

September 1995   Drought Report

Bottled water for drought hit Yorkshire towns

March 1997

Motorway Madness

100-vehicle pile-up in thick fog on the M1

JANUARY 1998

Worst Storms Since 1987 Hurricane

Falling tree kills driver as gales bring power cuts and floods

▲ **Figure 1** Newspaper headlines.

▲ **Figure 2** Haweswater in the Lake District, August 1995. Instead of a reservoir full of water to supply Manchester, it became a tourist attraction.

Drought in the UK

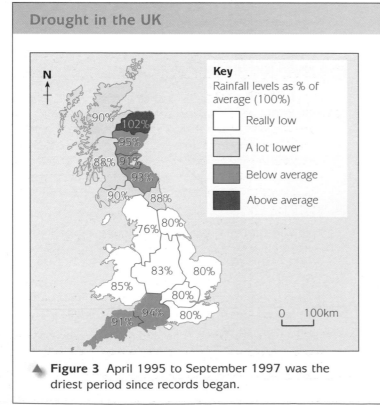

Key
Rainfall levels as % of average (100%)

☐ Really low

☐ A lot lower

☐ Below average

☐ Above average

90%
102%
95%
88% 91%
93%
90% 88%
76% 80%
83% 80%
85%
80%
91% 94% 80%

0   100km

▲ **Figure 3** April 1995 to September 1997 was the driest period since records began.

Even England, which is normally wet, suffered from a drought in the mid-1990s (Figure 2). Farmers faced some extra costs for water supply and lost income when crop yields were reduced. Yorkshire Water paid for the distribution of bottled water to places most badly affected by shortages. However, for most people in the UK, measures such as the ban on the use of hosepipes were a nuisance, but not a matter of life and death as in countries in Africa.

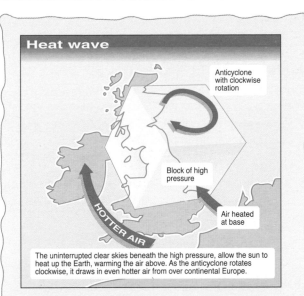

Heat wave

Anticyclone with clockwise rotation

Block of high pressure

Air heated at base

HOTTER AIR

The uninterrupted clear skies beneath the high pressure, allow the sun to heat up the Earth, warming the air above. As the anticyclone rotates clockwise, it draws in even hotter air from over continental Europe.

Summer of '95 blazes its way to a new record

Another water authority stepped in last night to ban hosepipes, as weather forecasters confirmed that the summer of 1995 looks set to become the driest since records began in 1727.

North West Water introduced hose-pipe bans and standpipes have been installed in Bradford in case of emergency.

Forecasters also confirmed that June, July and August could be the third hottest summer spell since thermometer measurements first began in 1659.

The problem – the stubborn anticyclone system over the British Isles – shows no sign of going away. There has been no rain in London since 26 July nor in Sheffield since 27 July. The book-makers William Hill were offering odds of 4/1 on the first totally dry August for London since 1924.

The weather has been bad for potato growers and some dairy farmers are reported to be using winter feed because of dry pastures. But the hot weather has helped cereal growers to an early harvest.

▲ **Figure 4** Adapted from *The Guardian*, 17 August 1995.

The sun and heat have come as a welcome fillip to British seaside resorts, with hotels full and seafront stalls doing a roaring trade. Spending in Kent, Surrey and Sussex reached a record £1.5 billion last month, the South East England Tourist Board reported.

By contrast, halfway through the busiest tourist period of the year, more than a million foreign holidays worth £350 million remained unsold this weekend.

Supermarkets announced record sales of soft drinks and ice-cream so far this month. A spokesperson for one of the big chains said 'We listen to the weather forecasts and change or move our stock around accordingly. Hot weather usually means good sales for salad produce and for any kind of drinks, so we extend our shelf space for these items. On the meat counter, people just aren't interested in joints of meat for roasts, but chops, burgers and sausages are selling as soon as we put them out. Everyone must be having barbecues!'

▲ **Figure 5** Cuttings from other newspapers in August 1995.

Activities

1 Look at **Figure 3**.
 a (i) Where was the only area to have above average rainfall between 1995 and 1997?
 (ii) In which part of England was the lowest percentage of average rainfall recorded?
 (iii) Name the part of the UK with rainfall 15 per cent below average.
 b Trace or sketch a small outline map of England and Wales. Shade on it the areas where rainfall was 15 per cent or more below average at that time.

2 a Make a table with two columns, one headed 'Winners' and the other 'Losers'. In the hot dry summers of 1995 and 1996, which of the following groups of people were winners and which were losers? Complete your table.
 the Water Boards   Dairy farmers   Makers of soft drinks
 Potato farmers   UK hotel owners   Ice cream factory
 Package tour companies   Cereal farmers
 Seafront arcade workers   Sausage factory
 Charter airlines   UK bed and breakfast owners
 b Choose two of the winners. Explain how and why each one benefited.
 c Choose one of the losers. Explain why it lost money.
 d Some supermarkets made extra money during these dry summers, some did not. Suggest reasons for this.

3 Explain as fully as you can why drought is a much more serious hazard to people in African countries than in the UK.

Tropical storms

Tropical storms are areas of very low pressure. They form over warm tropical oceans. One example is hurricanes, which affect the Caribbean and Florida between August and November each year.

Causes of the damage and destruction

1 **High winds** – between 150 and 300km per hour, which can blow down everything in their path.

2 **Torrential downpours** – 500mm of rain falling within 24 hours is not unknown. This is the same amount that falls in Cambridge in a full year.

3 **Storm surges** – walls of sea water up to 10m high whipped up by the winds and waves.

▼ **Figure 1** Summary of the effects of Hurricane Andrew in 1992.

- 58 people killed
- US $27 billion damage
- 50 000 homeless in the southern suburbs of Miami
- 90 per cent of houses in estates around the Homestead Air Base hit
- Route 1 highway south of Miami blocked by broken power lines and debris
- Roadsides lined by smashed and flooded shops and businesses

Effects

It is possible for everything to be destroyed. Coastal and low-lying areas are flooded. On steep hillsides landslides of soil, stones and rock are set off. People are trapped and killed. Homes and crops are flattened.

Hurricane watch in the USA

The USA spends millions of dollars trying to predict a hurricane's course. When a hurricane is on course to hit a populated area, they

- issue warnings to people and businesses
- prepare the emergency services
- tell people to board up their homes and offices
- advise people to go into underground shelters or move inland where the risk is less.

Improved forecasting has saved lives, but the cost of hurricane damage keeps on increasing as property values go up (**Figure 2**). However, the forecasters do not always manage to get it right. Hurricane Andrew changed its course at the last minute and started to head straight for Miami. It happened too late for all the normal warnings, which is why so many were killed (**Figure 1**).

Imagine how much worse the effects of tropical storms are in poor, low-lying and densely populated countries such as Bangladesh and the Philippines.

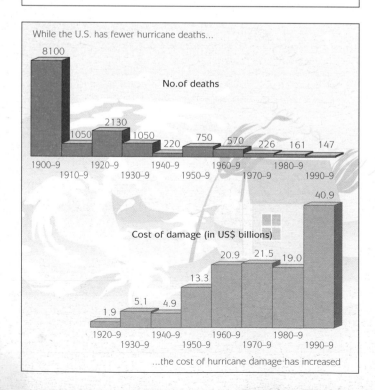

While the U.S. has fewer hurricane deaths...

No.of deaths

8100

2130
1050   1050
220   750   570   226   161   147

1900–9   1920–9   1940–9   1960–9   1980–9
   1910–9   1930–9   1950–9   1970–9   1990–9

Cost of damage (in US$ billions)

40.9

20.9   21.5   19.0
13.3
1.9   5.1   4.9

1920–9   1940–9   1960–9   1980–9
   1930–9   1950–9   1970–9   1990–9

...the cost of hurricane damage has increased

> **Activities**
>
> 1 a What is a tropical storm?
>   b State three reasons why tropical storms can cause so much damage and destruction.
>
> 2 a Name one tropical storm.
>   b Describe the damage caused **(i)** to people and **(ii)** to property by this storm.
>
> 3 a Describe two ways for reducing the number of people killed in a tropical storm.
>   b Explain why some tropical storms cause more loss of life than others.
>
> 4 Do your own research. Search out details about another tropical storm in a less economically developed country (e.g. Bangladesh, Philippines, Honduras). Write about its effects.

◀ **Figure 2** Deaths and damage in the USA as a result of hurricanes in the twentieth century.

Chapter 7

Ecosystems

A young boy in Nigeria takes the measure of an old and once mighty ironwood tree, which has just been felled by clearance of the tropical rainforest.

Key Ideas

Physical factors of three different global ecosystems – coniferous woodlands, tropical rainforests and savanna grasslands:
- the main factor controlling the world distribution of ecosystems is climate
- the nature of the soils associated with these ecosystems is influenced by both climate and vegetation.

Human activity has an impact on natural ecosystems:
- tropical rainforests and savanna grasslands are under pressure as human uses increase
- there is need for management of the world's natural forests.

Global distribution of ecosystems

An **ecosystem** is a living community of plants and animals within a natural environment. This environment includes climate and soil. Plants depend upon the climate and soil for growth. However, plants also affect the type of soil and the climate. This means that there are two-way relationships between different elements in an ecosystem. This is why some arrows in the ecosystems diagram (**Figure 1**) go in two directions.

On a world scale, climate is the main factor determining the type of vegetation in an area. **Figure 3** shows a world map with three of the world's main ecosystems.

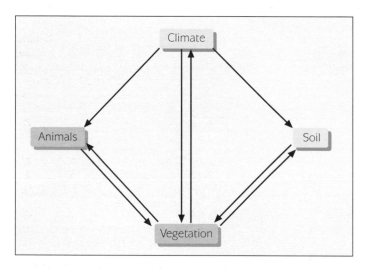

▲ **Figure 1** Ecosystem – systems diagram.

1 Tropical rainforest

Take a careful look at where these forests are located in **Figure 3**. Then turn back to the world map in **Figure 1** on pages 76–77 and look where places with an equatorial climate are found. Are they almost the same?

In other words, the tropical rainforest ecosystem is found in places with a hot and wet equatorial climate. Rainforests grow close to the Equator. Trees and plants grow quickly in the hot, wet climate and the vegetation forms dense jungle. Plants grow all year.

2 Savanna (tropical) grassland

Figure 3 shows that these are located next to the tropical rainforests. The largest areas are in Africa. Temperatures are high all year. However, unlike in the rainforests where it is wet all year, one season of the year is dry. The savanna climate has a hot, wet season and a hot, dry season. Grasses and trees need to adapt to drought for part of the year. Lack of rain limits the growth of plants.

3 Coniferous forest

These grow in North America, Europe and Asia in places a long way north of the Equator, in much colder climates. It is very cold in winter and the growing season is short. Low temperatures limit plant growth. Only a few varieties of trees and plants can grow. Great areas are covered by coniferous trees. Look back again to **Figure 1** on pages 76–77. What type of climate matches the location of coniferous woodlands?

◀ **Figure 2** Savanna grassland, Zimbabwe. These tropical grasslands are a mixture of grasses and trees. The umbrella-shaped tree is an acacia.

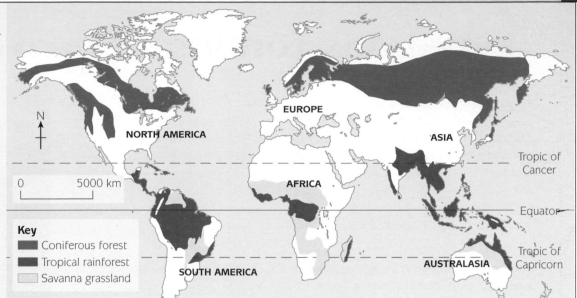

Tropical rainforest
Climatic summary. Hot all year – average temperature 27–30°C. Wet all year – annual precipitation 2000–3000mm

Coniferous forest
Climatic summary. Warm summers – 16-20°C. Very cold winters – well below freezing point. Precipitation mainly in summer – low annual total – less than 500mm.

Savanna grassland
Climatic summary. Hot all year 25–35°C. Variable rainfall totals but always a marked season of drought. 500–1000mm rain per year

Key
Coniferous forest
Tropical rainforest
Savanna grassland

▲ **Figure 3** World distribution of three ecosystems.

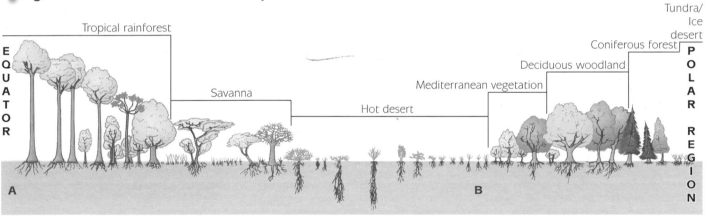

▲ **Figure 4** The changing pattern of vegetation cover from the Equator to the Polar regions in the northern hemisphere.

Activities

1 a Give a definition of an ecosystem.
  b (i) Draw the systems diagram for an ecosystem.
  (ii) Use different colours or shading to distinguish between its living and natural elements.
  c (i) Name one link in the ecosystem where two way arrows are used.
  (ii) Suggest a reason why the arrows are two way.

2 Use an atlas and **Figure 3**.
  a Name one country covered by large areas of tropical rainforest in each of these continents: South America, Africa and Asia.
  b Name the continent with the largest continuous area covered by tropical rainforest.

  c Describe where tropical rainforests are located in Africa.
  d Name one country covered by large areas of coniferous forest in each of the following continents: North America, Europe and Asia.
  e Name the continent with the largest continuous area covered by coniferous forest.
  f Describe where coniferous forest are located in North America.
  g Name one country covered by large areas of savanna grasslands in Africa and South America.
  h Name the continent with the largest continuous area covered by savanna grasslands.

  i Describe where the savanna grasslands are located in Africa.

3 Look at **Figure 4**.
  a Describe the ways in which the vegetation changes as you move away from the Equator (between points A and B).
  Use the following headings: height of vegetation; density of vegetation; length of roots.
  b What features of the vegetation suggest that there is less and less rain as you move away from the Equator towards B? Answer as fully as you can.

Coniferous forests

Characteristic features

The forests are evergreen. The coniferous trees, such as fir, pine and spruce, are similar in shape, height and size (**Figure 1**). There may be only two or three species of tree in an area so that the forests look the same over large areas. Often there is only one layer of vegetation – the tree layer. Trees grow close together in the darkness in the forests. Little else grows. The forest floor is covered by a thick mat of dead pine needles. The dark woods do not attract bird life because little food is provided. Deer are some of the few animals that can feed on the leaves of the trees.

The trees reproduce from cones, which protect their seeds. The trees have a conical shape with branches that slope downwards along the whole length of the trunk. They are softwoods. Their leaves are small needles which give the trees their evergreen appearance. They have thick barks which contains resin. Tree roots are shallow, spreading only small distances near the surface.

Adaptations to climate

Coniferous trees have adapted to survive in the temperate continental climate.

- In winter it is very cold. The ground is covered by snow and there are strong, cold winds. It is one of the most challenging climates for any kind of plant or animal life to survive in.

- Summers are short. They are not particularly warm and rainfall is low.

The temperature and precipitation figures for Irkutsk in **Figure 1** on page 77 show you what the climate is like.

Some of the ways in which coniferous trees adapt to this climate are explained in **Figure 2**.

▲ **Figure 1** Coniferous forest.

Tree characteristic	Adaptation to the climate
Conical shape	They are flexible and bend in the strong winds.
Downward sloping branches	Snow slides off them more quickly.
Evergreen	Leaves are always present so that trees can begin to grow as soon as it is warm enough in spring/early summer; necessary because of the shortness of the growing season.
Needle leaves	They reduce water loss by transpiration; necessary when water is not available (e.g. when the ground is frozen in winter and when little rain falls in summer).
Thick bark	This protects trunk from extreme winter cold.

▲ **Figure 2** Adaptations of coniferous trees to climate.

Activities

1 a Look back at the climate graph for Irkutsk in **Figure 1** on page 77.
   (i) State the highest temperature.
   (ii) State the lowest temperature.
   (iii) How much precipitation falls in the wettest month?
   (iv) In which part of the year does most precipitation fall?
   (v) What is the annual total precipitation approximately?
  b State two features of this climate which make it difficult for trees to grow.

2 a Draw a large coniferous tree. Add labels to describe its characteristic features.
  b Choose three of the features described in **(a)** and explain how each is an adaptation to the climate.

Soils

Soil is the name for the loose materials found above solid rock. **Podsol** is the name given to the type of soil that forms under coniferous forest.

Characteristic features of a podsol

Look carefully at **Figures 3** and **4**. These show the **soil profile** of a podsol. Start from the surface and work downwards. Try to recognize the following layers within the soil.

1 Just below the surface – can you see a narrow layer, dark in colour? This is the humus layer. The humus gives it the dark colour.

2 Next, can you spot a much lighter coloured layer, almost grey? This is known as the **A horizon**. It has lost its colour because the minerals from this layer have been washed downwards by **leaching** (see below).

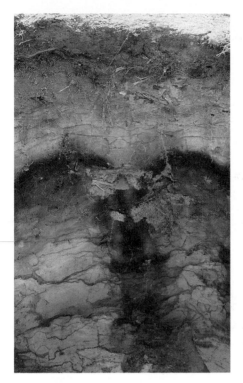

▲ **Figure 3** Profile of a podsol soil below a coniferous woodland (like the one shown in Figure 1).

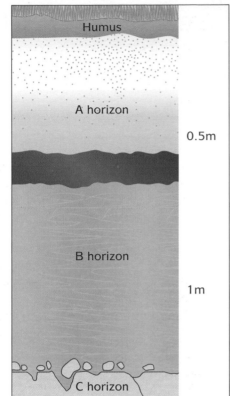

▲ **Figure 4** Profile of a podsol soil – summary of its main features.

3 About 0.6m down, find a narrow reddish-brown layer. This is the top of the **B horizon**. Minerals, lost from the layers above, are re-deposited here. This is why the colour is darker. A **hard pan** is formed.

4 Below this, there is a wider layer, which is mainly orange-brown but with some darker stains. This is the lower B horizon. Its colour comes from deposited clays.

5 In **Figure 4** the profile has been extended to show rock. This is the beginning of the **C horizon**. Below this it is all rock and no soil.

Formation of a podsol

A podsol has very clear layers within the profile.

One factor in its formation is climate:

• In a cold climate the amount of rainfall and snow is higher than the amount lost by evaporation and transpiration. Rainwater and melted snow drains downwards through the soil and carries minerals, such as iron and clay, with it. These are washed out of the upper layers – the A horizon. This is called **leaching**. They are re-deposited lower down in the B horizon. At the top of the B horizon the minerals such as iron are compressed to form a hard pan.

Another factor is vegetation:

• The conifers do shed the needles but not all together. The needles collect on the soil surface. Because the climate is so cold and there are few organisms in the soil, the litter does not decompose very quickly. This gives an acid humus. This litter is not well mixed into the soil because there are so few earthworms. They do not like the cold and acid conditions.

Activities

1 a Draw a large diagram to show the profile of a podsol.
   (i) Colour it in and label the colours of the different horizons.
   (ii) Add the letters for the different horizons.
  b State one reason why the A horizon is a lighter colour than the B horizon.
  c In what ways is the C horizon different from the horizons above it?

2 a What is meant by leaching?
  b Where does it occur in a podsol?
  c Explain the effects of leaching upon a podsol soil.

Tropical rainforests

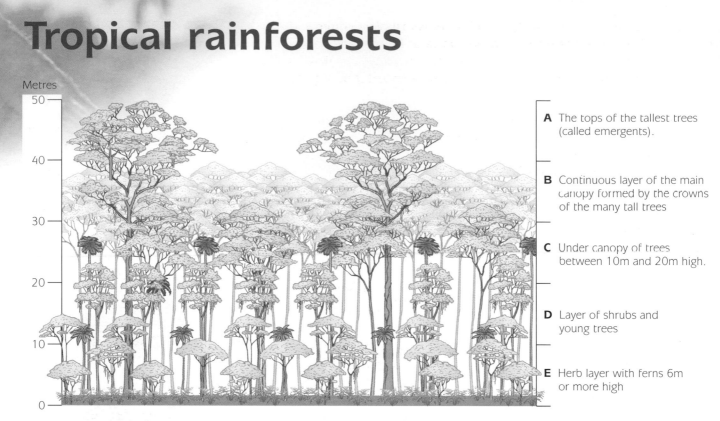

▲ **Figure 1** The five layers in a tropical rainforest.

Metres

A The tops of the tallest trees (called emergents).

B Continuous layer of the main canopy formed by the crowns of the many tall trees

C Under canopy of trees between 10m and 20m high.

D Layer of shrubs and young trees

E Herb layer with ferns 6m or more high

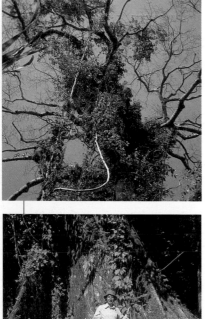

▲ **Figure 2** Trees showing some characteristic features of the tropical rainforest ecosystem.

Characteristic features

Tropical rainforest is different from the vegetation of all other ecosystems because of its **biodiversity**. This is the term used to describe the huge number and great variety of living organisms found in the rainforests. A 100ha block of coniferous woodland may contain only two or three different types of tree. In the same area in a tropical rainforest there may be over 500 species of tree, and double this number of species of flowering plants.

There are five forest layers. These are shown by the letters A–E in **Figure 1**. The canopy provides a habitat for monkeys and numerous birds such as macaws and parrots; on the ground floor there are some larger animals such as jaguars and anteaters. There are countless insects everywhere. However, it is the plant life that is really abundant.

The forests are evergreen. However, the tall trees are deciduous. The forests always look green because the tall trees shed their leaves at different times of the year. It is also only for a short time (usually six to eight weeks each year). The tallest trees, up to 50m high, are hardwoods and include types such as mahogany and ironwood. They have long trunks with all their branches at the top. Their leaves are an oval shape and have points at the end of them known as drip tips. The smooth bark of the trees is thin. Even the tall trees have shallow roots. These extend sideways below the ground and extend above the ground as buttress roots (**Figure 2**).

Adaptations to climate

Climate is the main factor responsible for the biodiversity and great height of the trees in rainforests.

*   The equatorial climate is hot and wet all year.
*   Temperatures are high all year – about 27°C.
*   Rain falls all year and the total per year is high – about 2000mm.

There is no more favourable climate on Earth for plant growth.

There is great competition for sunlight and water within plant communities. It is survival of the tallest as trees are drawn upwards by light and heat. This is why all the branches and leaves of tall trees are at the top (layer A in **Figure 1**). The drip tips of the leaves help them shed water during the heavy rains.

In contrast, little sunlight reaches the forest floor. Ferns survive in the lowest layer because they can use a high percentage of the light that reaches there (layer E in **Figure 1**). In between layers A and E, shrubs and trees of many different heights fill the gaps wherever light exists to allow them to grow.

Soils

Figure 3 shows the profile of a **latosol**. This is the type of soil that forms under tropical rainforest. As you can see, latosols are red or yellowish-red. The red colour comes from the oxides of iron and aluminium in the soil. They are very deep soils, much deeper than podsols. The heavy rain leads to leaching, which washes out minerals from the top of the profile. This is why the top of the profile in **Figure 3** is a lighter colour.

Nutrient recycling

The most important part of the soil is at the top of the profile. This is where the rapid recycling of nutrients takes place. Life in the forest depends on this recycling (**Figure 4**). Falling leaves and branches provide a continuous supply of litter on the forest floor. This decays quickly in the hot, wet climate. Leaves are soon decomposed into humus by the many organisms living in the topsoil.

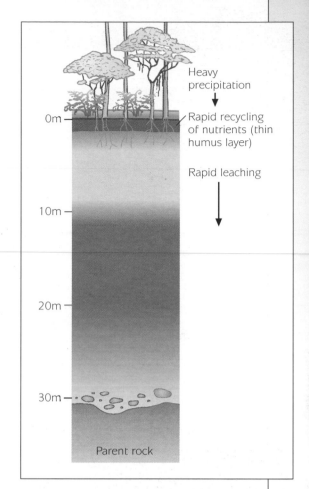

▲ **Figure 3** Profile of a latosol.

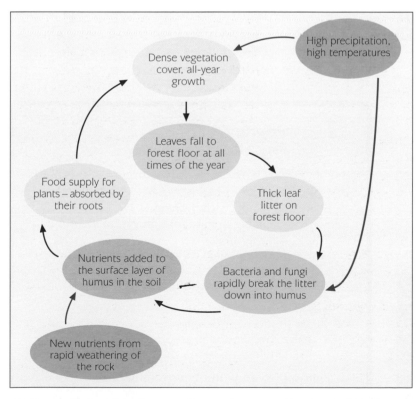

▲ **Figure 4** Systems diagram for nutrient recycling in a tropical rainforest ecosystem.

Activities

1 **a** Draw a labelled diagram to show the characteristic features of a tropical rainforest.
   b Draw one of the tall trees in the forest. Add labels to describe its characteristic features.
   c State two characteristic features of the forest shown in **Figure 2**.
   d Choose three of the features labelled in **(a)**, **(b)** or **(c)** and explain how each is an adaptation to climate.

2 **a** Look at **Figure 4** on page 93 and **Figure 3** on this page.
   (i) State one similarity between a latosol and a podsol.
   (ii) State one difference between a latosol and a podsol.
   (iii) Explain this difference.
   b **(i)** What is meant by nutrient recycling in tropical rainforests?
   (ii) Explain how it works (**Figure 4** helps).
   (iii) Why is it of great importance in the rainforests?

Human use of tropical rainforests

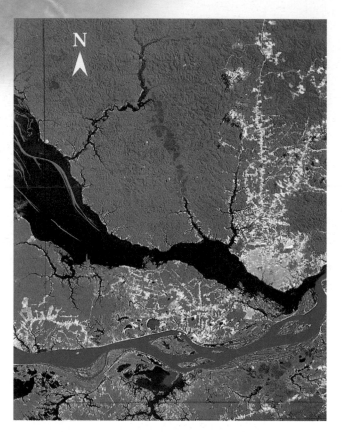

▲ **Figure 1** Satellite photograph of the Amazon Basin near Manaus. The black coloured river which flows past Manaus is the Negro. The river which shows up as dark blue is the Amazon itself. The two rivers can be seen joining up east of Manaus.

Large areas of tropical rainforest remain, despite recent deforestation. **Figure 1** shows the forested land (in red) around the largest town in the Amazon Basin with over two million people – Manaus (in blue). The cleared areas have lost their bright red colour.

Groups of Indians in the Amazon Basin have lived in the rainforests for centuries. They live by one or more of the following ways:

- collecting fruits, hunting animals and fishing, i.e. using food sources provided by nature
- practising shifting cultivation – growing crops such as manioc on plots cleared of trees.

Cleared areas of forest are small. The Indians cultivate each cleared area for only two or three years, only for as long as the soil remains fertile. Then they move to another part of the forest. The forest quickly takes over again as soon as crop growing stops, so that hardly a mark is left on the forest.

The Indian way of life is an example of **sustainable** use of rainforests. No long-term damage is done.

In contrast, recent human activity has been more destructive. Governments, as well as logging and mining companies, are keen to use the Amazon Basin's rich resources.

ℹ Development of the Amazon Basin

Some reasons why the Brazilian government wanted the Amazon region to be developed in the 1960s.

1 Economic (to do with money):
- export minerals, gain foreign exchange and pay off international debts
- use the minerals in its growing manufacturing industries
- become a more economically developed country.

2 Social (to do with people):
- relieve population pressure in the coastal areas
- give landless peasants the chance to own land.

3 Political (to do with the government):
- so that the government gains prestige from its big new schemes
- take people's minds off problems such as poverty.

▲ **Figure 2** Forest clearance for cattle ranching in Brazil.

Rainforests are damaged in the following ways:

- Roads are built, then forested areas along the road sides are cleared for farming and settlement. The satellite photograph (**Figure 1**) shows this happening north of Manaus. A network of roads passes through the Amazon Basin and crosses Brazil (**Figure 4**). Settlers follow the road builders.

- The main type of farming is cattle ranching. The ranchers clear all the forest for pastures. The trees are knocked down and cleared with bulldozers (**Figure 2**). Much of the wood is piled up and burnt.

- Logging companies use only a few types of tree, but in order to reach the trees they want they cut down all the others.

- Mining companies destroy the forest, because they only care about the Amazon's rich mineral wealth. At Carajas (named in **Figure 4**), there is one of the world's largest iron ore reserves and major deposits of bauxite, gold, nickel, copper and manganese. When gold is found, gold-rush fever takes over and thousands flock there (**Figure 3**).

▲ **Figure 3** Gold rush at Serra Pelada; at its peak 40 000 *garimpeiros* (miners) were working here.

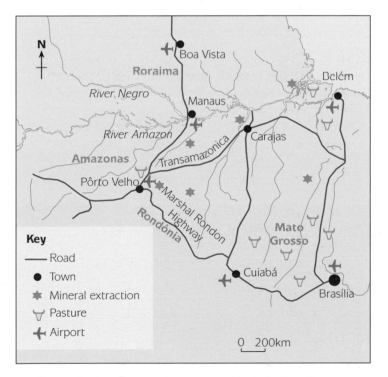

▲ **Figure 4** Opening up the Amazon Basin in Brazil.

Activities

1 a Draw a frame the same size as **Figure 1**. Show and label the following:
   (i) the courses of the rivers
   (ii) the town of Manaus
   (iii) areas of cleared forest
   (iv) areas of natural forest.
  b (i) Describe where most of the cleared areas are located.
   (ii) Suggest reasons why the rainforest has been cleared from some areas more than from others.

2 a (i) Name one example of sustainable living in the Amazon rainforests.
   (ii) Why is it sustainable?
  b (i) Describe what **Figures 2** and **3** show.
   (ii) Do they show sustainable or non-sustainable activities? Explain your answer.
  c (i) The policy of Brazilian government was to open up the Amazon Basin in the 1960s. Give three reasons for this.
   (ii) Do you agree with the government's policy? Explain your answer.

Savanna (tropical) grasslands

Characteristic features

Savanna grasslands lie to the north and south of the tropical rainforests. An example of an area of savanna vegetation is shown in **Figure 2** on page 90. Notice that there are only two layers of vegetation in this ecosystem – the grasses and the trees. Grasses are tall and form a continuous cover, whereas trees are dotted around and there can be wide spaces between them. A denser covering of trees shows places where more water is available, such as along the banks of rivers.

The savanna grasslands of Africa are famous for their great herds of wild animals – elephants, zebra, gazelles and wildebeest. These are the food supply for the big cats, such as lions, leopards and cheetahs.

Adaptations to climate

Figure 1 is a temperature and rainfall graph for Kano in northern Nigeria, which has a savanna climate. There are two seasons in this type of climate:

1 **A hot, wet season** – with temperatures around 30°C and between 500 and 1000mm of rain.

2 **A hot, dry season** – with temperatures around 30°C or a little higher, and little rainfall or none at all.

These seasons affect the vegetation. The main problem is survival during the dry season. Grasses turn brown and die back. Trees adapt to drought in special ways:

- They lose their leaves in the dry season to reduce water loss.

- Leaves are small and waxy to reduce transpiration.

- Roots are long to reach underground supplies of water.

- Acacia trees (like the one shown in **Figure 2** on page 90) have the umbrella shape which shades the ground above its roots, so reducing evaporation from the soil.

- Baobab trees (like the one shown in **Figure 2** on this page) store water in a soft spongy layer in their massive trunks.

In the wet season, the savanna lands look completely different. Grasses grow quickly, often to more than 3m high. These make a good food supply for the herds of grazing animals. The trees come back in leaf. The brown landscape changes to green as new life bursts forth everywhere under the tropical downpours.

Soils

During the dry season, minerals in the soil, such as calcium, are drawn upwards by the high temperatures and high rates of evaporation. During the wet season it is all change. Heavy rains cause leaching, which washes minerals such as silica lower down the profile. This means that the soil profile shown in **Figure 3** is quite varied and depends on the time of year.

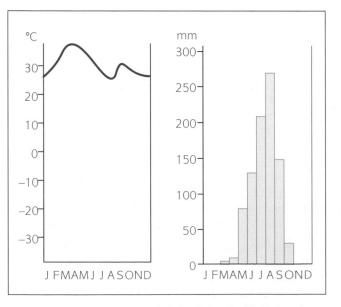

▲ **Figure 1** Climate graph for Kano in Nigeria.

▶ **Figure 2** A baobab tree in Zambia in the dry season.

Human uses of savanna grasslands

Local people keep domestic animals (especially cattle and goats) and grow crops on the African savannas. One major problem here is desertification, which means turning good land into desert. The three main causes of desertification are shown in **Figure 4**. The first one, climatic change, is a natural cause; the other two, overgrazing and population increase, are human causes. In each case, the result is the same – loss of the vegetation cover. Once the ground becomes bare, the surface is no longer protected against heavy rain and strong winds. The soil is eroded, leading to scenes of desertification like the one shown in **Figure 5**.

Many tourists visit the African savannas on wildlife safaris. These visitors bring a different set of problems, which are looked at in the section on tourism (see pages 203–5).

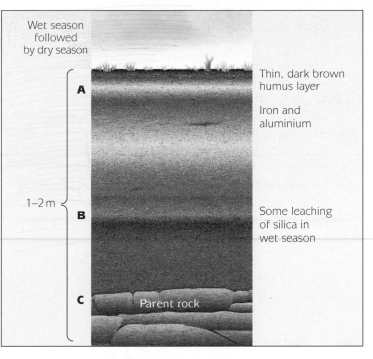

Wet season followed by dry season

A — Thin, dark brown humus layer

Iron and aluminium

1–2 m

B — Some leaching of silica in wet season

C — Parent rock

▼ **Figure 4** Desertification – causes and processes.

▲ **Figure 3** Profile of a soil under savanna grassland.

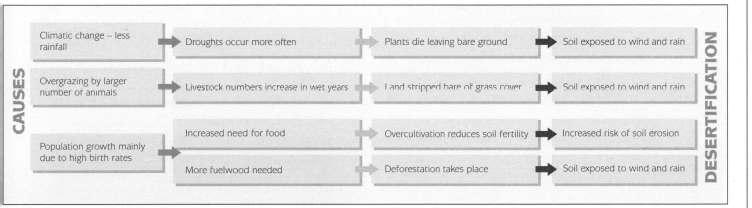

CAUSES

| Climatic change – less rainfall | → | Droughts occur more often | → | Plants die leaving bare ground | → | Soil exposed to wind and rain |

| Overgrazing by larger number of animals | → | Livestock numbers increase in wet years | → | Land stripped bare of grass cover | → | Soil exposed to wind and rain |

| Population growth mainly due to high birth rates | → | Increased need for food | → | Overcultivation reduces soil fertility | → | Increased risk of soil erosion |
| | | More fuelwood needed | → | Deforestation takes place | → | Soil exposed to wind and rain |

DESERTIFICATION

▲ **Figure 5** Land overgrazed in Kenya. The bare ground and deep gulleys in the soil show that desertification has occurred.

Activities

1 Look at **Figure 1**.
  a In which months is the wet season in Kano?
  b In which months is the dry season?
  c Approximately how much rain falls in a year?
  d What is the evidence that the climate is hot all year in Kano?

2 a Look at **Figure 2**. State two features of the vegetation that show that it is the dry season.
  b Look at the acacia tree and the grass in **Figure 2** on page 90. State two features of the vegetation that show it is the start of the wet season.
  c How is a baobab tree different to an acacia tree? Give two differences.
  d How do trees in savanna lands adapt to the dry season? State three ways.

Sustainable forestry

Malaysia is one of the economically better developed countries of Asia. About half of the country's land area is still under natural forest cover. The government of Malaysia is trying to protect this using its Forest Management Plan.

Sustainable methods of forestry in Malaysia

The methods being used include the following.

A Dividing the forest into two groups:

- conservation areas that cannot be logged such as Wildlife and Bird Sanctuaries and National Park
- production areas which can be logged.

B Using selective logging in the forests where logging is allowed.

- Only fully grown trees can be removed.
- Cut down only between 7 and 12 trees per hectare.
- Do not log again in the same area for 30 to 50 years to give time for the forests to recover.

C Improving methods of logging.

One example is heli-logging (using helicopters to haul out the logs). This is used in Sarawak and saves forest being removed for ground access.

D Keep monitoring what is happening.

- Check that the work is being done according to the plan.
- Check that no illegal logging is taking place.
- Give large fines and long prison sentences to anyone found breaking the rules.

E Re-planting trees in areas that have already been cleared.

- Plant faster growing trees, e.g. rubberwood used for making furniture.

Activities

1 **a** Of the total area of Malaysia: 25 per cent is not tree covered; 25 per cent is covered by plantation trees such as rubber; 50 per cent is covered by natural forest. Draw a pie graph to show these percentages. Colour or shade it in and make a key.

   b Describe three methods of sustainable forestry used in Malaysia.

2 Look at **Figure 1**.

   a Describe as many differences as you can between the two diagrams in **Figure 1**.

   b Explain the bad effects on soils of forest clearance.

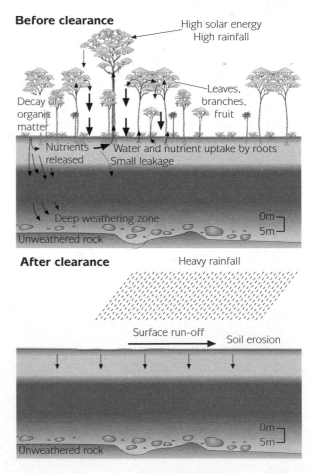

▲ **Figure 1** Nutrient recycling before and after clearance of tropical rainforest.

Chapter 8

Population

Places where there are many people ... places where there are very few people ... why are some parts of the world crowded with people while others remain empty?

Key Ideas

The global distribution of population is uneven:
- physical factors and human factors help to explain why some areas are crowded and others have few people.

Population change depends upon birth rate, death rate and migration:
- high birth rates and low death rates have led to rapid world population growth
- there are contrasting population problems between LEDCs and MEDCs
- there are many different types of migration.

Population change presents opportunities and problems:
- some countries need to reduce population growth, others need to encourage an increase
- different strategies are used to feed and house the growing numbers of people in LEDCs and MEDCs.

The world distribution of population

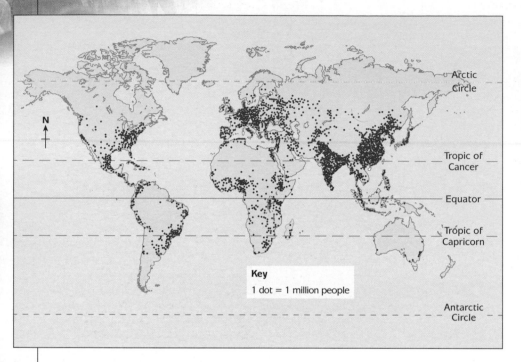

Key

1 dot = 1 million people

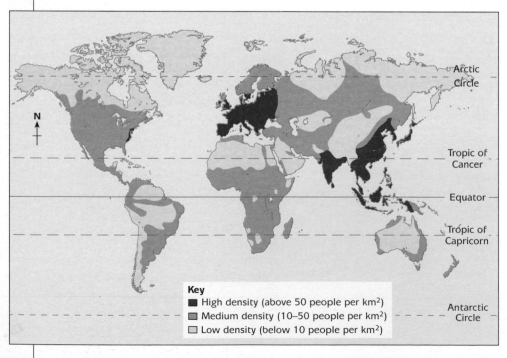

Key
■ High density (above 50 people per km²)
■ Medium density (10–50 people per km²)
□ Low density (below 10 people per km²)

▲ **Figure 2** Choropleth map showing world population density.

The world's population is very unevenly spread around the world. Some areas have many people while others are almost deserted.

◄ **Figure 1** Dot map showing world population distribution.

ℹ Information box

Population – means people
Population distribution – the way people are spread out across the Earth's surface (**Figure 1** shows a dot map of population distribution).
Population density – the number of people who live in an area, measured in people per square kilometre.
Figure 2 is a choropleth or shading map showing population density.

The world's population distribution can be divided into three main categories:

1 Areas with high densities of people (over 50 per km²): South and East Asia, Europe and the north-east of North America

2 Areas of medium population density (10–50 per km²): California, the coast of Brazil, the Nile valley in Egypt and south-east Australia

3 Areas with low population densities (less than 10 per km²): Sahara Desert in North Africa, northern Russia and Canada.

Key features of the world's distribution of population:

• 85 per cent population in Asia and Europe

• 64 per cent of the land area is almost empty of people

• Very few people in the southern hemisphere where there is less land

• Very few people north of 60°N

• 80 per cent of the population live between 20°N and 60°N.

Explaining the population distribution

HUMAN FACTORS	Reasons for areas of high population density	Reasons for areas of low population density
Economic	• Large, rich markets for trade • Good infrastructure (roads, railways, services) and access to imports and exports, e.g. Japan, Europe, USA • Skilled and varied labour force, e.g. in the large towns and cities, especially in MEDCs	• Poor trading links and markets • Poor infrastructure (roads, railways, services) and limited access, e.g. The Sahara, Amazon Basin, interior Australia • Limited job opportunities, including agriculture, e.g. Amazon Basin, Sahara, tundra, Alaska
Social	Some groups of people prefer to live together for security and companionship, e.g. Japanese, Americans	Some groups of people prefer to be more isolated,
Political	Stable government, e.g. Singapore, Taiwan	Unstable governments and civil war, e.g. Afghanistan

PHYSICAL FACTORS	Reasons for areas of high density	Reasons for areas of low density
Relief	Lowland which is flat or gently sloping such as river flood plains, e.g. Ganges valley, India	Mountainous areas with high altitude and steep slopes, e.g. Alps, Andes
Climate	Moderate climates with no extremes. Enough rain and heat to allow crop growth, e.g. UK, Japan	Extreme climates: very cold, very hot and too dry, e.g. tundra, Sahara
Soil	Deep fertile soils such as loam and alluvium, e.g. south-east England	Thin, rocky and acid soils, e.g. hot deserts, mountains
Vegetation	Areas of open woodland and grassland, e.g. Pampas, Argentina	Very dense jungle which is difficult to penetrate, and swamps, e.g. Amazon Basin
Accessibility	Coastal areas with easy access, e.g. South America, UK	Interior areas with poor access, e.g. central South America
Resources	Plenty of water, fishing, timber, minerals such as coal, oil, copper; e.g. coalfields in Western Europe	Few economic resources, e.g. southern Chile, Sahel

▲ **Figure 3** Reasons for different densities of population.

Where people choose to live depends upon physical and human factors. These are shown in **Figure 3**.

Densely populated areas have large numbers of people. These are areas where there are many advantages for people such as low, flat land with fertile soils and a water supply. **Sparsely populated** places have very few people. These are places where there are disadvantages for people such as in high mountains, cold climates and deserts. These areas are shown in **Figure 4**.

▼ **Figure 4** Limitations on population density.

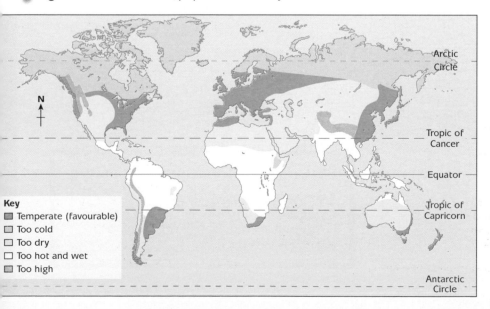

Key
- Temperate (favourable)
- Too cold
- Too dry
- Too hot and wet
- Too high

Arctic Circle
Tropic of Cancer
Equator
Tropic of Capricorn
Antarctic Circle

N

Activities

1 Write definitions for population, population density and population distribution.

2 State three features of the world's distribution of population.

3 What is the difference between sparsely populated and densely populated?

4 Explain why the UK is densely populated. Make sure you include both physical and human factors.

5 Choose two of the following areas and give the physical and human reasons why they are sparsely populated: Northern Canada; Sahara Desert; Himalayas; the Amazon Basin.

Population distribution in the UK

The UK is part of Western Europe, one of the areas of the world with a very high population density. However, as **Figure 1** shows, the population density is not high everywhere in the UK. The population distribution in the UK is very uneven. There are great differences from one area to another, from densities of under 10 per km² in the remote upland areas to densities of over 1000 per km² in the cities.

In the UK the sparsely populated areas – where there are few people – are mainly the upland areas, e.g. the Pennines, Dartmoor and the Scottish Highlands. The reasons for this are:

- cold and wet climate

- steep slopes and thin soils

- building roads and houses is difficult

- crops cannot be grown

- remoteness and isolation with few services

- limited job opportunities, e.g. sheep farming, forestry, tourism, quarrying.

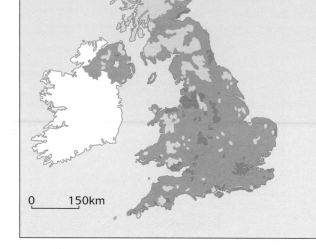

Figure 1 Britain's population density in 1994.

The densely populated areas in the UK are found in the **conurbations**, large cities and industrial areas (**Figure 2**). About 90 per cent of the UK population live in urban areas – the towns and cities. The reasons for this are:

- lowland areas with gentle relief

- warmer and drier climate

- fertile soils ideal for crop growing

- dense network of roads, railways and airports

- large number and wide variety of jobs available.

Large areas of the UK have a medium density of population, between 11 and 150 people per square kilometre. These are the fertile farming areas with market towns and villages, e.g. East Anglia or areas such as County Durham with its former mining villages and small towns.

Figure 2 Upland areas and conurbations in Britain.

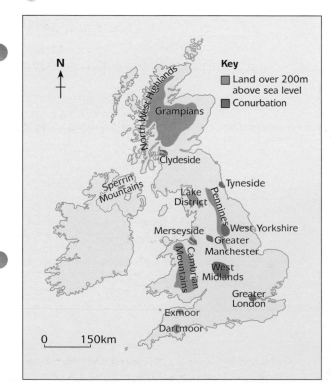

> **i Conurbations**
>
> A conurbation is a huge urban area created by the growth of one or more cities which merge with each other and engulf smaller towns and villages.

Population distribution in Brazil

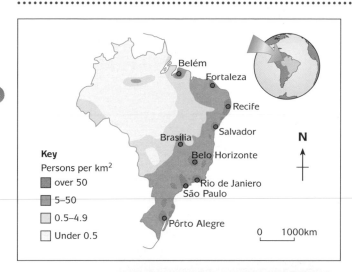

Key

Persons per km²

- over 50
- 5–50
- 0.5–4.9
- Under 0.5

0   1000km

◀ **Figure 3** Brazil.

Brazil's population is unevenly spread. The interior has very few people while the coastline is densely populated.

The Amazon rainforest

The main reasons why so few people live in the rainforest (less than 1 per km²) are the physical factors and the remote interior location:

- climate – equatorial hot (28°C) and wet (2000mm) all year round
- vegetation – dense jungle difficult to clear and travel through
- soils – infertile and easily eroded
- diseases, e.g. yellow fever
- remote from the coast and main towns
- poor communications
- few jobs available
- farming only supports a small population.

The south-east coast

High population densities are due to:

- less extreme climate
- flat land easy to build on
- fertile farmland used for vegetables, fruit and cattle
- large towns and cities, e.g. Rio de Janeiro, São Paulo
- excellent communications links
- wide variety of jobs in industries and services
- high birth rates in the urban areas.

▶ **Figure 4** Few people live in the Amazon Basin.

Activity

Choose either the UK or Brazil.

a Complete a map to show the distribution of population.

b Add labels to your map to give reasons for the high and low density areas chosen.

◀ **Figure 5** Very high densities of population are found in the coastal cities, such as Rio de Janeiro.

Population change

A population may increase or decrease over time. How a population changes depends on the birth rate, the death rate and migration (see information box). A population grows if the birth rate is higher than the death rate, i.e. there is a **natural increase**, but some countries have a natural decrease where the death rate is greater than the birth rate. In some countries migration can have a large impact on population size.

World population growth

Figure 1 shows that the population of the world grew very slowly up until the middle of the 20th century. Then there was a population explosion, when population increased very rapidly. Today the growth rate is still high, although the rate of growth seems to be starting to slow down. The world's population is continuing to grow because in many countries the birth rate is higher than the death rate, causing the population to increase.

Growth in the developed world

Figure 2 shows how the MEDCs began with high birth and death rates. Over time both birth rates and death rates in the MEDCs fell to a low level, although the birth rate remained slightly higher, leading to steady population growth. In many MEDCs natural increase today is low and in some, such as Germany and Sweden, the birth rate is actually lower than the death rate.

Growth in the developing world

The biggest contribution to world population growth, especially since the 1950s, has been in the developing countries in Africa, Asia and Latin America. Initially both birth rates and death rates were high (**Figure 2**) giving a low natural increase. However, in the LEDCs as death rates began to fall the birth rates remained high. This caused a massive population explosion and very high natural increase. Even today, although birth rates are still falling, population growth remains high in many LEDCs.

ℹ **Understanding population terms**

Crude birth rate – the number of live births per 1000 population per year.
Crude death rate – the number of deaths per 1000 population per year.
Natural increase – the birth rate minus the death rate.
Annual population growth – the birth rate minus the death rate plus or minus migration.
Migration – the movement of people either into or out of an area.

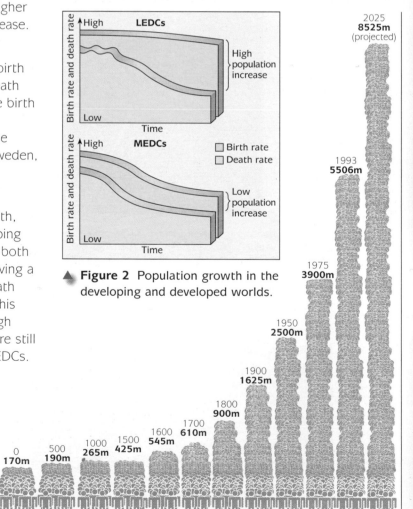

▲ **Figure 2** Population growth in the developing and developed worlds.

▲ **Figure 1** Growth of world population between 10 000BC and AD2025.
Each person on the graph represents four million people.

The population cycle

▼ **Figure 3** Many countries in the developed world have passed through four stages in their population growth in the population cycle sometimes called the Demographic Transition Model shown here.

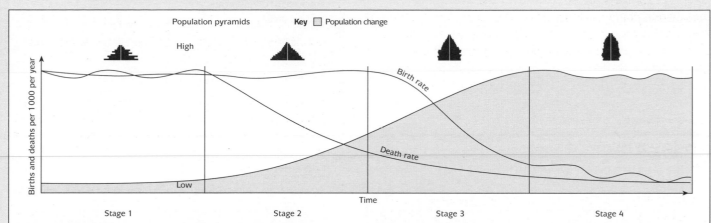

Stage 1 High birth and death rates

High birth rates and death rates give a low natural increase. The population total remains stable with very little change over time. There are very few places where Stage 1 exists, except perhaps remote tribes in the rainforests.

High death rates occur due to:
- high levels of disease such as plagues and cholera
- famine
- lack of clean water
- lack of medical care.

High birth rates are due to:
- lack of birth control
- need for large families to help work the land
- need to ensure some children survive as many die in infancy
- need to look after parents in old age.

Stage 2 High birth rates, death rates start to fall

The death rate begins to fall but the birth rate remains high. This means that more babies are being born and fewer people are dying. As a result there is a high natural increase and the population grows rapidly.

The UK passed through Stage 2 during the Industrial Revolution (1750–1900). Today some LEDCs (Less Economically Developed Countries) are still in Stage 2, e.g. Bangladesh and Nigeria where population growth is very high. The death rates fall especially in the towns because of:
- improved medical care and knowledge of hygiene
- vaccinations and medicines
- cleaner water supplies
- improved sewerage systems
- improved food supplies.

Stage 3 The birth rate starts to fall

In Stage 3 the death rate continues to fall but the birth rate also starts to fall. This means that the population is still growing but the growth is slowing down. The natural increase is less. The UK passed through Stage 3 between 1900 and 1950. Today many LEDCs are in Stage 3, e.g. Brazil. The birth rate begins to fall because:
- of the introduction of family planning and birth control
- improved medical care lowers the infant mortality
- there are fewer farmers needing large families
- in the cities it is more expensive to raise children
- people want holidays, cars, etc.
- old age pensions mean elderly do not depend on children
- women stay in education longer and have careers.

Stage 4 Low birth and death rates

In Stage 4 both the birth rate and the death rate are low. Overall there is little population growth – the population is stable. Many MEDCs (More Economically Developed Countries) are now in Stage 4, e.g. USA, Japan, Italy.

If all of the countries in the world were in Stage 4 then **zero population growth** would be achieved.

Stage 5 A decline in the population

The original model only had four stages but today some people feel that a fifth stage is needed. In some countries the birth rate has now fallen below the death rate e.g. Sweden, Germany. More people are dying than are being born and the population is falling – a negative natural increase.

Activities

1 Define the following terms: birth rate death rate natural increase infant mortality.

2 Using **Figure 2** and the text explain why population growth is much higher in LEDCs than in MEDCs.

3 Draw a large copy of **Figure 3** and add and complete a table like the one here to show the main features of the population cycle. Stage 1 has been done for you. You will have to add Stages 2–5.

	Stage 1
Birth rate	High
Death rate	High
Natural increase	Low – stable population
When the UK passed through the stage	Before 1750
Countries at this stage today	Remote tribes in rainforests only
Reasons	Primitive society with no birth control, high levels of disease

Population structure

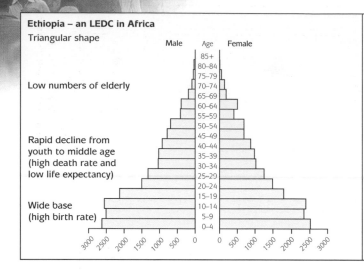

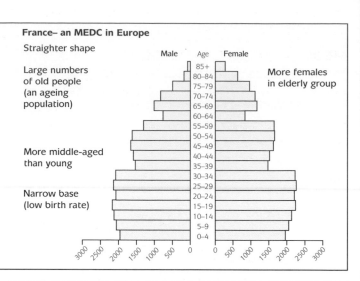

Figure 1 Population pyramids for Ethiopia and France in the 1990s.

Figure 2
A Age–sex pyramid for Eastbourne, UK;
B Age–sex pyramids for Zambia.

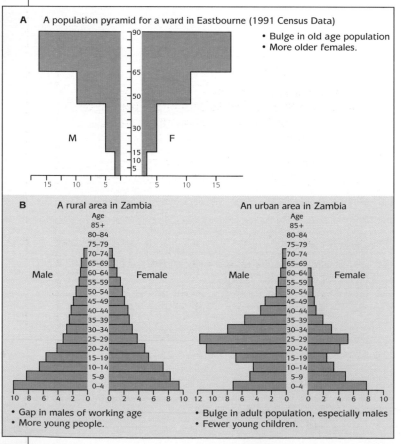

> ### ℹ Information box
>
> **A population pyramid** has horizontal bars showing the percentages or numbers of males and females in each age group. The age groups are usually 5 years apart e.g. 0–4, 5–9 years etc.
> **Life expectancy** – the average number of years a person is expected to live.

A **population pyramid** (**Figure 1**) shows the age and sex structure of a population. They are sometimes called age–sex pyramids. Countries can collect this information by a **census**. In the UK there is a census every ten years.

The shape of a population pyramid can be used to work out which stage in the population cycle a country is in. In **Figure 1** Ethiopia is in Stage 2 and France at Stage 4 of the population cycle.

Some pyramids have irregular shapes with bulges or gaps at certain age groups. Bulges, i.e. where the pyramid is fatter, are often a result of in-migration to an area. Many cities in developing countries have a bulge in males aged 20–40 years old as a result of the in-migration of young males looking for work, as do mining settlements or towns with an army barracks (**Figure 2B**).

In the UK some towns like Eastbourne have a top heavy pyramid with more elderly people. Often there are more women in the elderly population because on average women have a longer **life expectancy**. The top heavy pyramid is because the town is popular as a retirement town and many older people have moved in once they have retired from work (**Figure 2A**).

Population problems

In many LEDCs the main problem is still the rapid growth of population but in many MEDCs population growth has almost ceased and the main problems are the growing number of elderly people and a smaller workforce.

MEDCs – the ageing population

The numbers of elderly are growing because life expectancy has increased greatly (**Figure 3**). People are now living longer due to better health care, vaccines and surgery. At the same time birth rates have fallen and there are fewer people entering the workforce. This means that there are fewer people to work and pay taxes to look after the elderly. The elderly require a large number of specialist services as well as pensions, e.g. care homes, meals on wheels, warden assisted homes and geriatric medical care. With fewer children schools, youth clubs and hospital wards for sick children are likely to be closed and replaced with services for the elderly. More pressure will also be put on people to have private pensions with state pensions only paid to the most needy.

LEDCs – more and more people

The greatest problem is still the rapid growth in population. Many LEDCs still have very high birth rates and it will take a long time for the growth to slow down. In many LEDCs the high growth rates cause many problems (**Figure 4**) and lead to low living standards and poverty. There is also global concern that the Earth will not be able to support all of these people in the future. International conferences have called for population growth to be controlled so that there will be enough food, water and other resources in the future. They want to ensure that the world develops in a sustainable way – this means that the same amount of resources will be available in the future as there are today.

In rural areas:
- Overgrazing and overcultivation
- Water, land and air pollution
- Deforestation and soil erosion

In urban areas:
- Overcrowding and the growth of shanty towns
- Water, land and air pollution
- Traffic congestion

In the country as a whole:
- Shortages of resources, food and raw materials
- Unemployment
- Lack of money for basic health care and schooling
- Rising crime, political coups, huge debts
- Low living standards

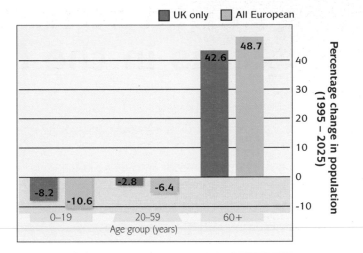

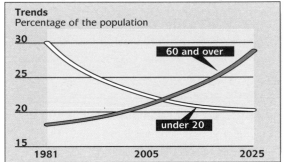

▲ **Figure 3** The generation gap.

Activities

1 What is a census?

2 Using **Figure 1**, draw a sketch of a population pyramid in Stage 2 and Stage 4 of the population cycle. Label each sketch to show the main features of its shape.

3 Using **Figure 2** draw sketches of the three pyramids shown. Give reasons for the shape of each one.

4 a What is the main population problem in
   (i) MEDCs
   (ii) LEDCs?
  b Explain how the MEDCs may cope with their population problem.
  c Describe the problems caused by the high population growth in many LEDCs.

5 Describe what the graphs show in **Figure 3**.

◀ **Figure 4** Problems of population growth in LEDCs.

Attempts to solve population problems in the MEDCs

The main problems in MEDCs are:

- the growing number of elderly people and paying for the services they need
- the fall in the birth rate leading to a decline in population and fewer in the workforce.

In the past some MEDCs encouraged population growth by:

- attempts to increase birth rates such as those shown in **Figure 1**
- allowing the in-migration of guestworkers.

Today such policies are rare. There is global concern about population growth and the cost of family allowances is too expensive.

A

The Shetland Islands want a population explosion

Residents of Fetlar are seeking 'youngish people or families with some capital and an entrepreneurial spirit' to travel to the island. Fetlar is a small island, just fourteen square miles in area. It lies nine miles east of Shetland's main island. Its population was once over 200 but is now down to just 80. The small primary school has only six children. The local shop is about to shut as the owners have decided to concentrate on crofting. Local people are worried that other services will close if the population continues to fall.

B

Attractive for migrants?	Unattractive for migrants?
• Fresh air, open space and a mild climate	• Strong winds – it feels cold because of wind chill
• Very few cars – no congestion or pollution	• No pub or hotel
• No crime	• High living costs – 15 per cent higher than on the mainland
• Licensed community centre	• Minimal shopping facilities – need to travel to the mainland for most shopping
• Electricity	
• Low taxes of £45 per year	• Lack of employment – the only people with full-time jobs are the schoolteacher and the nurse
• Relatively cheap housing	
• Birdwatching	• Remoteness

▲ **Figure 2 A:** Fetlar in the Shetland Islands advertises for inhabitants: report in *The Daily Telegraph*, 16 April 1991. **B:** Positives and negatives of living in Fetlar.

▼ **Figure 1** Attempts to increase a country's population.

ADVERTISING

Accepting immigrants

High family allowances

Tax incentives

Banning contraceptives

Crèches for working mothers

Medals for Supermums

3-year job protection for mothers

Advertising for people!

Islanders in the Shetlands have been so worried about their dwindling population that they have advertised in national magazines for people to set up home on the island (**Figure 2A**). Study the table in **Figure 2B** to find out what the island has to offer and why the advertisements may not work.

France

During the twentieth century the population grew very slowly in France. The government has tried to increase the birth rate by:

- giving tax incentives for large families
- increasing family allowances for families with three or more children
- discouraging the use of contraceptives.

However, most families have two or less children because of the cost of raising large families. Many women also want to return to their careers. In recent years the government has not been able to afford the costs of the family allowances and tax incentives. As a result the average number of children per family has fallen to 1.8.

The Netherlands

Creating more space

In many MEDCs a large proportion of the population live in towns and cities. In the Netherlands, one of the most densely populated countries in the world, extra living space had to be provided for homes, industry and farmland.

▼ Figure 3 The Zuider Zee scheme.

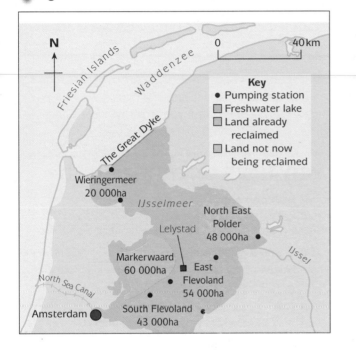

The table in **Figure 5** shows how the land use on the polders has changed. At first they were mostly used for farming but later polders have been used more for housing and recreation. On East Flevoland there is a new town called Lelystad that acts as an overspill for Amsterdam. The fifth polder, Markerwaard, will not now be built due to environmental opposition.

▼ Figure 5 Land uses on the polders.

	Wieringer-meer	North East Polder	East Flevoland	South Flevoland
Total area (ha)	20 000	48 000	54 000	43 000
Period of development	1930–40	1942–58	1957–70	1968–present
Percentage of:				
Farmland	87	87	70	50
Residential land	1	1	8	18
Woodland, nature reserves and recreation	3	5	16	25
Canals, dykes and roads	9	7	6	7

The Zuider Zee scheme

The solution was the Zuider Zee scheme in the north-west of the country. The scheme involved:

1 The Great Dyke, a dam across the mouth of the inland sea:

   • to help stop flooding
   • to create a freshwater lake
   • to carry a road to connect the north of the country to the south.

2 Reclaiming five large polders. A **polder** is an area of land reclaimed from the sea. The polders are flat with very few trees. They are criss-crossed by drainage channels.

▼ Figure 4 Cross-section through a polder.

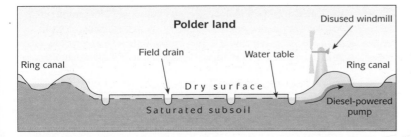

Activities

1 What are the two main population problems in MEDCs?

2 Suggest ways a government can try to:
   a increase birth rates
   b increase the workforce.

3 Using **Figures 2A** and **B** list the population problems of Fetlar in the Shetland Islands.

4 Give three reasons why people may not want to move to Fetlar.

5 What were the advantages of the Zuider Zee scheme in the Netherlands?

6 a Draw a pie chart for the land uses on the North East Polder and one for the South Flevoland Polder.
   b Describe the differences between the two.
   c Suggest why the two polders are used differently.

Solving population problems in LEDCs

The LEDCs have two problems:

1. to reduce birth rates so that the population growth slows down
2. to cope with the growing demands for housing, food, and other services from the large populations.

Controlling population growth

Figure 1 shows some different ways that countries such as India and Ethiopia have used to try to reduce high birth rates. In some countries, such as Sri Lanka, the government has used persuasion and incentives. In others, such as China, laws have been passed and strictly enforced. In other countries, e.g. Saudi Arabia, no attempt has been made to control population growth. In Catholic and Muslim countries this is due to religious beliefs that oppose any form of contraception.

▼ **Figure 1** What changes birth rates?

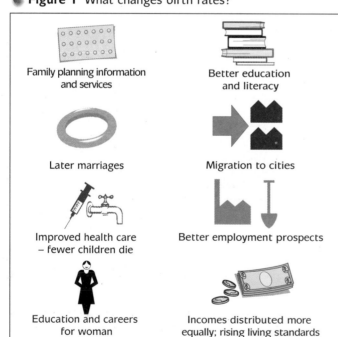

Family planning information and services

Better education and literacy

Later marriages

Migration to cities

Improved health care – fewer children die

Better employment prospects

Education and careers for woman

Incomes distributed more equally; rising living standards

China's one-child policy

In the 1980s China's population was over 1000 million. At the time the government had a 'two-child' policy but this would mean a population of over 1.8 billion by 2025. The government introduced the 'one-child' policy in the hope of slowing down population growth. They hoped to achieve a stable population of 1.2 billion early in the twenty-first century. **Figure 2** shows some of the advertising used by the Chinese government.

The one-child policy was very strict. It was almost illegal to have more than one child. Families were criticized and fined for having more than one child; there were forced abortions and sterilizations. The policy was more successful in the towns than in the rural areas. There were reports of infanticide where girl babies were killed because the Chinese people regard boys in higher esteem (**Figure 3**). There were concerns that the child in each family would be spoilt and that there would be a shortage of females in the future for marriage. Since 1989 the one-child policy has been relaxed.

WHY HAVE ONLY ONE CHILD?

For you with one child:

Free education for your one child.
Family allowances, priority housing and pension benefits.

For those with two children:

No free education, no allowances and no pension benefits.
Payment of a fine to the state from earnings.

To help you

Women must be 20 years old before they marry.
Men must be 22 years old before they marry.
Couples must have permission to marry and have a child.
Family planning help is available at work.

REMEMBER: One child means happiness.

▲ **Figure 2** Part of the Chinese Government's advertising campaign.

Chinese resist 'one child only' policy

By GRAHAM EARNSHAW
in Peking

A Chinese peasant grasped a double-headed axe and confronted three birth officials, shouting: "If you force me to have a vasectomy, I'll kill all of you." It was a small incident which ended in the peasant paying a large fine, and probably having a vasectomy.

The effects of the current policy, from forced abortion and sterilization to female infanticide, are extremely worrying. The one-child-only policy has been generally successful in the cities, but the peasants, who make up 80 per cent of China's population, are proving to be very stubborn.

The peasants want a lot of children to help work the fields and to look after them in old age. And they prefer boys to girls to the extent that they are willing to kill their daughters to make sure their one child is male.

▲ **Figure 3** China's 'one-child' policy – report in *The Daily Telegraph*, 30 May 1983.

Coping with high population growth

In many LEDCs population growth is still high. This is a particular problem in cities where there are still high birth rates as well as many migrants from the rural areas.

In LEDCs high population growth causes many problems in the cities.

In some countries population growth has also caused problems in rural areas. More people in the countryside leads to higher demands for shelter, food and water. More crops are grown, more animals reared and more timber cut down for fuel and building. In places like the Sahel in North Africa this has caused:

- overcultivation
- overgrazing
- wells to dry up
- loss of vegetation cover
- bare soil and soil erosion.

In some areas the land has turned into desert, a process called **desertification** (**Figure 6**).

▼ **Figure 6**

Environmental problems	Socio-economic problems	Political problems
Traffic congestion and overcrowding	Unemployment	Rapid growth of towns and cities
Air, water and land pollution, e.g. rubbish tips, litter	Poverty	High demand for housing and the growth of huge shanty towns
Soil erosion and landslides	Family break-ups and stresses	Demand for food, education, health care and other services
Open drains with sewage along the streets	High levels of disease	Unemployment

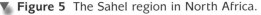
▲ **Figure 4** Problems of population growth in cities.

▼ **Figure 5** The Sahel region in North Africa.

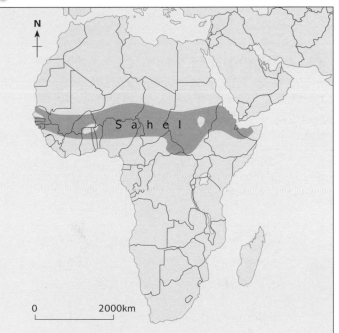

Activities

1 What are the main population problems in the LEDCs?

2 a Name two countries with birth control policies and two with weak or no policies.
b Give one reason why a country may not have a birth control policy.

3 a Describe the birth control policy in China.
b List four advantages of the policy for the people.
c List four disadvantages of the policy in China.

4 Using **Figure 4** and the text write two lists, giving the problems of population growth in:
a urban areas   **b** rural areas.

Case Study – Solving population problems

Transmigration in Indonesia

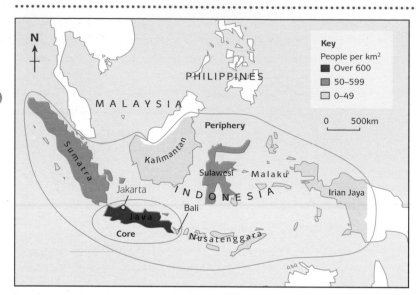

▲ **Figure 1** Indonesia, population density and core and periphery.

▲ **Figure 2** Resettlement in Indonesia's rainforest.

Indonesia is a collection of islands to the north of Australia (**Figure 1**). Most of the islands have an equatorial climate and are covered in rainforest. The population in 1995 was about 200 million and population growth is high, with a birth rate of 25 per 1000 and a death rate of 9 per 1000.

The islands of Java and Bali form the core of Indonesia. This is the most wealthy and attractive area with the capital city Jakarta and many jobs. The poorer areas surrounding these islands are called the periphery. Sixty per cent of the population live on Java and it is a magnet for people from the periphery.

The government wanted to reduce the number of migrants moving to Jakarta. They needed to provide places where the chance of getting a job was as high as in Jakarta. They did this with a transmigration policy. The policy resettles people from the core into the periphery in new farming areas set up by the government (**Figure 2**). The migrants are given free land, free transport to the area and food and fertilizer for 12 months.

The scheme has had some success but there have been problems:

Political problems

- It has had little impact because of the high rate of population increase on Java
- The costs of the scheme are very high
- The scheme relies on aid from the World Bank.

Environmental problems

- 10 per cent of settlements have failed due to infertile soils
- Some areas have been affected by volcanic activity and flooding
- 49 million hectares of rainforest have been destroyed in the last 30 years
- Soil erosion and leaching occurs when the forests are cleared.

Socio-economic problems

- There have been conflicts between local people and the newcomers
- People remain poor as they cannot grow enough food to feed themselves
- Native tribes have lost land and been forced to move to other areas.

Irrigation in Egypt

The Sahara Desert stretches across much of North Africa. Libya and Egypt include large areas of desert. Libya has a population of 5 million, but Egypt has 60 million people. How can Egypt support such a huge population? The answer lies with the River Nile. Over 99 per cent of Egypt's population live on only 4 per cent of the land area.

Since the 1960s Egypt has coped with the growing population by:

* increasing the water supply
* expanding the irrigated farmland.

The Aswan Dam

The dam was built in the 1960s to:

* control the flow of the River Nile
* stop the annual floods
* increase water supply for the cities and for irrigation
* allow more land to be reclaimed for housing and farming
* increase food supplies.

Since then about 20 schemes along the river have reclaimed more land for farming. This has doubled the area of farmland from 4 to 8 per cent, an extra 2 million hectares of land. The extra water supply allows the farmers to grow more than one crop a year – called double or treble cropping.

However, the building of the dam and the land reclamation has also caused some problems:

* Some irrigation schemes have made the soils salty and useless for farming.
* The creation of Lake Nasser flooded some important historical sites.
* Irrigation canals and the lake have increased water-borne diseases such as bilharzia.
* The silt that used to go on the land as fertilizer no longer does so and farmers have to buy fertilizers.
* The silt is now filling up the lake.
* The Nile delta is getting smaller as the silt no longer reaches the river mouth.

ℹ Information box

Irrigation is the artificial watering of the land.

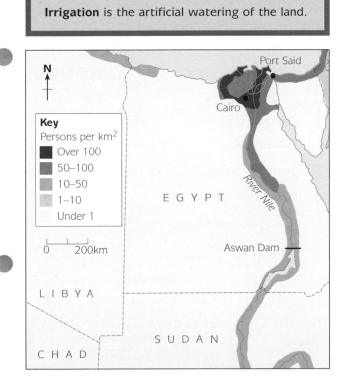

▲ **Figure 3** Egypt's population distribution.

Activities

1 You are working for an advertising agency in Jakarta, Indonesia, which has won the contract to design the advertising material for the transmigration programme. Design a poster suitable to be displayed around the city.

2 Imagine you are a migrant in one of the new resettlement areas. Write a letter to friends still in Jakarta who are thinking about moving too. Tell them about the advantages and disadvantages of your move.

3 a Why was the Aswan Dam needed in Egypt?
   b Make a copy of the table below and complete it to show the advantages and disadvantages of building the Aswan Dam.

Advantages of the Aswan Dam	Disadvantages of the Aswan Dam

Case Study – Solving population problems

Migration

Look at this table. How can we explain the fact that the annual growth rate does not match up with the natural increase?

The explanation lies in **migration** – the movement of people. More people have emigrated away from Jamaica but there has been movement into (immigration) Hong Kong. In any country people will both move in and move out – the difference between this immigration and **emigration** is the **migration balance**.

Country	Birth rate per 1000 (BR – DR)	Death rate per 1000	Natural increase	Annual growth rate – the actual population growth in a country	Comment
Jamaica	27	6	21	12	The actual population growth is less than the natural increase – emigration
Hong Kong	18	5	13	33	The actual population growth is much higher than natural increase – immigration

Types of migration

Figure 1 shows some different types of migration. **Forced migration** occurs when people have no choice about moving. They become **refugees** when they reach a different country (**Figure 2**). The reasons why they are forced to move include:

- natural disasters, e.g. floods, earthquakes, volcanic eruptions, famine
- war and persecution, e.g. the Jews in Europe during the Second World War.

Voluntary migration is when the person chooses to move. Today most migration is voluntary. The person will consider the advantages and disadvantages of the movement before making the decision (**Figure 3**). These are called:

- the push factors – the disadvantages of where the person lives now, e.g. low wages, poor climate, few services
- the pull factors – the advantages of where the person is hoping to move to, e.g. near to relatives, better education, higher standard of living.

▼ **Figure 2** African refugees.

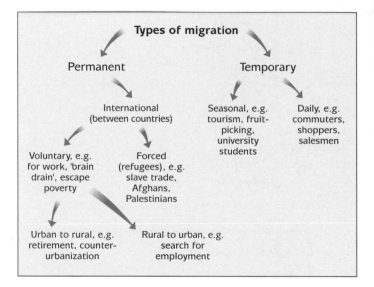

▲ **Figure 1** Types of migration.

IN THE COUNTRYSIDE	IN THE CITY
Push factors	**Pull factors**
Drought and famine	Better paid jobs in industry
Poverty	Better schools and hospitals
Pressure on the land	Shops and entertainment
Few jobs – little money	Improved housing
Lack of services	Water supply, electricity
Remoteness	Reliable food supplies

Obstacles
- Leaving family behind
- Poor and expensive transport
- Fear of the unknown
- International boundaries

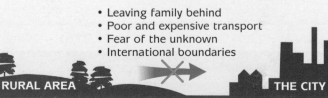

RURAL AREA   THE CITY

▲ **Figure 3** The push–pull model of migration.

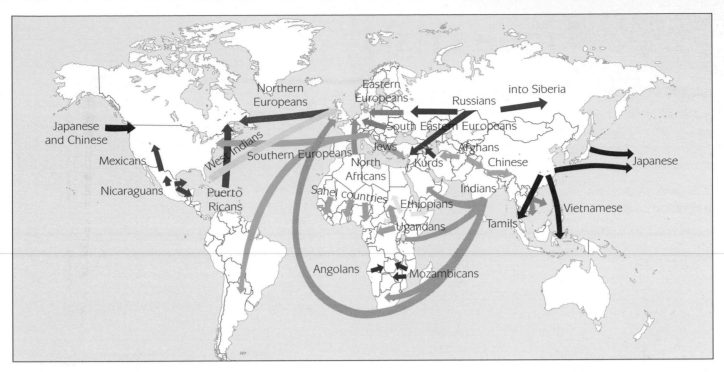

▲ **Figure 4** Some important international migrations in the twentieth century.

International migration

International migration is when people move across the borders of a country. They have decreased in importance in the twentieth and twenty-first centuries. In the nineteenth century there were many international migrations as people moved to different countries to settle new land. **Figure 4** shows some of the main international migrations in the twentieth century.

There are three main types:

- From poor to rich countries, e.g. from Mexico to the USA. Most move in search of work and higher living standards and are called economic migrants.
- From areas of drought and famine, e.g. from the Sahel to neighbouring countries in Africa.
- From persecution and wars – political refugees, e.g. Jews returning to Israel and Palestinians moving to Jordan and the Lebanon.

	Advantages	Disadvantages
For the host country Economic	An extra source of labour. May bring skills and money to the country, e.g. brain drain of doctors from UK to USA, voluntary workers to LEDCs, may help to develop areas and extract resources.	A strain on the country's resources, especially in the LEDCs. Increased unemployment. Need to provide housing, food, medical care, education.
Social	Cultural exchange brings new skills and ideas.	May increase racial tension, violence and discrimination.
For the losing country Economic	May reduce burden on the country, with fewer mouths to feed and provide for. Money sent back by migrants is important foreign exchange. Families improve local economy by spending in local shops and on services.	A loss of labour – often the voting males who have the entrepreneurial skills move.
For the migrant and family Economic	May earn more money and have a higher standard of living – stable employment with a salary/wage.	Higher living costs in the host country for housing, food, clothing.
Social	Meet new people and broaden cultural understanding.	May result in family separation if only the main worker migrates, e.g. Turkish males going to Germany to work.

▲ **Figure 5** Advantages and disadvantages of international migration.

The refugee crisis

Strictly speaking, refugees are people who have been *forced* to move out of their country. However, some definitions also use the term refugee for people who have been forced to move within their country. Most refugees are made to flee their homes by human or political causes rather than natural causes.

Political causes	Natural causes
• Religious, political or racial persecution • Civil war	• Environmental disasters, such as floods, droughts, earthquakes, volcanic eruptions

The numbers of refugees have grown enormously in recent years (**Figure 1**). In 1995 the United Nations estimated that there were over 14 million refugees in the world. Giving an accurate figure is difficult because most refugees are illegal immigrants and governments do not know exactly how many there are. Most refugees are women and children. Most refugee movements are between neighbouring countries. Over 80 per cent of all refugees are in LEDCs (**Figures 2** and **3**) – the very countries that are already finding it difficult to provide for their own populations.

Refugees living in other LEDCs often live in extreme poverty, lacking food, shelter, clothing, education and medical care. They have no citizenship, few, if any, rights and virtually no prospect of improvement. Very few refugees are ever able to return to their home country.

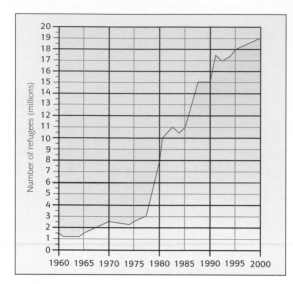

▲ **Figure 1** Growth of the world refugee population.

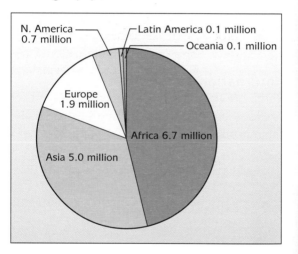

▲ **Figure 2** Refugees by region.

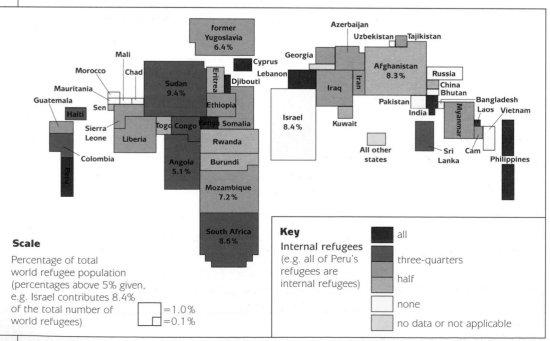

Scale

Percentage of total world refugee population (percentages above 5% given, e.g. Israel contributes 8.4% of the total number of world refugees) □ =1.0% □ =0.1%

Key
Internal refugees (e.g. all of Peru's refugees are internal refugees)
- all
- three-quarters
- half
- none
- no data or not applicable

◀ **Figure 3** Refugee makers – where the refugees come from. The larger the box the greater the number of refugees. (1994 data)

Palestinian refugees

For hundreds of years Arab Muslims formed the majority of people living in Palestine but there were also Christian and Jewish communities there. In the first half of the twentieth century Jewish migration to Palestine rose as a result of growing anti-Semitism in Europe. Immigration to Palestine increased greatly following Hitler's rise to power and the persecution of the Jews in the Holocaust. By the end of the Second World War many Jews were desperate for the creation of a Jewish state. For Jews, Palestine was the land promised to them by God since biblical times and they regarded it as their homeland.

In 1947 the United Nations agreed to the partition of Palestine into a Jewish state and a Palestinian state. In 1948 the state of Israel was proclaimed. War broke out between Israel and her Arab neighbours and as a result of this initial conflict over 800,000 Palestinians fled Israel.

Most of the refugees fled to neighbouring Arab countries, to Gaza and the West Bank. Syria and Jordan absorbed many refugees but many others, particularly those in Lebanon, had no option but to settle in refugee camps.

Destination	Number of refugees
Jordan	1 639 718
Gaza	852 626*
West Bank	607 770*
Lebanon	382 973
Syria	391 651

* Now under Palestinian self-rule. The status of the people and the daily reality of their lives still makes them displaced and disadvantaged.

Source: Data from UNRWA

▲ **Figure 4** Destinations of Palestinian refugees

◀ **Figure 5** Refugee camp in the Lebanon.

Impact on the Lebanon

- There were 17 overcrowded refugee camps. In 2001 twelve camps still existed, housing 215 000 of the refugees in Lebanon (**Figures 4** and **5**).
- Lebanon, already struggling to cater for the needs of its own population, cannot supply the refugees with shelter, clothing, food and medical supplies. The United Nations provides financial aid to help.
- Several wars have been fought between Israel and Palestinian groups within Lebanon. Israel occupied the border zone between 1982 and 2000, and it remains an area of instability.

Impact on Israel

- Wars in Lebanon have been costly in lives and money.
- The refugee problem is a major source of hostility and lack of trust between Israel and her Arab neighbours.
- Since 1948 frequent bombings and terrorist attacks have occurred in many parts of Israel.
- After 1948 more land was available for Jews to settle because the Palestinians had left.

Impact on the refugees in Lebanon

- They are free from the hostility they experienced in Israel.
- They have lost their homeland and livelihood.
- They suffer appalling living conditions in makeshift shelters with little food, clothing, money or other services.
- Unhygienic living conditions cause disease.
- They have lost their rights and have no say in their own destiny.
- Over time the refugee population has grown. Children and grandchildren of the original refugees are now living there.

Internal migration

Internal migration is migration within a country. Today this is the most common – just think of how many people must move house in the UK every day! **Figure 1** shows some different types of internal migration.

In the UK people began to move from the countryside to the towns during the Industrial Revolution (**Figure 2**). This is called **rural to urban migration** and Figure 3 shows some of the **push and pull factors**.

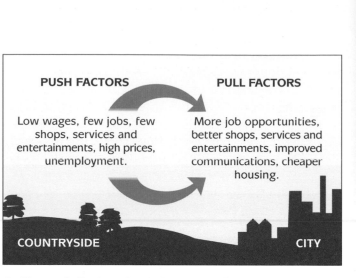

PUSH FACTORS

Low wages, few jobs, few shops, services and entertainments, high prices, unemployment.

PULL FACTORS

More job opportunities, better shops, services and entertainments, improved communications, cheaper housing.

COUNTRYSIDE   **CITY**

Figure 3 Push and pull factors for rural-to-urban migration in the developed countries.

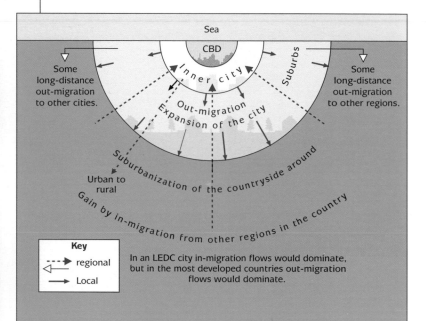

Key
- - -> regional
——> Local

In an LEDC city in-migration flows would dominate, but in the most developed countries out-migration flows would dominate.

Sea
CBD
Inner city
Suburbs
Some long-distance out-migration to other cities.
Some long-distance out-migration to other regions.
Out-migration
Expansion of the city
Suburbanization of the countryside around
Urban to rural
Gain by in-migration from other regions in the country

Figure 1 Types of internal migration.

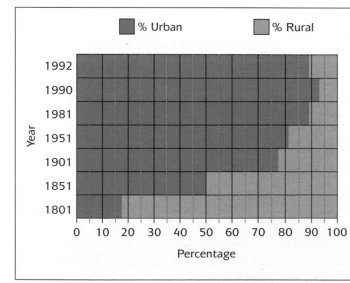

Figure 2 The urban population in the UK.

During the Industrial Revolution, industries such as coal mines, shipyards and textile mills were growing in the towns and workers were needed, while in the countryside new machines meant fewer workers were needed. This loss of people from the countryside is called **rural depopulation** and it has continued in many MEDCs. In the UK over 90 per cent of the population live in towns and cities. In recent years in some MEDCs there has been a reversal of this movement. People have been moving out of the cities – this is called **urban depopulation**. This has happened especially in the very large urban areas called conurbations (**Figure 4**). People want to escape the rising crime, air and noise pollution, poor housing, traffic congestion and overcrowding. They are moving into the countryside, into commuter villages or to New Towns. This is called **counter-urbanization**.

In the LEDCs rural to urban migration started much later (for many in the 1950s), but it has been much more rapid and has caused many problems for the governments of the LEDCs (see page 113).

Year	Liverpool	Manchester	Birmingham
1801	82 000	75 000	71 000
1851	376 000	303 000	233 000
1951	789 000	703 000	1 100 000
1991	510 000	449 000	1 007 000

Source: *Philip's Geographical Digest*, 1996–7

Figure 4 The changing population of Liverpool, Manchester and Birmingham.

Internal migration in the UK

Figure 5 shows how the population changed in the regions of the UK between 1981 and 1991. The main population movements are summarized below.

Out-migration from rural and upland areas

Examples: the Scottish Highlands, the Pennines.

Physical push factors:

- Harsh climate
- Steep and hilly land
- Poor soil
- Remote area with poor accessibility.

Human push factors:

- Few employment opportunities
- Limited services.

Out-migration from declining heavy industrial areas

Examples: north-east England, South Wales

These regions relied on heavy industries, e.g. steel, coal, engineering and textiles. They have been in decline since the Second World War. Many industries closed and unemployment soared to over 50 per cent in some areas. The regions found it difficult to attract enough new industries and so people moved away in search of new jobs.

Out-migration from the inner cities

Examples: Greater London, Birmingham, Glasgow and Newcastle upon Tyne

Many people have left the inner city areas in the UK because of a variety of social, economic and environmental push factors (**Figure 6**).

Areas of in-migration in the UK

The main areas of in-migration have been:

- London and the south-east where standards of living are high and employment is available
- Areas of countryside with small villages where commuters can still get to work in the big cities
- Holiday resorts especially on the south coast, e.g. Bournemouth, which are popular for people to retire to.

▼ **Figure 6** Push factors of the inner cities.

Environmental	Socio-economic
Old terraced housing	Declining industries
Air and noise pollution	Unemployment
Derelict land and buildings	Low incomes
Lack of open space	Poor access to motorways
Vandalism and graffiti	High crime rates

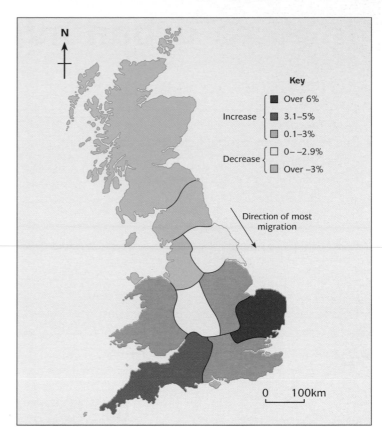

Key

Increase
- ■ Over 6%
- ■ 3.1–5%
- ▨ 0.1–3%

Decrease
- ☐ 0– –2.9%
- ▨ Over –3%

Direction of most migration

0   100km

▲ **Figure 5** Population change in England and Wales, 1981–91.

Activities

1 a Show on a single graph the data in **Figure 4**.
  b Describe and explain the changes shown on the graph.

2 Choose one area of decline and one area of growth from **Figure 5**. Describe the reasons for the growth and decline in your chosen areas.

3 Who are the winners and losers when internal migration takes place? A family chooses to leave the Scottish Highlands and move to London. In small groups choose one of the following and put together a list of ideas. Contribute to a class discussion:

- The advantages for the family that moves
- The disadvantages for the family that moves
- The disadvantages for the community where they lived in Scotland
- The advantages for the community where they move to in London
- The advantages and disadvantages for the government in Scotland
- The advantages and disadvantages for the government in England.

Rural to urban migration in LEDCs

Push factors
(the reasons why people leave the countryside):

- overpopulation resulting from high birth rates
- starvation as a result of too many people for the available food supply
- overgrazing and overcultivation causing soil erosion
- hard work, long hours and little pay for farmers
- natural disasters such as drought, hurricanes, floods and volcanic eruptions
- poor-quality housing
- shortage of education, health and welfare facilities
- lack of electricity, water and sewage services.

Pull factors
(the reasons why people move to the cities):

- a greater variety of jobs with higher wages
- improved housing with services such as water and electricity
- improved quality of life and standard of living
- the availability of schools, doctors, hospitals and entertainment
- more reliable sources of food
- the experience of life in modern, dynamic cities.

▲ **Figure 1** Rural push and urban pull factors.

In LEDCs people began to move from the countryside to the towns in the early twentieth century. The movement has increased since the 1950s. More and more people in LEDCs now live in the towns and cities, e.g. in Nigeria in 1991 30 per cent of the population lived in urban areas, up from just 5 per cent in 1921. The movement has been mostly of younger males so it is **age and sex selective**. The young men are looking for education, work and a better standard of living. More of the push and pull factors can be seen in **Figure 1**.

The rural migrant leaves the home village with a **perception** of city life based upon radio programmes, magazines and letters from relatives already in the city. The reality may be very different. Migrants often have little money and need either to build their own shanty or to stay with friends or relatives until they are established. Some end up sleeping rough in the streets (**Figure 2**). Life in the shanty towns is covered in more detail in Chapter 9.

▲ **Figure 2** Sleeping rough in Goa, India.

Activities

1 Define migration.

2 What are push and pull factors?

3 List four push and pull factors that lead to rural to urban migration in LEDCs.

4 Why is rural to urban migration in LEDCs said to be age and sex selective?

5 Sketch a population pyramid for an LEDC city.

Chapter 9

Settlement

Settlements
are unique and
dynamic places;
no two settlements
are identical and
most have areas
of both growth and
decline. In all towns
and cities different
zones of land use can
be recognized. This
is an aerial view of
Luton facing North.

Key Ideas

Settlements vary in site, size, structure and function:
- different siting factors affect settlement location
- there is a hierarchy of settlements
- settlement function may change over time
- cities can be divided into urban zones.

Urbanization is a global phenomenon:
- issues which result are related to inner city decline in MEDCs and shanty town growth in LEDCs.

Planning strategies are needed to control urban growth:
- attempts have been made to solve the problems of CBDs, inner cities and shanty towns
- there are conflicts about how best to develop or preserve the rural–urban fringe.

Settlement: site, situation and growth

Settlements are places where people live and work. In most countries there is a whole range of different-sized settlements, from individual farms and hamlets through to huge sprawling cities.

The site of a settlement is the physical land on which a settlement is built. Early settlements were built with great care because people had to:

- grow their own food
- find a water supply
- defend themselves from attack
- find building materials and fuel.

Today life is very different, especially in developed countries. Most families buy their food in large supermarkets; there is electricity, piped water and gas. Defence is no longer a factor.

Over time some settlements grew while others disappeared. **Figure 1** shows the remains of an abandoned settlement on the Isle of Arran in Scotland. Settlements that grew had a good **situation**. The situation is the location of the settlement in relation to the surrounding area – the type of relief (i.e. flat or hilly), the routeways and links to other settlements. A settlement at a route focus or bridging point encouraged trade and the settlement would grow.

Site factors
Water supply
All people need water but settlements also need to avoid flooding. In dry or arid areas settlements were built close to a river, spring or well. These are called **wet-point sites**.

▲ **Figure 1** An abandoned settlement on the Isle of Arran, Scotland.

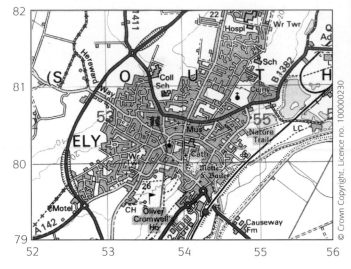

▲ **Figure 2** Ely, a dry-point site.

In the chalk and limestone areas of Britain there is often a line of spring-line settlements at the base of an escarpment (page 27).

In some places the land is marshy or there is a threat of flooding. **Dry-point sites** were chosen to avoid the water. These sites were on valley sides or the tops of small hills. Ely in Cambridgeshire (shown in **Figure 2**) is a good example in the Fenland area of Britain.

Aspect and shelter
In the northern hemisphere the south-facing (*adret*) slopes are warmer than the north-facing (*ubac*) slopes (**Figure 3**). The south-facing slopes are also sheltered from cold north or north-easterly winds. More settlements are sited on the south-facing slopes in the northern hemisphere and also on the lower hillslopes where there is even more shelter.

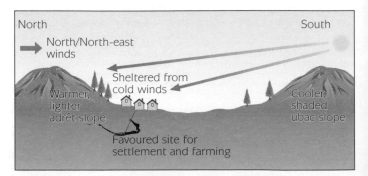

▲ **Figure 3** A cross-section through a valley in the UK running from west to east.

© Crown Copyright. Licence no. 100000230

Defence

Many settlements have the remains of castles, forts or town walls. This shows how important defence was in earlier times. **Figure 4** shows Durham City, a defensive site on the inside bend of a huge meander and with a castle. **Figure 5** shows Corfe Castle where the castle is sited on a hill in a gap in a ridge of high ground.

Food supply

Early people needed to grow their own food so areas with fertile soils often have more settlements, e.g. East Anglia. Areas such as the Chilterns and Pennines have thin, less fertile soils so there were fewer early settlements.

Building materials and fuel supply

Early settlements were often sited near a woodland. The supply of timber was needed for fuel and for building materials. Other settlements located close to quarries or mines for building materials and other minerals. Examples include the mining villages in County Durham and settlements in Alaska, which are close to the oil fields.

Communications

The settlements that grew larger were often located at:

- a bridging point or ford
- at a crossroads
- at a gap through hills, e.g. Corfe Castle
- at a junction of valleys.

All of these locations are a route focus and the settlement grew because trade developed. Some settlements had a castle, cathedral or monastery and this also helped the town to grow as more people were needed to provide the services for the soldiers or monks. The sketch map in **Figure 6** shows the site of Berwick-upon-Tweed in Northumberland and the reasons why it has grown into a town.

▲ **Figure 4** Durham City: a defensive site.

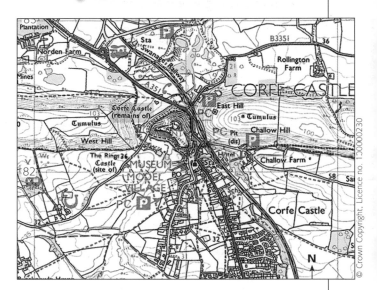

▲ **Figure 5** Corfe Castle: potential for growth?

◄ **Figure 6** Sketch map of Berwick-upon-Tweed.

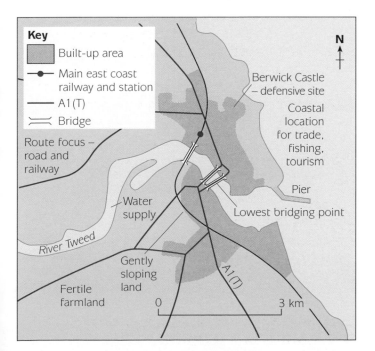

Activities

1 Write definitions for the site and situation of a settlement.

2 List six factors that affected the site of an early settlement.

3 Choose one of the OS map extracts. Draw and label a sketch map to show the site of the settlement. (Have a good look at **Figure 6** to help you.)

4 Using an OS map of your local area draw a sketch map to show the site of a town.

Hierarchy of settlement

A settlement hierarchy arranges settlements in order of size or importance. A settlement's position in a hierarchy depends on the following:

- the population size
- the range and number of services
- the sphere of influence or area served by the settlement.

Settlement size

Figure 1 shows a hierarchy of settlements based upon settlement size. Single farms and hamlets are at the bottom of the hierarchy and the largest city, usually the capital city, is at the top.

Services

The shops and services in a settlement provide for the needs of the local population. The larger a settlement, the more services are needed to provide for the population. **Figure 2** suggests a hierarchy based on the services in settlements of different sizes.

Sphere of influence

This is the area served by the settlement, sometimes called its **trade area** or **hinterland**. A large settlement has a large number and variety of shops and services. These attract people from a wide area who will travel to use the services. This is a place with a large sphere of influence. London attracts people from all over the country to visit its shops and services. Smaller settlements have far fewer shops and services and so people do not travel long distances to use them. A village, for example, will only serve the needs of the village and surrounding farms. It has only a small sphere of influence.

Small settlements such as villages often only have a general store, post office or small supermarket. These shops sell low order or **convenience goods**. These are goods that are needed more often and are quite cheap such as newspapers, bread and milk. People do not travel very far to buy such goods.

In large cities there are many more shops including department stores and specialist shops. Some sell larger, more expensive items that people will travel further to buy. These include furniture, jewellery, TVs and sports equipment. These are called **comparison goods** or high order goods.

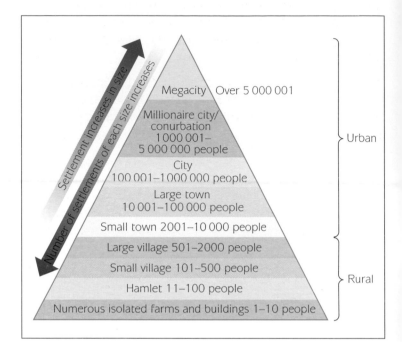

▲ **Figure 1** A hierarchy of settlements according to population size.

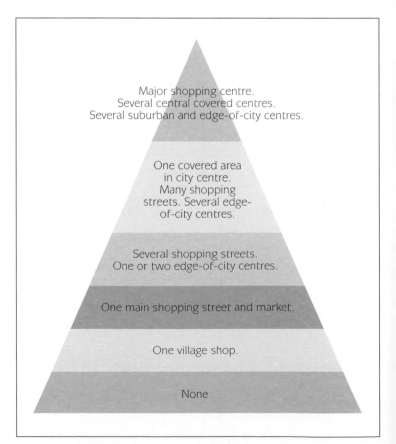

▲ **Figure 2** A hierarchy of settlements based on services.

Functions of a settlement

The function of a settlement is its purpose – the 'work' that it does. **Figure 3** shows some different settlement functions, e.g. a fishing town, a resort town. Notice how they are based on the main types of employment in the town. Many large towns and cities are multifunctional. This means there is a mixture of employment types.

Many settlements have changed their function over time. In some cases the original functions, such as defence or farming, have disappeared altogether. One example of change in the function of a village is shown in **Figure 4**. Shincliffe village began as a farming settlement.

Much later coal was discovered and a mine opened. The village expanded with pit head workings, rows of colliery terraces, railway lines and new services, e.g. churches and public houses. The mine closed in the twentieth century and the population of the village declined. People moved away to find work in mines in other places. Later in the twentieth century the village expanded greatly as new housing estates were added. Today the village is a commuter or dormitory village in which many of the residents live but travel to nearby towns and cities to work.

Description	Definition (percentage of workers in town)
Fishing towns	Fishing employs over 5 per cent
Mining towns	Mining employs over 20 per cent
Quarrying towns	Quarrying employs over 20 per cent
Engineering towns	Engineering employs over 15 per cent
Chemical towns	Chemical works employ over 15 per cent
Shipbuilding towns	Shipbuilding employs over 15 per cent
Transport towns	Transport employs over 15 per cent
Resort towns	Personal service and entertainment employ over 20 per cent
Commercial towns	Commerce and finance form the largest single group, employing over 10 per cent
Towns with a balanced occupational structure, e.g. London	No single employment group dominates.

▲ **Figure 3** A classification of towns by function.

▼ **Figure 4** A changing village: Shincliffe in County Durham.

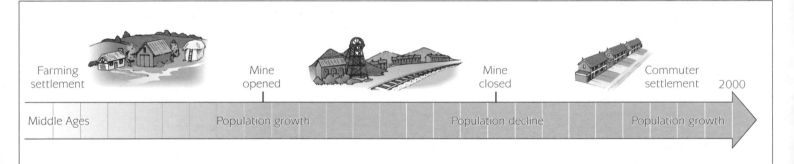

Farming settlement — Mine opened — Mine closed — Commuter settlement — 2000

Middle Ages — Population growth — Population decline — Population growth

Activities

1 Using a map of your local area and **Figures 1** and **2**, complete a copy of the table below.

Settlement hierarchy	Population size	Example from my local area	Functions
Conurbation			
City			
Town			
Village			
Hamlet			
Isolated farms			

2 a Define the term **sphere of influence**.
  b Giving reasons, state where you and your family would go to buy:
   (i) a magazine and some sweets
   (ii) the weekly food shopping
   (iii) a new three-piece suite and clothes.

3 Study **Figure 4**.
  a How has the function of the village changed over time?
  b Describe and explain how the population of Shincliffe has changed.

Urban growth

Urbanization is a process of urban growth that leads to a greater percentage of the population living in towns and cities. In the UK about 90 per cent of the population lives in urban areas. **Figure 1** shows how the urban population has changed in the UK since 1800.

Cities in developed countries (MEDCs)

Towns and cities in MEDCs grew rapidly during the Industrial Revolution, mostly in the 1800s. At the time jobs were being lost in the country-side. An agricultural revolution brought new machinery that meant less work was available in the rural areas. People moved from the country-side to the towns for new jobs in the shipyards, mines and factories. They lived in the rows of terraced housing built in the inner cities.

People continued to move into the urban areas in the twentieth century especially from the remote rural areas. **Figure 3** on page 120 shows some of the pull and push factors that caused the migration.

In the late twentieth century the very large urban areas began to lose population especially from the run-down areas of inner cities. Development schemes in many cities are now trying to attract people back into the cities.

Cities in developing countries (LEDCs)

Cities in LEDCs began to grow rapidly particularly after 1950. This was much later than in MEDCs. The growth has also been much faster, double the rate of the MEDCs. Urbanization in LEDCs was caused by:

* rural to urban migration, a result of push and pull factors (page 122)

* high birth rates in the cities.

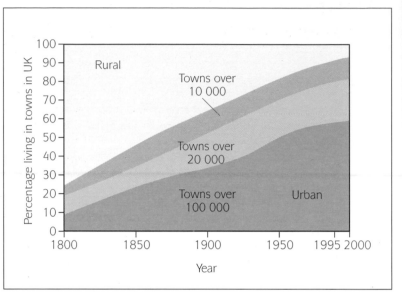

▲ **Figure 1** Urban population growth in the UK, 1800–2000.

World urbanization

Figure 2 shows just how rapid world urbanization has been. The world's population doubled between 1950 and 1990 but the percentage living in towns and cities trebled. The main features of world urbanization in the late 1900s are as follows:

1   The LEDCs now have most of the world's largest cities; they are mostly located in the tropics (**Figure 3**)

2   In LEDCs, many more people live in urban areas than in MEDCs. However, within the LEDCs, the urban population is still lower than the rural population, i.e. more people still live in rural areas in LEDCs.

3   It is the very largest cities that have grown the most.

In 1900 there were only two cities with over one million people – London and New York. These were called **millionaire cities**. Now there are over 300 millionaire cities.

In 2000 the ten largest cities had over 10 million people. These are called **megacities** and most of them are in the LEDCs (**Figure 4**).

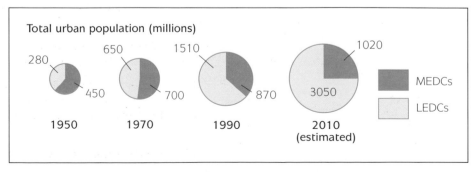

▲ **Figure 2** The world's urban population, 1950–2010 (in millions).

Urbanization in the LEDCs has advantages and disadvantages:

Advantages

1 **Improved economy** Farms surrounding city increase production to provide food for sale in the cities.

2 **Better services** People have access to water supply, electricity, medical care and education

3 **Improved income** Casual, poorly paid work in the informal sector, e.g. selling fruit, shoe cleaning, still pays more than farmwork in rural areas.

4 **Opportunities for improvement**
   - Living in shanty towns is seen as a step on the ladder to improvement
   - Jobs in the informal sector may provide some skills and training
   - It eases some of the population pressure in rural areas
   - Funds flow back to the migrants' villages.

Disadvantages

1 **Poor housing** Problems of housing provision lead to vast illegal shanty towns. Living conditions are appalling.

2 **Unemployment** Lack of jobs leads to a large informal sector.

3 **Increased congestion and pollution** in cities.

4 **Widening of gap between rich and poor** Growth highlights the gap between the rich and poor, which can lead to strikes and protests.

5 **Problems in the rural areas** The rural areas may have insufficient able-bodied workers to farm the land. Agricultural production can fail.

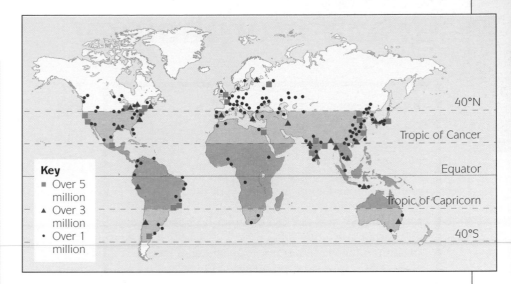

▲ **Figure 3** Growth and distribution of 'millionaire' cities.

Rank order	1970		1995		2010 (estimated)	
1	New York	(16.5)	Tokyo	(26.8)	Tokyo	(28.7)
2	Tokyo	(13.4)	São Paulo	(16.4)	Mumbai	(24.3)
3	London	(10.5)	New York	(16.3)	Shanghai	(21.5)
4	Shanghai	(10.0)	Mexico City	(15.6)	Lagos	(20.8)
5	Mexico City	(8.6)	Mumbai	(15.1)	São Paulo	(20.1)
6	Los Angeles	(8.4)	Shanghai	(15.1)	Jakarta	(19.2)
7	Buenos Aires	(8.4)	Los Angeles	(12.4)	Mexico City	(18.2)
8	Paris	(8.4)	Beijing	(12.4)	Beijing	(17.8)
9	São Paulo	(7.1)	Calcutta	(11.7)	Karachi	(17.6)
10	Moscow	(7.1)	Seoul	(11.6)	New York	(17.3)

Source: United Nations Population Division, 1995

▲ **Figure 4** The world's largest cities (figures in millions of people).

Activities

1 Write a definition of urbanization.

2 Study **Figure 1**. Copy and complete the table below.

Year	% of the population in urban areas in UK
1800	
1900	
1950	
2000	

3 In 1995 what percentage of the population lived in:
   (i) towns over 100 000
   (ii) towns between 20 000 and 100 000
   (iii) towns between 10 000 and 20 000
   (iv) rural areas?

4 Give two differences between the urbanization in LEDCs and MEDCs.

5 a Using an atlas and an outline map of the world mark and label the location of the ten largest cities in 1995 (from **Figure 4**).

   b Describe where they are located.

6 Give four advantages and four disadvantages of urbanization in LEDCs.

Urban morphology

> **ℹ Information box**
>
> **Urban land use** – how the land is used in towns and cities. It includes the shops, industries, offices, housing and parks.
>
> **Urban zones** – in urban areas the different land uses are not all jumbled up. They are in distinct zones of housing or industry or shops and offices.
>
> **Morphology** – the way the different land uses are arranged in a town or city.
>
> **Urban model** – it shows how the land uses may be arranged in cities in both MEDCs and LEDCs.

Key

- ■ Central Business District (CBD)
- ■ High class housing
- ■ Zone of upgraded self-built houses
- □ Modern factories along main road
- ■ Zone of active improvement of housing
- ■ Shanty towns/ squatter settlements

High-quality commercial spine develops

▲ **Figure 2** Land-use zones in a developing city.

Key

- ■ Central Business District (CBD)
- ■ Light manufacturing ⎫ Inner city
- ■ Low-class residential ⎭
- □ Medium-class residential ⎫ Suburbs
- ■ High-class residential ⎭

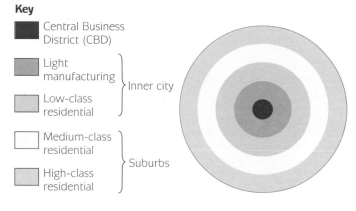

▲ **Figure 1** The Burgess model.

The Burgess model for an MEDC city

The Burgess model has five rings of different land uses. The Central Business District or CBD is at the centre. The other zones are arranged in a circular pattern around the CBD. The Inner City is the zone closest to the CBD with the suburbs beyond.

The Burgess model was developed in the 1920s and based on two main ideas:

1 Cities grew outwards from the original site so the oldest properties are in the centre and the younger properties at the edges of the cities. The original site is generally where the CBD is located today.

2 The most expensive land is in the centre of the city where the CBD is located. Here only the high profit-making shops and offices can afford to locate. On the edges of the city the land is cheaper and there is more land available. Here industries and housing can afford to locate.

An urban model for an LEDC city

The urban model in **Figure 2** is based on cities in Brazil. The model has one similarity with the Burgess model. The CBD is in the centre. All cities have CBDs that are similar with skyscrapers and Western-style shops. However there are many more differences between the two models. In the LEDC city:

- The model is much less regular, there are more zones

- The land uses are not as well zoned – the land uses are more mixed up

- The high-class sector is very small and close to the CBD or on prime sites such as near the coast

- There are no middle-class housing areas such as the suburbs in MEDC cities

- The largest zone is the shanty towns stretching to the outskirts of the city

- There are no traditional industrial areas but modern factories have been built along roads.

> **Activity**
>
> Study **Figure 3** and the photo on page 123.
>
> **a** Which urban zone is represented by each of the six grid squares outlined in black?
>
> **b** Describe the land uses in each of the six squares.
>
> **c** In pairs or small groups discuss whether Luton's pattern of land uses fits the Burgess model. Try to explain any differences. Contribute your ideas to a class discussion.

Urban zones in British cities

1 The **Central Business District** is at the heart of the city, where the settlement was originally sited. You can recognize it on an OS map by identifying the historic buildings, where several main roads meet, or where there is a high density of buildings. Bus and railway stations are often at the edge of the CBD.

2 The **inner-city zone** grew during the Industrial Revolution. It is a mixed zone of terraced housing and industry. The terraces were built along narrow streets, giving them a grid-like appearance. Some of the industries cluster together in an industrial zone alongside railway sidings, canals or rivers. Some inner-city areas have been redeveloped with high-rise blocks of flats with open spaces between.

3 The **suburbs** began to expand after the First World War. These housing estates have an irregular road pattern with avenues and culs-de-sac. Houses are more varied, with semi-detached and detached properties.

4 In the **rural–urban fringe**, different land uses may be found, some rural, such as farmland and forestry, and some connected to the city, such as golf courses, airports and out-of-town shopping centres.

5 Throughout the urban area **recreational facilities** may be found, such as parks and sports fields.

6 **Industrial estates** have been built on the fringes of many towns and cities, where there is more space for single-storey factories and car parks.

▼ **Figure 3** OS map of Luton, Beds. 1: 50 000 (2cm = 1km).

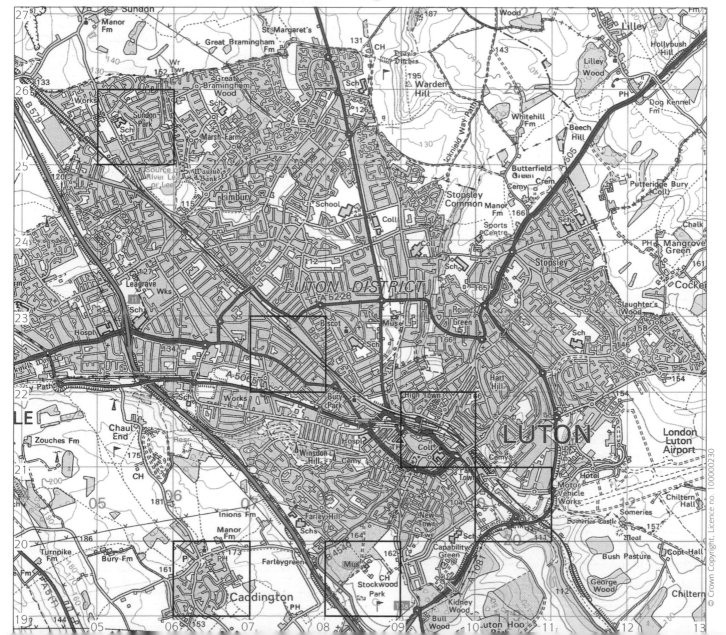

© Crown Copyright. Licence no. 100000230

The Central Business District

Figure 1 shows the Central Business District (CBD) of Leeds. As in many large cities the CBD is easy to recognize by:

- the tall skyscrapers
- the neon lights at night
- the very high density of buildings
- the focus of roads with nearby bus and rail stations
- the high density of people during the day working, shopping or seeking entertainment
- traffic congestion.

Main functions of the CBD
Shops

- The CBD has the widest range of shops and the largest department stores
- The shops mainly sell high order or comparison goods
- The CBD has a large sphere of influence or trade area
- Some shops such as those selling shoes, clothes or jewellery cluster together.
- Shops such as newsagents and chemists are more spread out
- The department stores and chain stores that make the greatest profits locate in the centre or core of the CBD
- Smaller shops are located on the edges or frame of the CBD (see **Figure 2**).

Offices
Banks, building societies, solicitors, company headquarters, insurance companies and government offices occupy high-rise office blocks or the upper floors above shops in the CBD.

Culture and entertainment
Parts of the CBD 'come alive' at night such as London's West End and the Newcastle Quayside. These are the areas where there are theatres, clubs, cinemas and restaurants.

The CBD is constantly changing with areas that are decaying and others that are improving. The CBD also has problems of traffic congestion, parking, pollution and a shortage of land.

▲ **Figure 1** Leeds CBD.

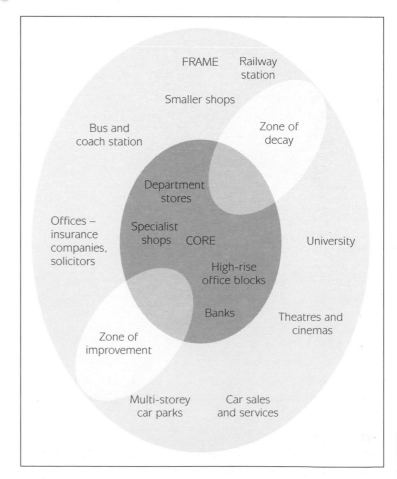

▲ **Figure 2** The core and frame in the CBD.

Problems and attempted solutions in the CBD

Traffic congestion

Towns grew before the motor car was invented. Many city centres had only narrow streets with few pavements. Today there is very high car ownership and many people need to be in the CBD for work, shopping and entertainment. This makes the CBD very congested with people and traffic and there are parking problems. Many local authorities have tried to solve these problems by one or more of the following:

- ring roads and by-passes to divert traffic not going into the city centre
- urban motorways and flyovers
- public transport schemes such as 'park and ride', the Newcastle Metro (**Figure 3**), trams in Manchester
- multi-storey car parks
- pedestrianization of high streets.

Today schemes are more environmentally friendly and try to reduce the traffic in city centres, e.g. tolls, traffic bans, electric cars and buses that run on gas and metro systems.

◀ **Figure 3**
The Newcastle Metro.

Pollution

Water, land, air and noise pollution are all common in city centres. Pollution is thought to contribute to the stresses of living in urban areas and to some diseases, such as asthma and bronchitis. Attempted solutions include:

- laws against litter and dumping sewage in rivers
- improved provision of litter bins and road sweeping
- Clean Air Acts that allow only the use of smokeless fuels
- clean-fuel technology and vehicles that run on methane gas or electricity
- banning heavy lorries from passing through city centres
- increased planting of trees and shrubs.

Lack of space and the high cost of land

In the CBD land is expensive and there is competition for the land. To cope with this tall skyscrapers have been built to increase the area available. Out-of-town shopping areas and business parks have been built on the edges of towns.

▲ **Figure 4** The Gateshead MetroCentre.

Urban decline

Parts of some CBDs have declined. There are empty shops and offices that are boarded up and vandalized. CBDs also have to compete with out-of-town shopping areas. Attempted solutions include:

- redevelopment of areas that have declined, e.g. Covent Garden in London
- expansion of the CBD into the inner city, clearing away old factories and poor quality terraces.

▲ **Figure 5** Decline in the West End of Newcastle upon Tyne.

Activities

1 List six characteristics of the CBD.

2 Using **Figure 2**, describe four differences between the core and the frame of the CBD.

3 Suggest reasons why so few people live in the CBD.

4 a Name the four main problems in the CBD.
  b Describe how planners can attempt to solve one of these problems.

The inner city

▲ **Figure 1** Terraced housing for workers in the inner city.

The inner city is the zone between the CBD in the centre and the suburbs. In Britain the inner city grew during the Industrial Revolution. Factories were built on the edges of the CBD. Streets of terraced housing (**Figures 1** and **2**) were also built for migrants from the countryside who came for the jobs in the factories. The terraces were cheap and sometimes poor quality but they were close to the factories so the people could walk to work. Services were also built including corner shops, schools, public houses and parks. There is a real mixture of land uses in the inner city.

In the 1960s and 1970s large parts of the inner cities were in decay. There were two main problems:

- poor housing with no proper kitchens, bathrooms or central heating
- a decaying environment.

▲ **Figure 2**   Once Victorian terraces for the middle classes, now multiple occupancy flats and bedsits for students and ethnic minorities.

▶ **Figure 4** The environmental, social and economic problems of British inner cities.

▲ **Figure 3** High-rise flats – the 1960s answer to the problems of inner cities?

The answer at the time was the high-rise flat (**Figure 3**). In Glasgow 262 multi-storey blocks of flats were built that were up to 31 storeys high. In most cities the flats have been a disaster and many have been demolished.

In the 1980s and 1990s the inner cities continued to decline and the problems worsened (**Figure 4**). In some cities there were riots e.g. Brixton, Liverpool and Manchester. The riots led to an enquiry and a report by Lord Scarman after which a new phase of inner-city regeneration began.

Environmental problems

Housing:
- Decaying terraced housing
- Poorly built tower blocks.

Pollution and decay:
- Air, land and water pollution
- Derelict warehouses and churches
- High levels of graffiti and vandalism
- Traffic congestion.

Poor services:
- Lack of open space and poor facilities.

Social problems
- Above-average concentration of pensioners, lone parents, ethnic minorities and students
- High levels of disease, illness and overcrowding
- Rising crime rates
- Poor police and community relations.

Economic problems
- Poverty and low income
- High unemployment, often over 50 per cent male unemployment
- Declining industries
- Poor access to motorways and airports
- High land values.

Improving the inner cities

Millions of pounds have been spent on improving the inner cities in Britain and to stop people moving away. Today many of the schemes involve the local communities in planning the changes. In other areas schemes have tried to attract people back to the inner cities. Attractive, modern executive apartments have been built as part of many riverside development schemes, e.g. London Docklands, Salford Docks, Newcastle Quayside. These aim to attract wealthier people to return to the cities. It is called gentrification.

> **i Information box**
>
> **Urban renewal** – the renovation and improvement of existing buildings.
> **Urban regeneration** – 'knock it all down and start again'.

Improving Glasgow's inner city areas

1950–74 Comprehensive Development Areas (CDAs)

The CDAs were the areas targeted for improvement and the policy was 'knock it all down and start again'. Large numbers of tenements (**Figure 5**) were demolished and replaced with high-rise flats. During this time thousands of people left the inner cities creating a 'dead heart'.

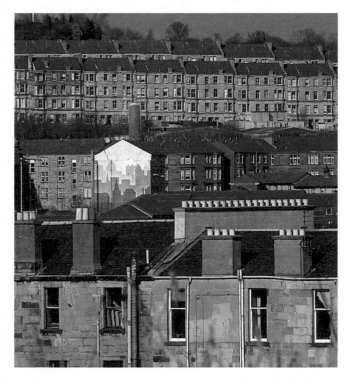

▲ **Figure 5** A Glasgow tenement.

1988 The Glasgow Garden Festival

The Garden Festival was held on 39 hectares of derelict land in the dockland area of Glasgow's inner city. The area now has 1100 new houses and flats, a new road, a business park and 4.5 hectares of open space based upon one of the parkland theme areas of the festival.

TURNING TOWER BLOCKS INTO PAGODAS

A renovation scheme is going to great lengths to disguise two grim towers of 1960s council flats in Paisley near Glasgow. The architects have decided to replace the flat roofs with Japanese pagoda-style roofs in blue aluminium. The two towers have also received blue and grey panelling bolted on top of the original concrete.

The original high-rise flats were cold, poorly insulated and prone to condensation. They had become sordid places to live. It cost £1 477 000, a fraction of the cost of building 112 new homes from scratch. The scheme has been so successful that there are plans to refurbish five similar tower blocks.

▲ **Figure 6** Adapted from *The Daily Telegraph*, 14 October 1994.

1986–94 The Govan Initiative

Many schemes in the past had only tried to improve the housing and environment. The Govan Initiative aimed to improve the economy and create much needed jobs by:

- financing 'start-up' units for businesses
- landscaping schemes to improve vacant land
- education, training and advice on home and industrial security
- the reopening of the one remaining shipyard
- skills training programmes.

Housing in cities

In most British cities the sprawling suburbs cover the greatest land area. The suburbs are mostly residential, housing the population of the city. Moving towards the outskirts of a city the housing becomes younger and the density decreases.

Local Authority housing

In the 1930s, new council estates were built in the suburbs, often still within walking distance of factories or close to main roads with access to public transport. In the 1960s, as inner city terraces were cleared, new council estates were built further out in the fringes of the suburbs. A greater effort was made to vary the size and type of the accommodation provided, with single-storey terraces, maisonettes with two or three storeys, and high-rise tower blocks. The estates often had free-standing garages and more open space.

The Victorian terraces of the inner city

High-density housing was built in Victorian terraces. Built in long straight rows, they give a grid-iron street layout. They were originally built as two-up two-down houses with no separate bathroom and kitchen. They each had a backyard with an outdoor toilet and coal store. No gardens or garages were provided. Today many have been improved with the addition of a two-storey extension to provide kitchen and bathroom, double glazing and central heating. Car parking can still be a problem as there is no space for garages.

Since the 1950s large areas of terraced housing in a substandard state have been cleared. Early redevelopment schemes built high-rise flats in their place. Today, remaining terraces have been improved to provide housing for people with a variety of incomes.

Rural–urban fringe   Suburbs   Inner city   Cent

Inner city redevelopment

Two phases of redevelopment can often be recognized:

1. The high-rise flats built in the 1960s by local authorities to rehouse people from the demolished terraces.

2. More recent modern housing built by private builders in varied styles, sizes and prices. Some are aimed at first-time buyers, while executive apartments have been built in prestigious locations, for example on riversides, in an attempt to diversify the social structure of the inner city. This is called gentrification when housing leads to a rise in the social class of an area.

Inter-war housing

Typically these are semi-detached houses with bay windows and metal window frames. Most have front and back gardens but at first, few had garages as car ownership was still unusual. Some of the housing was in estates, and some was built along main roads as ribbon development.

These housing areas were mostly private and built in culs-de-sac and avenues. The irregular street pattern is easy to recognize on Ordnance Survey maps. Most inter-war housing is in the inner suburbs adjacent to the inner city.

Post-war private housing

More recent housing has a greater variety of styles and designs. Some large private hosing estates have been built, while smaller patches of land within the suburbs have been used for in-fill housing development. Since the early 1990s there has been an increase in the building of very expensive executive-type housing, costing over £250 000 per unit. These estates are well planned and spacious and less uniform in their layout.

District   Inner city   Suburbs   Rural–urban fringe

The rural–urban fringe

The rural–urban fringe is another area of mixed land uses. It lies beyond the suburbs at the edge of the built-up area.

Urban sprawl

Urban sprawl is the growth and spread of cities into the countryside around. Land is in demand for new housing, industrial estates, business parks, shopping centres, bypasses, airports and golf courses. The growth has engulfed villages, farms and woodland. At first the growth was not well planned but today planners are trying to control the growth of urban areas. There are many conflicts caused by the spread of urban areas into the rural–urban fringe.

Motorways and bypasses

In the 1980s car ownership and road building were encouraged. This caused the following problems:

- pressure on the road network
- congested town centres
- pollution from exhaust fumes
- noise and heavy traffic in villages.

At the time the solutions were to build more roads including motorways and bypasses. Many of these schemes were opposed by local people and conservation groups (**Figure 1**) and in the 1990s government policy changed. Today schemes try to reduce traffic by improving public transport, charging tolls and raising fuel and car park charges. Many road schemes planned for the 1990s and early 2000s have been scrapped.

11 January 1996
Protesters Halt By-Pass Work Again

6 May 1994
Road Protesters Ready for Battle on Solsbury Hill

14 June 1995
Carriageway duel to save the Blackdown Hills

18 February 1996
Newbury protesters told how to destroy

▲ **Figure 1** No more roads, please!

Out-of-town development

Out-of-town locations have many advantages to developers for business parks (**Figure 2**), shopping centres and industrial estates:

- plenty of space for large superstores, single-storey factories and car parks
- cheaper land than in urban locations
- access to motorways and airports
- a large labour pool and market from the nearby suburban population
- open space, pleasant countryside
- cleaner, less congested environment.

▲ **Figure 2** The Solar Building at Doxford International Technology Park on the outskirts of Sunderland.

In the late twentieth century many cities grew rapidly as new developments were built in the rural–urban fringe. New shops and industries are attractive to the people living in the suburbs but there are also disadvantages:

- increasing urban sprawl
- loss of agricultural land and public open space
- loss of trade in traditional city centres
- increasing pollution and traffic congestion.

Increasingly, local authorities are applying stricter planning controls in the rural–urban fringe to protect the environment and to counter the damage caused to existing city centres and industrial areas.

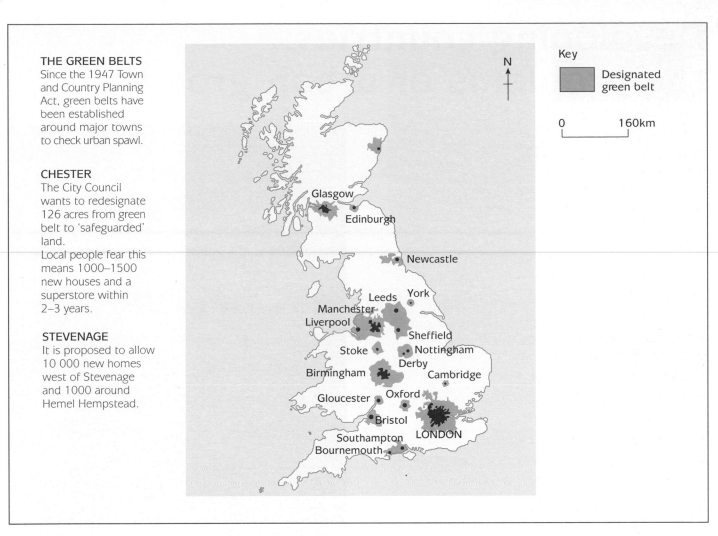

THE GREEN BELTS
Since the 1947 Town and Country Planning Act, green belts have been established around major towns to check urban sprawl.

CHESTER
The City Council wants to redesignate 126 acres from green belt to 'safeguarded' land.
Local people fear this means 1000–1500 new houses and a superstore within 2–3 years.

STEVENAGE
It is proposed to allow 10 000 new homes west of Stevenage and 1000 around Hemel Hempstead.

Key — Designated green belt

0   160km

Glasgow
Edinburgh
Newcastle
Leeds   York
Manchester
Liverpool
Sheffield
Stoke   Nottingham
Derby
Birmingham   Cambridge
Gloucester   Oxford
Bristol
Southampton   LONDON
Bournemouth

▲ **Figure 3** Green belts in the UK, 1995.

Conservation and green belts

Green belts were the first attempt to stop the sprawl of cities into the countryside. Green belts are areas of green and open land on the edges of cities in which urban development is restricted.

Britain's first green belt was created around London in the 1940s and many more towns and cities have established them since (**Figure 3**). The green belts have been quite successful in stopping sprawl although since the 1990s there have been pressures for green belt land to be released for development. Some people also argue that too many exceptions have been allowed to the no building rule, such as parts of the M25 around London.

Today planners are forced to redevelop brownfield sites rather than looking at land beyond the city boundary. These are areas of derelict land and empty properties within the existing urban area.

Activities

1 Give four causes of urban sprawl in MEDCs.

2 In small groups, take on one of the following roles and discuss the advantages and disadvantages of urban sprawl for each role. Report your findings to the rest of the class.

   - A developer wishing to build a business park in the rural–urban fringe.
   - A young family living in the outer suburbs
   - A farmer in the rural–urban fringe
   - A conservationist and environmental campaigner
   - A couple wanting to set up a smallholding
   - A representative from the planning authority.

3 When you have heard each of the presentations, choose a role and write a letter to the local paper giving your views on a proposed development in the rural–urban fringe.

Developing countries: the problems of urban growth

In cities in the LEDCs there are very few rich people but vast numbers of poor people living in huge shanty towns. The numbers of poor continue to grow as more and more people move from the rural areas into the cities. Urban growth has been so rapid and on such a large scale that the cities are facing serious problems.

Traffic

- Huge problems of congestion
- Air and noise pollution
- High accident rates.

In Mexico City in 1992 all children were told to stay at home as the air pollution was at a dangerously high level.

Unemployment and poverty

- New factories cannot keep pace with the need for jobs
- Massive unemployment
- Huge informal sector such as shoe shiners, street traders or domestic servants
- Many jobs are low paid
- A large sector of the population live in poverty in the cities.

Housing

The huge numbers of migrants to the cities has created a shortage of housing, especially low-cost housing that the migrants can afford. This has caused the growth of the vast shanty towns.

Problems caused by the growth of shanty towns

Housing

In many LEDC cities such as Mexico City, Calcutta and São Paulo, over 50 per cent of the population live in the shanty towns. The shanties are sited on any spare land the migrants can find including steep slopes, swamps and rubbish tips. Here, the land has not already been built on because of the threat of landslides, floods or pollution.

The shacks are homemade and built from anything the migrants can find such as bits of wood, corrugated iron, cardboard and polythene. The building materials and the high density of the shacks make them a real fire hazard.

▲ **Figure 1** Shanty town on a hillside in Rio de Janeiro, Brazil.

Most shacks lack the basic services such as running water, electricity, gas, drainage and toilets. Several families may share a water tap and sewage can run down the streets. Diseases such as cholera and typhoid are common and spread quickly. Many shanty towns do not have any rubbish collection and it collects on any spare land which is another cause of disease.

Transport

In many shanty towns transport is a problem. Some people are unable to take jobs in parts of the city that cannot be reached easily. In the shanties roads are often only dirt tracks. Most people rely on walking, few own a bicycle and even fewer a car. There are limited bus services and they are expensive.

Food and health

Families live in poverty with little money for food or clothes. The children often suffer malnutrition. The people live on one or two cheap basic foods that do not provide a balanced diet. Many babies die due to high rates of disease.

There is a lack of clean water and water-borne diseases are common, e.g. typhoid and diarrhoea. Disease spreads quickly because of the large numbers of people living so close together. Health care is often expensive and may be too far away.

Education

Many children do not go to school or may only manage to attend a primary school. Many children leave school early and are illiterate and without skills. They often need to earn money to support the family. Children as young as 6 years old may do some shoe shining or roadside selling.

Employment

Jobs are few in the shanty towns and many work in the informal sector street selling, shoe cleaning or as domestic servants. A few may get jobs in factories but travel can be expensive, the wages poor and the hours long.

Activities

1 Complete a table like the one below to show the problems in the shanty towns.

Environmental problems	Socio-economic problems

2 Draw and label a sketch of **Figure 1** to show the characteristics of a shanty town.

3 a Give three possible sites for a shanty town.
  b Describe the housing in a shanty town.

4 Imagine that you have recently migrated to the city and live in a shanty town. Write a letter to your family back in the rural area to explain what life is like in the shanties.

Figure 2 Sewage running down an open drain in Goa, India.

Solving the problems of cities in the developing world

The main problems in cities in the LEDCs are:

- the vast shanty towns
- the lack of services
- poor transport
- land, air and water pollution.

However, the LEDCs have very little money to try to solve the problems. Brazil has tried to solve some of the problems by schemes within the city and in the countryside to try to stop the growth of the cities.

Schemes in the city

Self-help schemes

Although the shanty towns are illegal, the Government has realized that they cannot remove them. The people are so poor that it is difficult to build them homes and charge the rents necessary. One solution in São Paulo in Brazil has been to establish **self-help schemes** (Figure 1). The Government puts in basic services such as water, sewerage and electricity and provides cheap building materials, such as breeze-blocks. The families then build single-storey homes with a water tank and indoor bathroom. The building helps to develop a community spirit and the houses are relatively cheap, hygienic and fire-resistant. However, the residents must be able to co-operate with each other and to plan the improvements. In Brazil these 'improved' shanty towns are known as the *periferia*.

Transport and pollution

In São Paolo an underground train system (**Figure 2**) has been constructed to reduce the numbers of cars on the road, to cut down on accidents and to help control pollution. The system is also a reliable cheap alternative for people travelling from the shanty towns to the CBD where most employment is available.

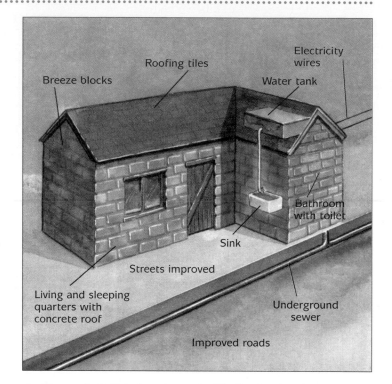

Figure 1 Self-help scheme in São Paulo, Brazil.

▼ **Figure 2** The underground train system in São Paulo, Brazil.

Opening up the interior

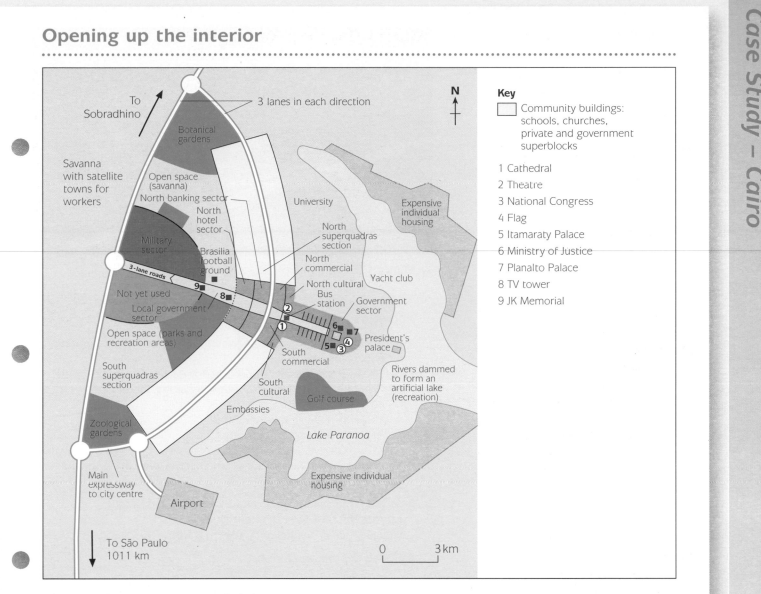

▲ **Figure 3** Brasilia, a new capital city.

New towns

In Brazil a new capital city, Brasilia, was planned and opened in 1960 (**Figure 3**). One aim was to divert some of the rural migrants away from the already overcrowded cities at the coast, such as Rio de Janeiro and São Paulo. The population of Brasilia has grown to over 1 million, but the shanty towns of the coastal cities are still growing and *favelas* (the Brazilian word for shanty towns) have begun to appear in Brasilia where the housing is too expensive for many rural migrants.

Activities

1 Using an atlas draw a sketch map to show the location of Brasilia in Brazil.

2 What was the aim of creating Brasilia?

3 Give two reasons why it has not worked.

4 Study **Figure 3**.
   a Name three features of Brasilia that show it is the capital city with the seat of Government.
   b List some of the facilities provided for the residents of Brasilia.
   c Describe the accommodation and attractions available for tourists visiting Brasilia.
   d Explain the location of the expensive individual housing.

Developing the Amazon rainforest

The Brazilian Government has tried to reduce the number of people moving from the countryside into the towns. In Brazil large numbers of people have come from the north-east region which has suffered serious droughts. They have moved into the very large cities of São Paulo and Rio de Janeiro on the south-east coast of Brazil.

The Government has developed parts of Amazonia in the north and west of the country and encouraged migrants from the north-east to settle in the rain forest. In the rainforest the Government has built huge roads such as the Trans Amazonian Highway (**Figure 1**). Along the roads plots of land have been cleared for farming. In some areas small houses have been built and services provided for the settlers. However, the resettlement schemes have not always been a success:

- The soils soon become infertile so more land has to be cleared

- Some migrants arrived to find the land had not been cleared and no services had been provided

- Many are a long way from any towns or markets and transport is difficult and expensive.

The Government is also trying to solve other problems in rural areas to try to reduce the out-migration of people to the cities. One scheme has improved land ownership by breaking up the very large estates and giving the land back to the tenant farmers.

▲ **Figure 1** Development in the Amazon rainforest.

Activities

1 a What is the difference between the site and the situation of a settlement?
b List four site factors important for early settlements.
c Give one reason why the following siting factors are no longer important:
- being close to a water supply
- fertile soils to grow food
- a defensive site.
d Suggest two reasons why some settlements grew more than others.

2 Arrange the following into a hierarchy of settlement, putting the largest settlement first:
village　　city　　hamlet　　town　　farm.

3 Define the following terms:
- Low order (convenience goods)
- High order (comparison goods)
- Sphere of influence.

4 Explain why large settlements have a greater number and range of shops and services.

5 a Draw a labelled diagram to show the location of the following urban zones of a city in an MEDC:
suburbs　　　industrial area
Central Business District　　　inner city.
b Describe the characteristics of two of the urban zones named in (**a**).
c List four problems of inner cities in developed countries.

6 a What is a shanty town?
b Give two reasons why shanty towns have grown in many LEDC cities.
c Describe and explain the problems of the shanty towns for the inhabitants and local authorities.
d Describe how the problems of shanty towns are being solved.

Chapter 10

Agriculture

Wheat growing in the British countryside. Why did the farmer choose to grow crops on the land?

Key Ideas

The farm as a system:
- farming is a system with inputs, processes and outputs.

Agricultural activity varies from place to place:
- physical factors (relief, soils, climate) and human factors (market, capital, labour, politics) result in different farm systems
- farming systems may be commercial or subsistence, intensive or extensive
- there is a wide range of farm types in the UK.

Agricultural change can have advantages and disadvantages:
- in LEDCs farming has been affected by the Green Revolution, irrigation, soil conservation and the use of appropriate technology
- in countries in the European Union, farming has been affected by hedge removal, soil erosion, quotas and subsidies.

Types of farming

The farm as a system

A farm may be studied as a system with a series of inputs, processes and outputs.

Inputs ⟶ Processes ⟶ Outputs

Inputs – what goes into the system, e.g. soils, climate and relief (physical inputs) and labour, money and machinery (human inputs).

Processes – the activities in the farm that turn the inputs into outputs.

Outputs – the products of the system, e.g. crops, wool, meat, money.

To make a profit the value of the outputs must be greater than the cost of the inputs. **Figure 1** shows a range of possible inputs, processes and outputs.

Types of farming

There are many different types of farming (**Figure 3**). They can be grouped in different ways (**Figure 2**).

Inputs	Processes	Outputs
Physical environment:	Planting	Milk
Relief	Ploughing	Cereals, e.g. wheat, corn
Soils	Spraying	Vegetables, e.g. potatoes,
Climate	Harvesting	cabbage
Drainage	Feeding stock	Oilseed rape, sugar beet
		Fruit, e.g. apples, pears
Human environment:	Shearing	Eggs
Labour	Dipping	Cattle, pigs, sheep
Machinery and fuel	Milking	Wool
Fertilizers, chemicals	Crop storage	Poultry
Animal feeds		Hay and straw
New animals and seeds		Animal feedstuffs
		Wastes, including manure

Arable, pastoral or mixed
- Arable – the growing of crops
- Pastoral – the rearing of animals
- Mixed – farms that grow crops and rear animals

Subsistence or commercial
- Subsistence – farmers produce food to feed themselves and their family, no profit is made
- Commercial – animals and crops are produced for sale and profit is made

Intensive or extensive
- Intensive – high inputs, often of labour and/or capital to produce high outputs. Farms are often small
- Extensive – large farms with low inputs

▲ **Figure 2** Classification of farm types.

◀ **Figure 1** The farm as a system.

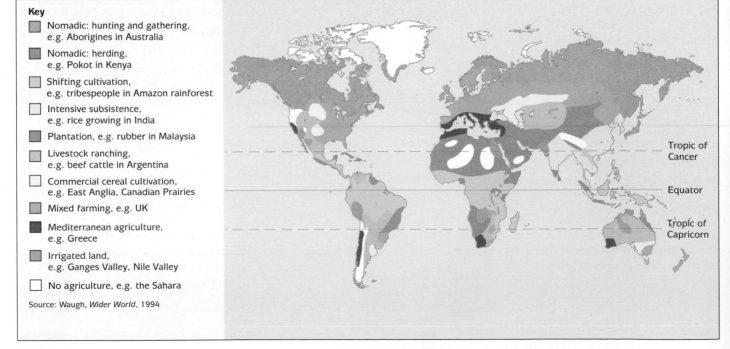

Key
- Nomadic: hunting and gathering, e.g. Aborigines in Australia
- Nomadic: herding, e.g. Pokot in Kenya
- Shifting cultivation, e.g. tribespeople in Amazon rainforest
- Intensive subsistence, e.g. rice growing in India
- Plantation, e.g. rubber in Malaysia
- Livestock ranching, e.g. beef cattle in Argentina
- Commercial cereal cultivation, e.g. East Anglia, Canadian Prairies
- Mixed farming, e.g. UK
- Mediterranean agriculture, e.g. Greece
- Irrigated land, e.g. Ganges Valley, Nile Valley
- No agriculture, e.g. the Sahara

Source: Waugh, *Wider World*, 1994

Tropic of Cancer

Equator

Tropic of Capricorn

▲ **Figure 3** Types of farming.

Factors affecting farming

The type of farming in an area depends on the physical conditions (soils, relief and climate) and human factors such as labour and markets (**Figure 4**). The physical conditions are often the most important especially if there are infertile soils or a lack of water. Then the farmer has little choice.

PHYSICAL FACTORS

Rainfall

All crops and animals need a reliable source of water. Different crops require different amounts of water. Wheat, for example, does not need more than 600mm a year and grows well in south-east England.

Temperature

Most plants stop growing when temperatures fall below 6°C. The number of months the temperature is above 6°C determines the length of the growing season. In some countries the growing season is too short for any crops to be grown. Different crops also have different temperature ranges within which they grow well. Wheat grows well in areas with a temperate climate while rice prefers hot temperatures in tropical and sub-tropical locations.

Sunshine hours

The number of sunshine hours is important, especially for the ripening of crops. Grapes need long hours of sunshine to ripen.

Soil type

Crops grow best on deep, fertile, free-draining soils, while less fertile soils are best used for pastoral farming. In the upland areas of the UK soils are thin, acidic and often rocky, and are unable to support crops (**Figure 5**), whereas in the lowlands the richer, fertile brown earths are more suited to agriculture.

Relief (height and shape of land)

Mountainous areas are colder than the lowlands and slopes are often too steep for farm machinery so most farming is pastoral. The lowlands with gentle relief are more easily farmed.

▲ **Figure 5** Hill sheep farming dominates in uplands such as the Lake District where the poor physical conditions make crop growing difficult.

HUMAN FACTORS

Labour

Labour is in abundance in some countries, such as India and Bangladesh. Here, rice growing absorbs huge numbers of people in planting and harvesting. In other areas such as the Pennines in the UK the population density is low and hill sheep farming is adapted to low inputs of labour.

Finance

The profit a farmer makes affects the amount that can be invested in machinery, fertilizers, seeds and animals, and how much the farmer can afford to pay in wages for the family and any farmworkers.

Market

If a farmer is to make a profit there must be a market for the produce. In the past, farms close to towns and cities in the UK often concentrated on dairying and market gardening in order to supply fresh foods quickly to the large urban population. Today, many farmers have contracts with supermarkets, e.g. Sainsbury's, and other food companies such as Bird's Eye which guarantee a market for their produce.

Politics, loans, grants and subsidies

In some LEDCs loans have been available to farmers to buy machinery, seeds and fertilizers. In the European Union there is a complicated system of subsidies which has encouraged farmers to specialize in different crops.

Tradition

Many farms have practised the same type of farming for generations. Tradition is important in rural communities. Also, it is very costly to change farming practices. Imagine the cost of converting from a cereal farm with its seed drills and combine harvesters to a dairy farm with milking parlours and cattle.

▲ **Figure 4** Factors affecting farming.

Farming in the UK

In the UK many farmers combine a number of different activities on their farms. However, as **Figure 1** shows, in certain areas particular crops or types of livestock are dominant.

Cereals

The most important arable crops in the UK are wheat and barley. Most arable farming is in the south and east of the UK because:

- the relief is low lying, mostly below 200 metres and flat or gently sloping – this means that large tractors and combine harvesters are easily used

- soils are mostly fertile boulder clay or loam soils that are easy to plough

- summer temperatures average over 16°C and long hours of sunshine help to ripen the crops

- cold winters with frost help to break up the soil and to kill soil pests.

Sheep

Sheep are raised for their meat and wool. Most sheep farming is in the upland areas (over 400m), in the north and west of the UK because:

- steep slopes make it impossible to use machinery for growing crops

- the sheep are sturdy and sure-footed and can cope with the steep slopes

- the thin, acid soils are infertile and only support grasses that the sheep can graze and survive on

- winters are cold with snow and summers cool – crops do not grow and ripen well and even the sheep need to be brought down to the lowlands in the winter

- rainfall is high, over 1000mm per year, so the grass grows well but arable crops would rot in the ground.

Market gardening

This is the growing of vegetables, fruit and flowers. This type of farming is very intensive and commercial. Most market gardens are quite small in area but have very high inputs of finance and labour. There is a large input of labour for planting, irrigating, spraying and harvesting. Expenditure is high on fertilizers, seeds, sprays, heating and lighting for greenhouses (**Figure 4**).

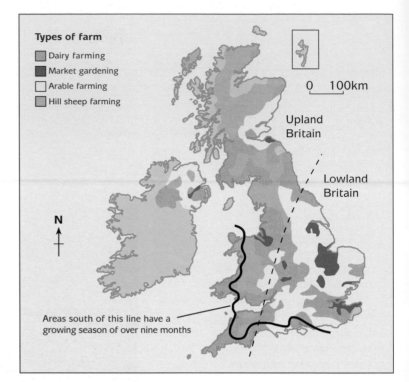

Types of farm
- Dairy farming
- Market gardening
- Arable farming
- Hill sheep farming

0   100km

Upland Britain

Lowland Britain

N

Areas south of this line have a growing season of over nine months

▲ **Figure 1** The pattern of farming in the UK.

Market garden crops are often very perishable. This means they need to reach their market quickly before they begin to rot. Before improvements in refrigerated transport many market gardens were close to large cities to reduce transport time and cost.

In the UK most market gardens are in the south and east. This is due to:

- flat, low-lying relief
- adequate rainfall
- warm, sunny summers to ripen the crops
- fertile, light, stone-free soils
- no need for greenhouses for all of the crops
- large market in London and the south-east
- excellent road and rail links.

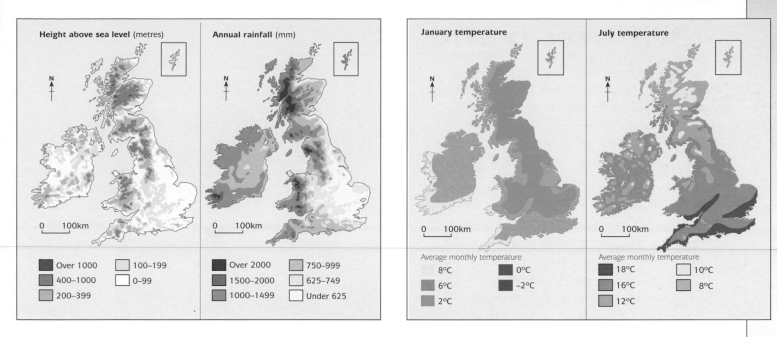

Height above sea level (metres) | Annual rainfall (mm)

N

0   100km

Over 1000 | 100–199
400–1000 | 0–99
200–399

Over 2000 | 750–999
1500–2000 | 625–749
1000–1499 | Under 625

▲ **Figure 2** Relief and rainfall in the UK.

January temperature | July temperature

N

0   100km

Average monthly temperature
8°C | 0°C
6°C | –2°C
2°C

Average monthly temperature
18°C | 10°C
16°C | 8°C
12°C

▲ **Figure 3** January and July temperatures in the UK.

Dairying

Dairying in the UK is both intensive and commercial. It is the main type of farming in south-west Britain because:

- high rainfall encourages good grass growth
- flat or gently sloping land allows the cows to graze easily
- warm summers and mild winters (over 5°C) so the grass grows all the year round
- the cows can graze out of doors almost all year
- farmers only need to provide very small amounts of winter fodder.

◀ **Figure 4**
Market gardening.

▲ **Figure 5** Dairy cattle.

Activity

Copy and complete the table to show the factors that affect the pattern of farming in the UK:

	Cereal growing	Hill sheep farming	Market gardening	Dairying
Distribution in the UK				
Named example(s)				
Physical factors: Relief				
Climate: Summer temperatures				
Winter temperatures				
Rainfall				
Sunshine				
Soils				
Human factors				

Arable farming

East Anglia (**Figure 1**) is the most important arable farming region in the UK. This is mainly because of the good physical conditions for growing crops (**Figure 2**).

There are also favourable human factors:

- a large and wealthy market in London and the south-east
- a dense network of roads, e.g. M11 and A1, and railways to transport the produce
- grants and subsidies from the European Union to grow certain crops, e.g. wheat, oilseed rape and linseed
- many local flour mills, freezing and canning factories and sugar refineries that buy the produce from the farms.

The main characteristics of the farming are as follows:

- intensive and commercial
- large farms, mostly over 200ha
- highly mechanized using huge tractors and combine harvesters
- growing cash crops which are sold to make a profit.

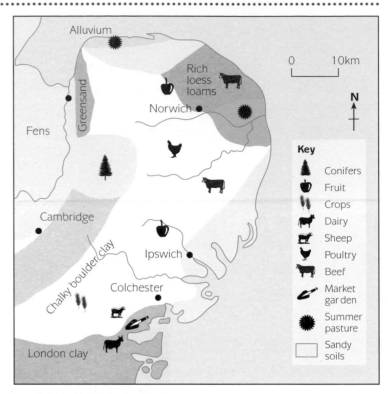

▲ **Figure 1** Soils and land use in East Anglia.

▼ **Figure 2** Physical conditions for farming in East Anglia.

Physical conditions	Impact on land use
Climate: • Warm summers, 17°C • Rainfall under 700mm per year • Slight summer rainfall maximum • Long hours of sunshine in summer • Winter frost	 Crops grow and ripen well Sufficient rain for crop growth, without waterlogging Rainfall in season when crops most need it Ripens the crops Breaks up the soil and kills pests, does not affect crop growth
Relief: • Flat or gently sloping • Lowland, most less than 100m above sea level	 Easy to use machinery Roads and railways have been easy to construct
Soils: • Mostly fertile boulder clay soils left behind by the ice sheets at the end of the Ice Age • Loam soils	 Fertile soils suitable for growing cereals, sugar beet and potatoes Very fertile – good for vegetables, fruit and cereals; retain plant foods and moisture, easily penetrated by roots

An intensive, commercial arable farm

Changes on the farm in East Anglia

Since the 1940s there have been many changes in farming in East Anglia:

- farms have joined together to become larger – amalgamation
- many farms now concentrate on just one or two crops; in the past farms were more mixed
- machinery has replaced labour – far fewer people are employed on the farms
- many hedgerows have been removed and fields enlarged to allow for the large machinery
- chemical fertilizers are used so that wheat and barley can be grown year after year
- agribusiness has developed.

ℹ️ Information box

Agribusiness – these are large scale farms run by large companies, which are sometimes not even linked to farming, e.g. insurance companies. Farm managers run the farms and they use high-technology to obtain maximum yields. The farms are intensive with high inputs of money, machinery and fertilizers.

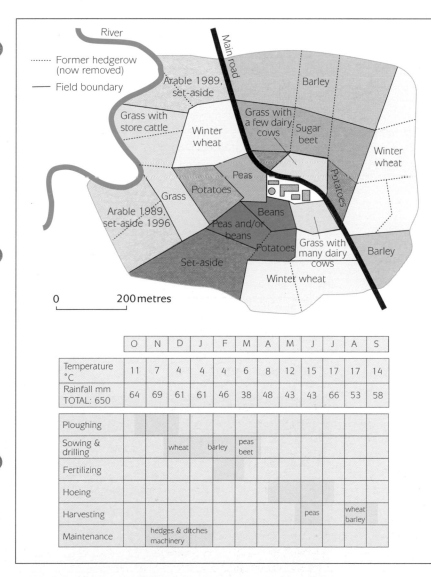

	O	N	D	J	F	M	A	M	J	J	A	S
Temperature °C	11	7	4	4	4	6	8	12	15	17	17	14
Rainfall mm TOTAL: 650	64	69	61	61	46	38	48	43	43	66	53	58

	O	N	D	J	F	M	A	M	J	J	A	S
Ploughing												
Sowing & drilling				wheat		barley	peas beet					
Fertilizing												
Hoeing												
Harvesting										peas	wheat barley	
Maintenance		hedges & ditches machinery										

▲ **Figure 3** An East Anglian arable farm.

Activities

1 a Give four physical factors that affect the farming in East Anglia. Say how each one encourages crops to grow,
  b Give four human factors that have encouraged arable farming in East Anglia.

2 Using **Figure 3**:
  a List the crops grown on the farm in East Anglia.
  b Suggest why the few dairy cattle are kept close to the farm buildings.
  c Explain why some of the hedgerows have been removed.

3 a Describe some of the changes that have taken place on farms in East Anglia.
  b In pairs discuss the good and bad points of the changes. Contribute your ideas to a class discussion.

Politics and farming in East Anglia

Farming in the UK receives a high level of support from the European Union (EU). Since joining the EU there have been many changes to farming in East Anglia through the Common Agricultural Policy (CAP). The initial aims of the CAP are shown in **Figure 1**.

The initial aims of the CAP were:
- to increase productivity and to achieve self-sufficiency
- to give all farmworkers a fair standard of living
- to keep prices of agricultural products stable
- to maintain food supplies
- to ensure 'reasonable' prices for customers.

▲ **Figure 1** The Common Agricultural Policy.

The CAP is funded from the VAT that member countries pay on goods. East Anglia has benefited from the CAP in the following ways:

1 Price support

If the market price for farm produce falls too low then the CAP buys up the produce so that the farmers get a good price for their products.

2 Subsidies

One of the first aims of the CAP was to increase food production. The EU needed to become more self-sufficient. This means that the EU countries would produce more of the food they needed to reduce imports. **Figure 2** shows how self sufficient the EU was in 1991.

This was done by giving subsidies to farmers to grow food products that were in short supply. In East Anglia the farmers received subsidies to grow more wheat. This increased the use of chemicals and led to the removal of hedgerows (**Figure 3**). However, these changes also caused problems. The chemicals flowed into rivers and threatened to kill fish and other river life. The creation of large fields has caused soil erosion and created a prairie type landscape (**Figure 4**).

▶ **Figure 4** 'Prairieization' – the monotonous East Anglian landscape.

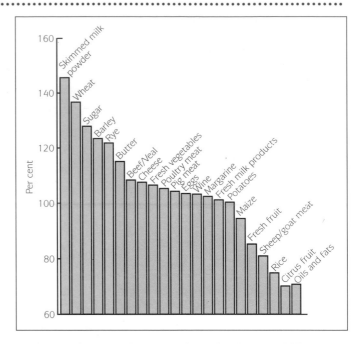

▲ **Figure 2** EU self-sufficiency in foodstuffs, 1991.

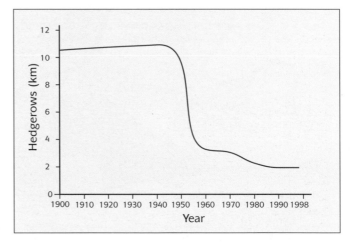

▲ **Figure 3** The decline in hedgerows in Cambridgeshire, East Anglia, 1900–1998.

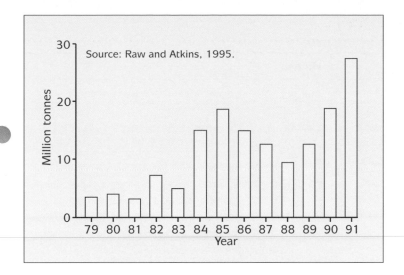

▲ **Figure 5** Stocks of EU cereals 1979–1991.

▲ **Figure 6** A hedgerow in Cambridgeshire.

Too much grain

The subsidies worked too well and the EU farmers overproduced grain. Huge grain mountains were created that cost a lot to store and dispose of (**Figure 5**). The CAP then introduced set-aside where farmers are not allowed to use at least 20 per cent of their land for five years. The land can be left fallow, planted with trees or used for other non-farming activities. In 1995 UK farmers were paid £253 per hectare of land left fallow.

Too little oil

The EU did not produce enough vegetable oil so the CAP paid subsidies to the seed-crushing companies who then had to pay the farmers a good price. The amount of oilseed rape being grown increased greatly in the UK. The crop made a good profit for the farmer and also had other advantages:

- once the oil is removed the remainder makes good animal feed
- the crop improves the soil fertility.

In 1996 the EU had almost achieved self-sufficiency in oilseed. The subsidy was removed so the growth of oilseed may decline.

Damaging the environment

Between 1945 and 1975 over 45 per cent of the hedgerows in Norfolk disappeared. Hedgerows limit the size of fields and the use of large machines but they have advantages:

- They are important as the homes and food supply for wildlife
- Without them the landscape becomes flat and monotonous.

The increased use of chemical fertilizers pollutes the land and water supplies. Whole streams may be starved of oxygen killing the fish and other stream life. Strict laws are now in force about the types and amounts of chemicals that can be used.

Hill sheep farming

Physical		Human	
Relief	– High mountains, steep slopes and little flat land	Market	– a small local market and limited transport
Soils	– Thin, rocky, acid and leached (podsols)	Labour	– the uplands are sparsely populated so little labour is available. The farms cannot afford many workers and are well adapted to a small labour force.
Climate	– Temperatures fall by 1°C for every 160m above sea level. Temperatures are much lower than in the lowlands (14°–15°C in summer). The growing season is short and there is high rainfall, over 2000mm on the Fells. There is more cloud cover, snowfall and hill fog.	Capital	– there is often little profit to reinvest so farming methods stay the same.
		Tradition	– the farming has changed very little over the years, retaining the 'One man and his dog' image.
Accessibility	– Twisting steep gradients make access difficult; many roads are very narrow. The main access routes are along valley floors in the Lake District. Today, the M6 passes along the eastern edge of the area.	Politics	– subsidies and grants have been paid to the farmers to guarantee a minimum standard of living.

▲ **Figure 1** Factors affecting farming in the Lake District.

In the upland areas the grazing of sheep is the main farming activity. **Figure 1** shows the physical and human reasons why.

The main characteristics of the farming are:

- it is pastoral and extensive
- the farms have a very large land area for grazing the sheep
- the sheep are the hardy breeds, e.g. Swaledales that can survive the cold weather and rough grazing and are sturdy on the hillsides
- the farmers sell the animals for meat or for fattening in the lowlands, the wool is also sold
- little machinery is used and little labour, often only the farmer and his family.

A farm in the Lake District

Figure 3 shows the three zones of land use on a hill sheep farm:

1. The **open fell**, usually over 300 metres, is grazed by the sheep in the summer months. The farmer rarely owns this land but shares the grazing rights with other farmers. The land is open moorland with no walls or fences.

2. The **intake** is owned by the farmer. It is enclosed by stone walls and may be improved by fertilizers. It is on the lower slopes and is grazed most of the year.

3. The **inbye** is the land on the valley floor closest to the farm buildings. The soils are more fertile and the land is sheltered. The sheep use the inbye in the winter and during lambing and shearing when they need to be closer to the farm. Some of this land may be used to grow some hay and turnips during the summer that is used as fodder for the animals in the winter.

Hill sheep farming does not always make a profit.

◄ **Figure 2** The hardy breeds of sheep are sure-footed on the rugged terrain in the Lake District.

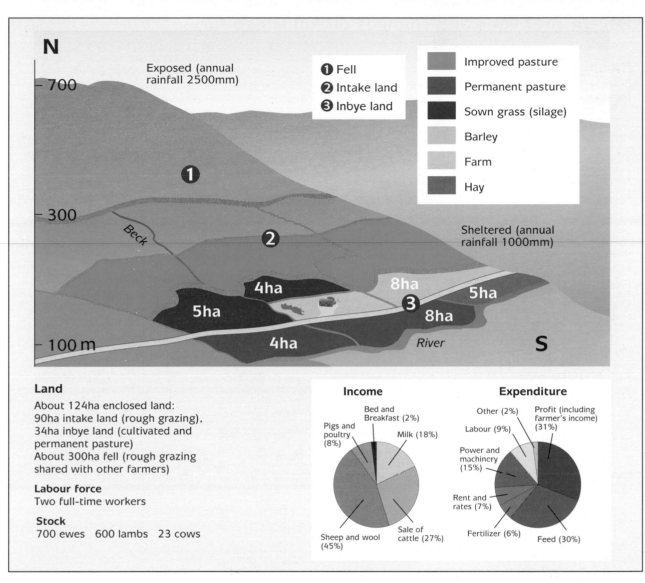

Land
About 124ha enclosed land:
90ha intake land (rough grazing),
34ha inbye land (cultivated and permanent pasture)
About 300ha fell (rough grazing shared with other farmers)

Labour force
Two full-time workers

Stock
700 ewes   600 lambs   23 cows

Income
- Bed and Breakfast (2%)
- Pigs and poultry (8%)
- Milk (18%)
- Sale of cattle (27%)
- Sheep and wool (45%)

Expenditure
- Other (2%)
- Profit (including farmer's income) (31%)
- Labour (9%)
- Power and machinery (15%)
- Rent and rates (7%)
- Fertilizer (6%)
- Feed (30%)

▲ **Figure 3** Profile of Fell Farm in the Lake District.

Activities

1 Give three physical and three human reasons why hill sheep farming takes place in upland areas.

2 Fit the following words into a table like the one below to show the farm as a system:

one shepherd   wool   shearing   meat
fat lambs   lambing   hay   turnips
winter fodder   fertilizing   sheepdog

Inputs	Processes	Outputs

3 From **Figure 3** describe the location of each of the three areas of the farm and what each part is used for.

4 Using **Figure 3**,
a What is the total area of the farm?
b How many animals are reared on the farm?
c Give two reasons why the crops are grown on the valley floor.
d Why is there permanent pasture next to the river?
e Other than sheep farming what other activities take place? Can you suggest why?

Recent problems and changes on hill sheep farms

Problems

In recent years the profits have decreased due to:

- rising costs of fuel and machinery
- marginal land and severe winters kill many animals
- reduced EU subsidies
- disasters such as the foot and mouth epidemic
- the collapse in lamb prices.

Fewer young people are taking over the farms. Young people prefer the more attractive work and higher wages in the towns and cities or in tourism in the National Parks. **Figure 4** shows the decline in the number of hill sheep farmers. Tourists can cause problems for farmers as some of them leave gates open, trample crops, allow their dogs to worry sheep and leave litter. Another problem for the farmers is the strict planning regulations in the National Parks, which prevent some farmers from making the changes needed to keep their farms profitable.

	1977	1986	1995
Farmers (full-time)	980	893	828
Farmers (part-time)	270	302	331
Total	1250	1195	1159

▲ **Figure 4** The numbers employed as hill farms decline.

Changes – improvements in farming

- Increased quality and quantity of meat and wool by improved breeding
- Grants for new farm buildings
- Subsidies from the CAP for Less Favoured Areas (LFAs), e.g. £6.75 for each breeding ewe
- Grants for conservation of the countryside, e.g. building dry stone walls, renovating old barns, planting trees
- Diversification into other activities

> **ℹ Information box**
>
> **Diversification** – when the farmer carries out other activities that may or may not be linked to farming, e.g. fish farms, bed and breakfast, tree planting, horse livery, campsites and farm shops.

Some farms have not been able to survive and have been sold. Sometimes the land has been sold to a nearby farm to make it more profitable. In some cases the farm has been sold as a second home and the land used for forestry.

Grow crops? Oilseed rape, barley, oats, potatoes?

Organic farming? Increased demand for organic products

Tourism? Campsite, farm holidays, open days, farm shop?

Environmental initiatives Tree planting, repairing walls, only cut meadows after flowering

Forestry? High demand for softwood paper pulp, but no profit for 15–30 years

Sports activities Pony trekking, quad biking, war games

Farm other animals? Deer, goats, rabbits, snails, trout farming?

▲ **Figure 5** Diversification in the Lake District.

Market gardening and bulb growing in the Netherlands

Figure 1 shows the market gardening concentrated in a strip of land in the west of the Netherlands. The most important area is Westland, which is well known for the production of tomatoes, cucumbers and lettuce. In recent years over 60 per cent of the farmers have begun to grow flowers. They have diversified to increase profits to pay for rising heating costs and competition from other growers in the EU. Most of the produce is exported to other EU countries and to Canada and the USA.

The physical conditions are ideal:

- The relief is low lying and flat
- The soils are light and sandy, they warm up and dry out quickly.

The climate is not important as the crops and flowers are grown in glasshouses. Seen from the air Westland looks like a 'sea of glass'.

The market gardens are small and the farming is intensive. Large amounts of labour and capital are needed. The farming is very high-tech and uses the latest scientific advice. The farmers are organized into co-operatives that:

- supply fertilizers, irrigation equipment and other products
- provide grants and credit terms
- arrange the auctions for the sale of the produce.

▲ **Figure 2** Bulb growing in the Netherlands – the flowers attract many tourists in the spring but they are cut off quite early so that the bulbs are not exhausted.

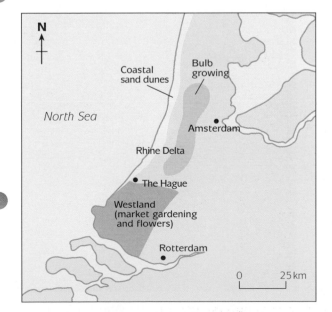

▲ **Figure 1** Farming in the Netherlands.

Activities

1 Complete a table like the one below to show the market gardening as a system:

Human inputs	Physical inputs	Processes	Outputs

2 Give three reasons why the farming is intensive.

3 How do the co-operatives help the farmers?

4 What are the two main problems the farmers have faced in recent years?

5 How has the farming changed to cope with the problems?

Farming in the developing world

Over 70 per cent of people in LEDCs are farmers. Most of the food grown is for subsistence, to feed the farmer and the family.

Shifting cultivation

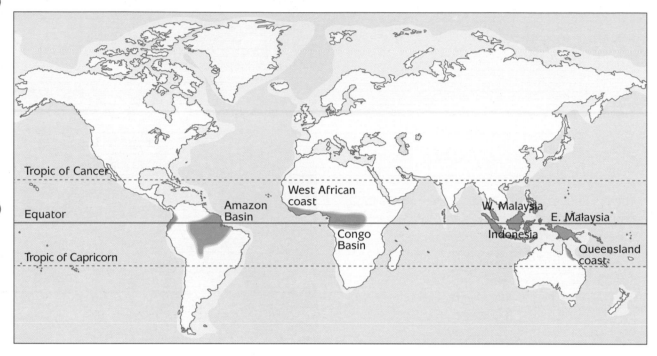

▲ **Figure 1** The world distribution of areas of shifting cultivation.

Figure 1 shows the main areas of the world where there is shifting cultivation. In the Amazon Basin the Amerindians practise shifting cultivation by:

- clearing a small patch of forest with machetes
- allowing the vegetation to dry out and then burning it; the ash produced fertilizes the soil
- planting crops such as yams and manioc in the clearings called *chagras* (**Figure 2**)
- 'shifting' to another part of the forest and clearing another area when the soil loses its fertility.

All of the farm work is done by hand with only simple tools. The men supplement the diet by hunting and fishing. Although only a small patch of land is cleared, overall the tribes need a lot of land as they need to clear new plots every few years. Each clearing needs to be left for over 50 years for the soils to recover and for the forest to grow back. This makes shifting cultivation an extensive type of farming.

▲ **Figure 2** A *chagras* in the Amazon Basin.

Shifting cultivation works in harmony with the environment. It is a **sustainable** form of farming. It does not destroy the forest resources permanently and the forest eventually grows back.

However, in recent years the developments that are taking place in the rainforest are making the system less sustainable. Developments such as mining, road building, ranching and plantations are leaving the Indians with smaller and smaller areas of land. The Indians are forced to clear patches of land that have not had time to fully recover. This damages the soils so that they cannot recover and the rainforest cannot grow back. The forest may be suffering permanent damage. Large numbers of Indians have also died from Western diseases such as measles or have been killed by developers. Others have decided to leave the rainforest and join other migrants in the shanty towns in the cities.

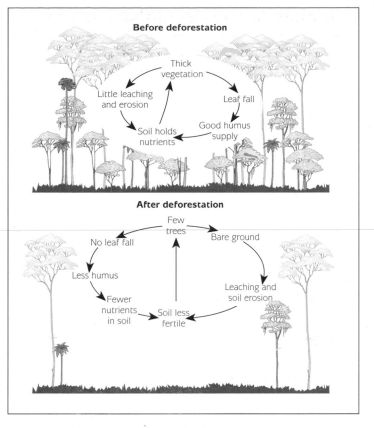

▲ **Figure 3** The nutrient cycle in the rainforest.

Activities

1 Why is shifting cultivation:
  a extensive
  b subsistence farming?

2 Using the list of words complete the table below to show the farm as a system:

hand labour   yams   hoeing   manioc
clearing   planting   beans   seeds
high temperatures   harvesting   high rainfall

Inputs	Processes	Outputs

3 Describe how shifting cultivation takes place in the rainforest.

4 Using **Figure 3** describe what happens when the forest cover is removed.

5 a Why is shifting cultivation a sustainable type of farming?
  b Give three developments that are taking place in the rainforest.
  c In pairs or small groups discuss the effect of these changes on:
    (i) the soils and the forest
    (ii) the Indians.
    Contribute your ideas to a class discussion.

6 Put together a five point plan that would allow shifting cultivation to be sustainable in the future.

Plantation agriculture

A plantation is a vast agricultural estate in the tropics. The main features of plantations are:

- intensive and commercial farming
- very large estates, often 2000–3000ha
- high inputs of labour and capital (money)
- often only one crop grown – monoculture
- cash crops mostly exported to MEDCs
- many owned by the powerful transnational corporations (TNCs) which have their headquarters in MEDCs, e.g. Dunlop, Unilever and Nestlé.

Plantations bring both advantages and disadvantages to developing countries. These are shown in **Figure 2**.

▲ **Figure 1** A banana plantation.

▼ **Figure 2** The advantages and disadvantages of plantations.

Advantages
- Exports earn foreign exchange used to improve the economy and services in a country.
- TNCs bring expertise, skills and knowledge which can be taught to the local people.
- Many jobs are provided for the local people, raising their living standards and having a spin-off in the local economy.
- Plantations provide houses, schools, health clinics and services, such as electricity and water, which improve standards of living.

Disadvantages
- Plantations often occupy the most fertile soils which would be better used to grow food crops for the local people.
- Some countries export plantation cash crops only to import food crops which they could be growing themselves.
- TNCs take most of the profits back to the developed countries.
- Local people may be exploited as cheap labour.
- The growth of a single crop makes plantations very susceptible to disease, poor weather and world market prices.

Unilever

Unilever is an Anglo-Dutch TNC and one of the largest companies in the world. It has over 500 companies in 80 countries around the world. Some of the famous names are Flora, Oxo, Persil, Bird's Eye and Walls. The HQ, manufacturing and research are concentrated in the MEDCs but many of its products begin on the plantations in LEDCs (**Figure 3**). In 1992 Unilever employed 120 000 people in LEDCs.

▼ **Figure 3** Unilever's plantations (1993).

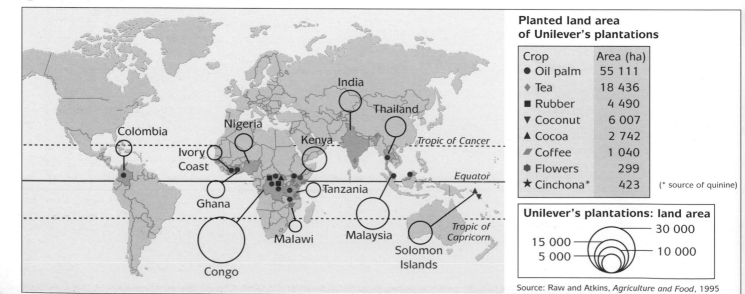

Planted land area of Unilever's plantations

Crop	Area (ha)
● Oil palm	55 111
◆ Tea	18 436
■ Rubber	4 490
▼ Coconut	6 007
▲ Cocoa	2 742
◢ Coffee	1 040
✷ Flowers	299
★ Cinchona*	423	(* source of quinine)

Unilever's plantations: land area

30 000
15 000
10 000
5 000

Source: Raw and Atkins, *Agriculture and Food*, 1995

A rubber plantation

Rubber is one of Malaysia's main cash crops and the country has many advantages for growing rubber:

- the hot wet equatorial climate (pages 76–77) means the rubber grows well
- gentle relief
- every area is close to the sea and ships for exporting the rubber.

The Jengka Triangle project is a large plantation in Malaysia. It has 500ha of oil palm and rubber, and housing for over 9000 families. Each plantation is divided into separate sections with trees at different stages of growth. About 60 per cent of the trees are mature and able to be tapped for their latex rubber, 20 per cent are young trees and 20 per cent are being cleared and replanted.

Problems and effects on the environment

Plantations replace the natural forest so the natural ecosystem is destroyed. Once the forest is cleared the bare ground may be eroded by the heavy rain and the soils leached. The soil may be washed into rivers increasing floods. The heavy machinery compacts the soil, which increases run-off. The soils are not very fertile and so many plantations use soil conservation techniques to keep the soil as healthy as possible.

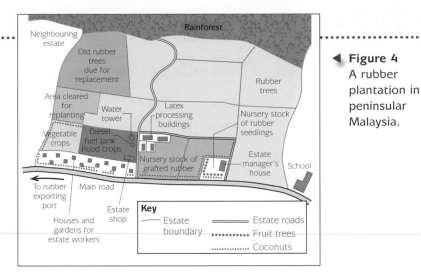

◀ **Figure 4** A rubber plantation in peninsular Malaysia.

Soil conservation techniques

1 **The growing of cover crops** Leguminous crops (beans, lentils, peas) are planted between the rows of young oil palm and rubber trees to protect the topsoil and help to restore fertility by adding nitrogen to the soil.

2 **Bunds and pits** Bunds are raised banks of soil which enclose a depression or pit. They are constructed near young trees to slow down soil erosion and trap the soil as it is washed away.

3 **Terracing** Terracing is used on steep slopes to prevent soil erosion. The steep slopes are levelled by building steps or terraces which follow the contours of the slope.

4 **Fertilizers** Plantations have a high capital expenditure on fertilizers such as potash and nitrates. In recent years fertilizers have been applied by spraying from aeroplanes or helicopters.

Activities

1 a What is a plantation?
  b Give five features of plantations.
  c Give three advantages and three disadvantages of plantations to developing countries.

2 Using **Figure 2**:
  a List some of the products grown on Unilever's plantations.

  b In which continents does Unilever have plantations?
  c Describe the distribution of the Unilever plantations.

3 a Describe the main features of the Jengka triangle project.
  b Suggest why vegetables are grown on the plantation.

  c What facilities are provided for the workers on the plantation?

4 List the problems that plantation farming causes for the soils, rivers and forest.

5 Draw and label sketches to show how the soil can be conserved on a plantation.

Rice growing in south Asia

South Asia (**Figure 1**) is one of the most densely populated areas in the world. Rice is the staple or main food crop and it is ideally suited to the monsoon climate (**Figure 2**) and the high populations. Most farmers are subsistence farmers, growing the rice to feed their families. The farming is labour intensive and the whole family is involved at various times of the year. **Figure 3** shows the typical farmer's year. In some years the farmer may grow a second crop of beans, peas or lentils and often a few chickens are also kept for eggs and meat.

Problems of rice growing

1 Sometimes the floods are much larger than normal and cause devastation. The rice crop is destroyed, people lose their homes and land and there may be great loss of life. In normal years the rivers flood and bring valuable water and fertile silt for the paddy fields.

2 In some years the monsoon rains 'fail', rainfall is lower than expected and the rice crop is ruined.

3 Many farmers are landless peasants because they do not own their land. Also as land is passed down through the generations the plots are divided up and now many are too small to support a family.

4 The rapid growth of the population in south Asia meant that new methods of farming were needed to produce more food.

Physical factors
- A monsoon climate (**Figure 2**) with heavy rains and high temperatures provides ideal conditions for rapid growth of rice.
- Heavy alluvial soils provide an impervious muddy layer.
- Flat flood plains make the flooding of fields easier; terraced hill slopes can be used for 'dry rice' in areas such as Assam.
- There is a water supply from the River Ganges and from wells.

Human factors
- Rice gives high yields per hectare which helps to feed the large population.
- Water buffaloes are used for work and as a source of manure for the fields.
- Rice seeds are stored from one year to the next for the next year's crop.
- Rice growing is labour-intensive: many people can work in the paddy fields ploughing, planting, harvesting and threshing.

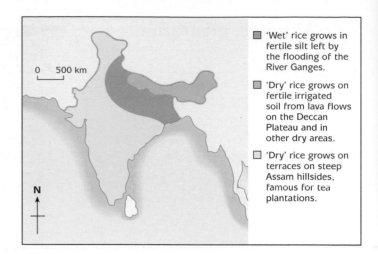

- 'Wet' rice grows in fertile silt left by the flooding of the River Ganges.
- 'Dry' rice grows on fertile irrigated soil from lava flows on the Deccan Plateau and in other dry areas.
- 'Dry' rice grows on terraces on steep Assam hillsides, famous for tea plantations.

▲ **Figure 1** Rice-growing areas in India and Bangladesh.

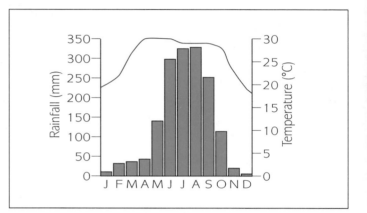

▲ **Figure 2** The monsoon climate.

Month	Things to do
January	Plant crops: peas, beans and lentils.
February	Weed fields. Look after crops.
March	Harvest crops.
April	Finish off odd jobs before monsoon starts.
May	Get seed bed ready for rice, weed, spread ash and manure on fields. When the rains come, sow rice seed.
June	Weed fields.
July	Plough in manure.
August	Move rice plants to another field. Plant them out 25cm apart.
September	More weeding. Add manure.
October	Rice plants begin to flower. Weeding.
November	Monsoon is over. Rice ripens.
December	Harvest and thresh rice.

▲ **Figure 3** The lowland rice farmer's year.

Source: Adapted from: Longman *Geography for GCSE*, 1997: 162

The Green Revolution

In the 1960s India needed more and better food to feed the growing population. This was achieved through the Green Revolution. The Green Revolution involved the following:

- high-yielding varieties (HYVs) of rice introduced – rice production trebled
- drought-resistant varieties grown
- plants ripened more quickly so that a second crop could be grown – double cropping
- fertilizers used more
- tractors and mechanized ploughs used instead of water buffalo
- grants and loans introduced for new seeds and equipment
- irrigation schemes needed to ensure adequate water supplies.

The Green Revolution had both its successes and its failures; these are shown in **Figure 5**. Overall the Green Revolution widened the gap between the rich and the poor.

▲ **Figure 4** Planting rice.

Irrigation

Irrigation was needed in south Asia because:

- the monsoon rains are irregular and sometimes fail
- the new HYVs and the double cropping require more water supplies.

In the Ganges Valley several different methods of irrigation are used:

1 **Wells** are dug to reach underground water supplies. Each well can irrigate 1–2ha of land. Today modern electric or diesel pumps are being used to raise the water. Modern tube wells run by electric pumps can irrigate up to 400ha of land.

2 **Inundation canals** are dug alongside the rivers. When the river floods the water goes into the canals and is led to the paddy fields. This also carries the fertile silt which means that expensive fertilizers are less necessary. However, a lot of water is lost by evaporation and the canals attract disease-carrying insects.

Successes	Failures
• Farmers who could afford the HYVs and fertilizer increased yields by three times.	• Many poor peasants could not afford to buy HYVs and fertilizer so their yields did not change.
• Faster growing plants allowed multiple cropping each year.	• Poorer farmers who borrowed money could not pay it back and their debts increased, forcing some of them to move to the city.
• Farmers could grow wheat, maize and vegetables as well as rice, giving more variety in the diet.	• The HYVs need more fertilizers and pesticides, which are expensive.
• Increased output created a surplus to sell in the cities, raising the farmers' income and standard of living and reducing the costs of imports.	• Irrigation schemes were needed and many farmers lost their homes and land.
• Higher incomes allowed more fertilizer and machinery to be bought.	• In large areas irrigation has led to salinization – the soils have become so salty that the land has had to be abandoned.

▲ **Figure 5** Successes and failures of the Green Revolution.

Appropriate technology

The Green Revolution brought a need for irrigation and cheap sources of power for new machinery. Some LEDCs built huge dams like those in MEDCs but they caused problems:

- Local people lost their homes and best farmland.
- No compensation was given to the people.
- The dams and reservoirs increased water-borne diseases.
- People lost the natural floodwaters and fertile silt so they had to buy pumps and fertilizers.
- Many borrowed money to pay for pumps, seeds and fertilizers and ended up in debt.
- The foreign workers brought diseases and different moral standards.

For many subsistence farmers appropriate technology would have been the best answer. It takes more account of the education and skills, the money and local resources available in the local area. It involves:

- using small dams and individual wells (**Figure 1**)
- using renewable energy sources such as wind, solar power and biogas (**Figure 2**) rather than expensive electricity or imported oil
- setting up labour-intensive projects to use the cheap labour force rather than machines
- providing tools and techniques designed to use local resources and skills
- avoiding high-tech machines which need expensive fuel and spare parts imported from abroad
- setting up low-cost schemes using technologies the local people can afford, understand and control
- establishing projects that are sustainable and in harmony with the environment.

▲ **Figure 1** Appropriate technology – a well in northern India.

▲ **Figure 2** A biogas plant.

Activities

1 a What is subsistence farming?
  b Name a country and precise location where rice farming is practised.
  c Describe the physical factors which favour this type of farming.
  d Explain why rice farming is so well suited to the:
    (i) monsoon climate
    (ii) high density of population.
  e List the problems faced by the rice farmer in south Asia.

2 a Describe the changes brought by the Green Revolution.
  b How would the changes improve the life of the people?
  c Give three advantages and three disadvantages of the Green Revolution.

3 a What is appropriate technology?
  b Give three reasons why building large dams is not appropriate technology.
  c Give two examples of schemes that use appropriate technology.
  d For one example explain why it is appropriate.

Chapter 11

Industry

Cambridge Science Park, an example of a modern development on a greenfield site

Key Ideas

Industrial activity can be classified:
- primary, secondary, tertiary and quaternary are the four types of industry.

Industry is a system:
- as with all systems there are inputs, processes and outputs.

Industrial location is influenced by many factors:
- locational factors include raw materials, energy, capital, labour, transport and government
- the relative importance of these varies according to the type of industry.

Industry changes over time:
- on a global scale the changing nature of industry has led to the growth of newly industrializing countries (NICs) and transnational corporations.

Types of industry

1 Primary industry

Primary means first. These industries grew first because people used raw materials first. Raw materials are natural products from land or sea. Mining, quarrying, forestry, farming and fishing are all examples of primary industries. People who work in these industries have jobs in the primary sector.

> ### ℹ Examples of raw materials
>
> Minerals, e.g. crude oil
> Metals, e.g. iron ore and bauxite
> Vegetation, e.g. wood
> Plants, e.g. cotton
> Plant products, e.g. cocoa and rubber
> Animal products, e.g. wool and hides

▲ **Figure 1** Herding in Egypt – starting young in primary industry.

2 Secondary industry

Secondary industry came second, when people started to make products from raw materials. A factory in which clothes are made (or manufactured) from raw cotton is one example of a secondary industry.

In a factory, raw materials are changed into something different by one or more of the following:

* hand labour

* use of machines

* being heated up

* having water or chemicals added.

People working in factories work in secondary industries.

> ### ℹ Examples of manufacturing industries
>
> | Raw material (from land or sea) | Manufacturing process(es) (way in which the raw material is changed by manufacturing) | Manufactured goods (goods that can be bought) |
> | --- | --- | --- |
> | Crude oil → | Refining using heat → | Petrol, plastics, polythene |
> | Wood → | Hand carving → | Wooden ornaments |
> | Cotton → | Spinning and weaving by machines → | Clothes, sheets, towels |
> | Oranges → | Squeezing with machines and adding water → | Fruit juice |
> | Fish → | Cleaning and cooking → | Fish fingers, fish in tins |

▲ **Figure 2** A factory making dyes in Leicester – an example of secondary industry.

3 Tertiary industry

Tertiary means third. Tertiary industries are those which provide services. The long list of services in the Information Box on page 167 still misses out some important services, such as education (teachers) and media (working in TV and radio). From the list, some are:

* used every day, such as water, gas and electricity

* needed from time to time, such as doctors and dentists

* used mainly at weekends and in holidays, such as those connected with leisure and tourism.

People in services are working in tertiary industries. Numbers increase as countries and people become richer.

ℹ️ Types of services

Health, e.g. doctors and dentists
Local Council, e.g. refuse collection and care services
Local services, e.g. water, gas and electricity
Communications, e.g. phone and cable companies
Transport, e.g. buses and trains
Retail, e.g. supermarkets and stores
Financial, e.g. banks and building societies
Sport and leisure, e.g. sports centres and tennis clubs
Tourism, e.g. hotel staff and tourist guides

Figure 3 The downtown business district (CBD) in New York (after September 11, 2001), where the offices of many well-known companies and big banks are located.

4 Quaternary industry

Quaternary means fourth. This industry is based upon high-tech. It is number 4 because it is newer than the other three types of industry. High-tech now plays a big part in the lives of people and companies in MEDCs. Computers are being used for more and more tasks. High-tech industries, which spend a lot of money on researching new products, are called quaternary industries.

People with jobs in the quaternary sector are often very skilled and well paid. In the UK, many jobs in quaternary industries are found in

- 'Silicon Glen' in the central lowlands of Scotland
- the 'High-tech Corridor' west of London near the M4
- over 40 'Science Parks' attached to universities (e.g. Cambridge Science Park on page 165).

Activities

1 a What is a raw material?
  b Name one example of a raw material from the sea.
  c Some jobs in the primary sector are listed below:
    Logger   Sheep and cattle farmer   Oilrig worker
    Cotton picker   Miner   Plantation worker

    Mix and match. Which job in the list above matches which raw material listed in the first Information Box on page 166? List the raw materials and name the job next to it.

2 a How are manufactured goods different from raw materials?
  b Make a table like the one below. Finish it off by naming two manufactured goods made from each raw material.

Raw material	Manufactured goods
Crude oil	*Petrol and plastics*
Iron ore	
Trees	
Cocoa	
Wool	

3 Name the main raw material used for manufacturing each of the following:
  (i) bread **(ii)** cheese **(iii)** beer **(iv)** soft drink cans **(v)** paper.

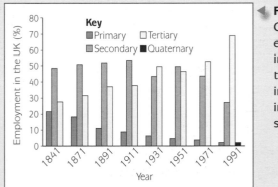

◀ **Figure 4** Changes in employment in different types of industry in the UK since 1841.

4 a From **Figure 4** state the year
    (i) when primary employment fell below 10 per cent for the first time
    (ii) when secondary employment was at its highest
    (iii) after which tertiary employment has always been the highest.
  b Describe how each of the following changes are shown in **Figure 4**.
    (i) The primary sector went down.
    (ii) The tertiary sector increased and became the most important.
    (iii) A small quaternary sector developed.
  c **(i)** For 1991, state the percentages for the four sectors of employment from **Figure 4**.
    (ii) Draw a pie graph to show them.
    (iii) Colour or shade in the sectors and make a key.

Industry as a system

All systems have inputs, processes and outputs. A simple factory system is shown in **Figure 1**.

- Raw materials (an input) go into the factory.
- Raw materials are changed in the factory (processes).
- Manufactured goods (an output) come out of the factory and are transported away to market.

A factory is also a business. To survive, a factory must make a profit. Look at **Figure 2**. The money from selling the outputs needs to be greater than the costs of inputs and processes.

More details about inputs, processes and outputs in a factory are given in **Figure 3**. Most factories produce wastes during the processing of the raw materials. Wastes are of two types:

1 Waste gases. They are burnt off into the atmosphere.
2 Liquid and solid wastes. These need to be treated before disposal on land or in rivers.

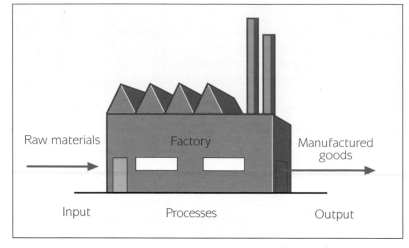

▲ **Figure 1**
A simple factory system.

▶ **Figure 2**
A factory that makes a profit.

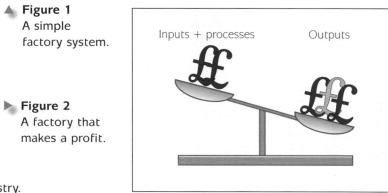

▼ **Figure 3** Factory system for a manufacturing industry.

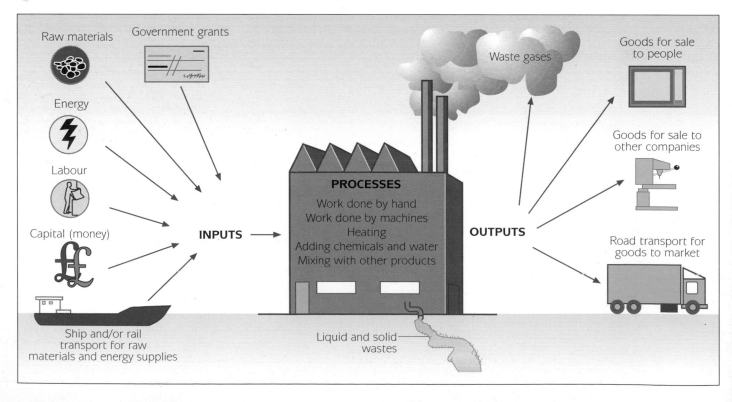

Types of manufacturing industry

The three main types of manufacturing industry are described in **Figure 4**.

Heavy industries	Light (consumer) industries	High-tech industries
Main features:	*Main features:*	*Main features:*
• Large-scale operations • Big factories covering large areas of land • A lot of money is needed to set them up • Large products are made (mainly bought by other industries)	• Small-scale operations • Small factory units often located on industrial estates • Only a limited amount of money is needed to set them up • Small products are made, mainly bought by people (consumers).	• High value products are made using modern technology • A lot of money is invested in research • Many are very small and are located on business parks
Examples: Steel, oil refining, chemicals, engineering and shipbuilding.	*Examples:* Electrical goods, clothing, food processing and toys.	*Examples:* Computers, business systems, mobile phones and telecommunications equipment.
Further information: The factory often covers a large area of land. Air pollution from chimneys may be obvious many kilometres away (**Figure 5**). Heavy industries may not be beautiful, but they are necessary. How would people cope without petrol for cars (from oil refining) or steel for making cars and football stadiums?	*Further information:* Many light industries are footloose industries. They have great freedom to choose where to locate. There are two reasons for this: 1 They do not use large raw materials. 2 The goods they make are low in weight and high in value, so that they can be distributed easily by road to any part of the UK.	*Further information:* These are also footloose industries. Factories are new and often located in pleasant locations on the edges of the towns. They are surrounded by countryside, which is why they are called greenfield sites (look again at the photograph on page 165).

▲ **Figure 4** Types of manufacturing industry.

Activities

1 a (i) Draw a diagram to show a simple factory system.
　　(ii) What is the difference between an input and an output in the factory system?
　b Draw another diagram like the one in **Figure 2** to show a factory that is in trouble and making a loss.

2 Look at **Figure 3** for answers to the questions below.
　a How many inputs are shown?
　b Name the input that fits each one of the following:
　　(i) It provides the power to drive the machines.
　　(ii) Skilled and unskilled workers.
　　(iii) Money not provided by the factory owner.
　　(iv) What the manufactured goods are made from.
　c Name the output that brings no profit to the factory owner.
　d (i) State the methods of transport used for carrying raw materials to the factory.
　　(ii) State the method of transport used for taking goods to the market.
　　(iii) Suggest reasons why the methods of transport are different.

3 a State two differences between a heavy industry and a light industry.
　b What is meant by a footloose industry?
　c Why are heavy industries less footloose than light industries?

▲ **Figure 5** View over Teesside, one of the largest concentrations of heavy industry in the UK.

4 Look at **Figure 5**.
　a Describe two features of the heavy industries shown in the photograph.
　b Some of the people from the housing areas on the photograph are happy to live there but others are not. Suggest why people have different views about living near heavy industries.

Factors affecting industrial location

Most companies consider a number of factors before choosing a location for their factory (**Figure 1**). The type of industry affects the location chosen. For example, a heavy industry, such as one making steel, wants to be near its raw materials. However, a light industry, such as one making soft drinks, is more interested in being close to its market.

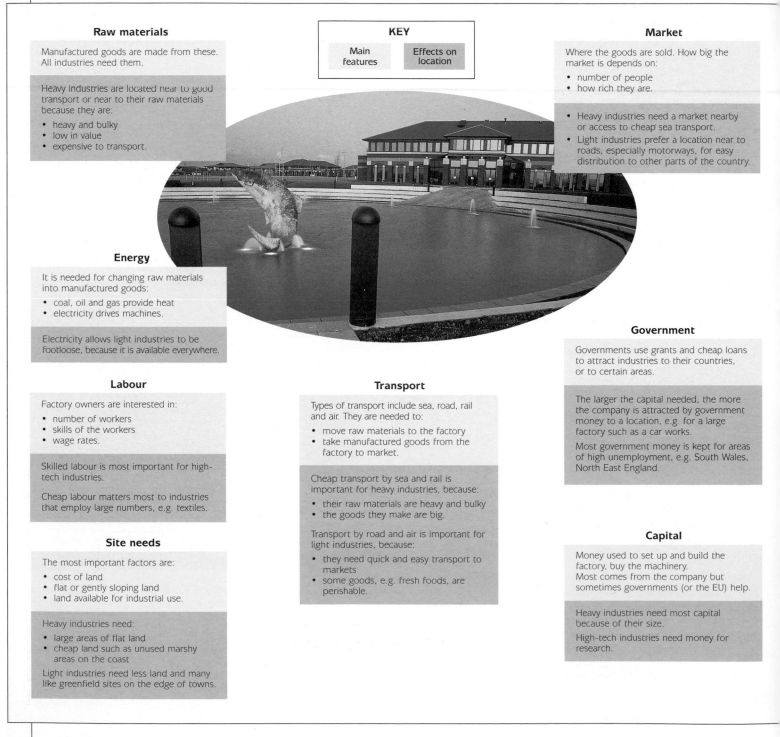

Raw materials

Manufactured goods are made from these. All industries need them.

Heavy industries are located near to good transport or near to their raw materials because they are:

- heavy and bulky
- low in value
- expensive to transport.

KEY

Main features	Effects on location

Market

Where the goods are sold. How big the market is depends on:

- number of people
- how rich they are.

- Heavy industries need a market nearby or access to cheap sea transport.
- Light industries prefer a location near to roads, especially motorways, for easy distribution to other parts of the country.

Energy

It is needed for changing raw materials into manufactured goods:

- coal, oil and gas provide heat
- electricity drives machines.

Electricity allows light industries to be footloose, because it is available everywhere.

Government

Governments use grants and cheap loans to attract industries to their countries, or to certain areas.

The larger the capital needed, the more the company is attracted by government money to a location, e.g. for a large factory such as a car works.

Most government money is kept for areas of high unemployment, e.g. South Wales, North East England.

Labour

Factory owners are interested in:

- number of workers
- skills of the workers
- wage rates.

Skilled labour is most important for high-tech industries.

Cheap labour matters most to industries that employ large numbers, e.g. textiles.

Transport

Types of transport include sea, road, rail and air. They are needed to:

- move raw materials to the factory
- take manufactured goods from the factory to market.

Cheap transport by sea and rail is important for heavy industries, because:

- their raw materials are heavy and bulky
- the goods they make are big.

Transport by road and air is important for light industries, because:

- they need quick and easy transport to markets
- some goods, e.g. fresh foods, are perishable.

Capital

Money used to set up and build the factory, buy the machinery. Most comes from the company but sometimes governments (or the EU) help.

Heavy industries need most capital because of their size.

High-tech industries need money for research.

Site needs

The most important factors are:

- cost of land
- flat or gently sloping land
- land available for industrial use.

Heavy industries need:

- large areas of flat land
- cheap land such as unused marshy areas on the coast

Light industries need less land and many like greenfield sites on the edge of towns.

▲ **Figure 1** Factors affecting the location of manufacturing industries.

Activities

1 a Write a heading 'Factors affecting the location of manufacturing industries'. Make a large table like the one here. Fill it in with information from **Figure 1**.

b Look at the photograph in the middle of **Figure 1**.
(i) Do you think it shows an area of heavy industry or light industry?
(ii) Give as many reasons for your answer as you can.

2 a By how many units is it cheaper to carry iron ore per tonne kilometre in
(i) a 200 000 tonne ship than in a 50 000 tonne ship;
(ii) a 200 000 tonne ship than in a 100 000 tonne ship?
b Explain why large steel works are more likely to be located next to deepwater ports than small ports.

3 Decision making

The directors of an oil company have already decided to locate an oil refinery and chemical works in the area shown in **Figure 3**. The letters A, B, C and D in **Figure 3** show the four sites that are being considered. The supply of crude oil will come by super-tanker.

a Study the map.
(i) Which one of the four sites A–D would be most suitable for the location of an oil refinery and chemical works?
(ii) Give reasons for your choice.
b Choose one of the other sites and explain why it would be less good.

Factor	Main features	Effect on location

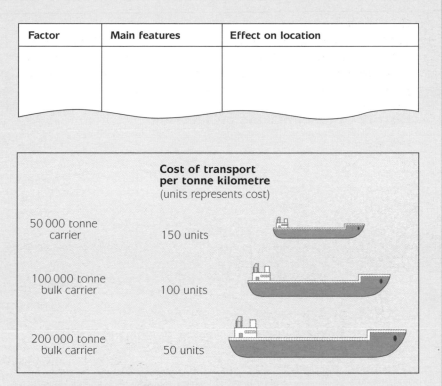

Cost of transport per tonne kilometre
(units represents cost)

50 000 tonne carrier	150 units
100 000 tonne bulk carrier	100 units
200 000 tonne bulk carrier	50 units

▲ **Figure 2** The relative cost of transporting iron ore by sea.

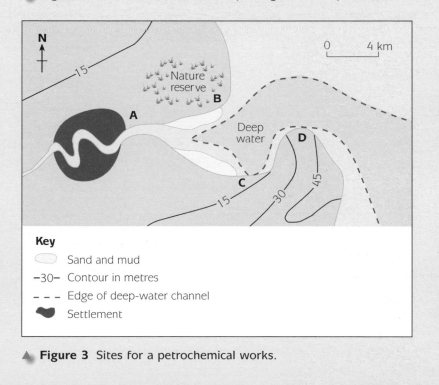

Key
⬭ Sand and mud
—30— Contour in metres
– – – Edge of deep-water channel
⬛ Settlement

▲ **Figure 3** Sites for a petrochemical works.

Heavy industry

The main heavy industries located around the estuary of the River Tees are steel, chemicals and oil refining. Look back at **Figure 5** on page 169. It shows that the heavy industries have a big effect on the landscape of Teesside.

History of steel making on Teesside

Iron and steel industries began along the south bank of the Tees between Middlesbrough and Redcar in the middle of the nineteenth century because of local raw materials and energy supplies. These included:

- iron ore from the Cleveland Hills
- coal from the Durham coalfield
- limestone from the east Durham plateau and Weardale.

These are shown in **Figure 1**. All were heavy and difficult to transport. Transport was not as easy as it is today. A location near to raw materials and energy supplies was essential. There was a market for steel in the shipyards of north-east England.

Steel making on Teesside in the 1990s

Most of the early advantages for steel making have gone – the iron ore has been worked out; coal mines and shipyards have closed. All that is left is limestone, which is not the most important raw material. However, Teesside has other advantages for the location of a modern steel works. The Redcar steel works, built in the 1980s, is shown in and around square 5625 in **Figure 2**.

Advantages of Teesside for a modern steel works include:

- **Transport** Perhaps the key factor – the Tees is a wide, deep and sheltered estuary which can be used by large bulk ore carriers. Iron ore can be bought from any country in the world where the price is right. The ships dock at the steel works' own terminal (squares 5425/5525 in **Figure 2**).

- **Markets** The River Tees is also useful for exporting steel to EU and other overseas markets. The railway line, which you can see running past the steel works in **Figure 2**, carries steel to customers in other parts of the UK.

- **Labour** The long history of steel making means that workers are skilled.

- **Site** This was ideal. The Redcar works were built on a large area of flat land, which was little used for anything else.

Other heavy industries on Teesside

Chemical works around the River Tees are named in squares 5223 and 5722 on the OS map. They were mainly located here because of their access to raw materials and energy – both are needed in large amounts:

- **Raw materials** Local deposits of rock salt and gypsum are used in making chemicals.

- **Energy supply** was coal from Durham. Today it is oil. A pipeline from the North Sea oilfields carries crude oil to the terminal near Seal Sands (named in square 5225). Super-tankers can use the Tees. Look again at the OS map. On the north bank there are many oil storage tanks. On the south bank, Wilton Works (square 5722) is a petrochemical factory making many different products from oil, such as plastics and synthetic fibres.

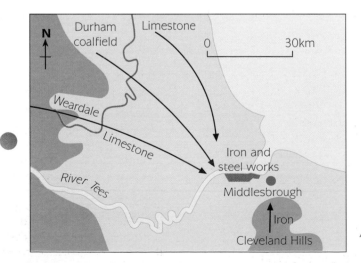

▲ **Figure 1** Sources of supply for the early iron and steel works.

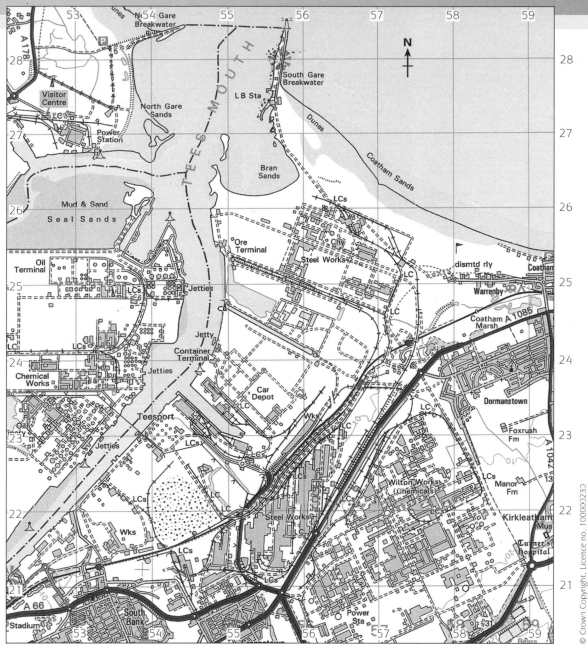

▲ **Figure 2** OS map of the Tees estuary at a scale of 1: 50 000 (2cm = 1km).

© Crown Copyright. Licence no. 100003233

Activities

Use the OS map for answering questions 1–3.

1 a Make a frame the same size as the OS map in **Figure 2**.
    (i) Trace or sketch in the coastline and course of the River Tees.
    (ii) Shade in the site of the Redcar steel works.
    (iii) Mark and name the ore terminal and main railway line.
b State and explain three advantages for the location of a modern steel works at Redcar.

2 Use the OS map in **Figure 2** again.
a (i) What has been built at Tees mouth to help ships sailing into the River Tees?
    (ii) Why are there no jetties for ships to dock in square 5526?
    (iii) All the jetties are in deep water. How is deep water shown on the map?
b The land on the sides of the River Tees is flat. How does the map show this?
c Find the A1085 road.

    (i) Describe its course.
    (ii) Suggest why it was not built further north or further south.

3 Write out the title 'Teesside – case study of a region of heavy industry'. Using information from these two pages, make notes under the following headings:
a Examples of heavy industries
b Where they are located
c Why they are located there
d Likely environmental problems (use OS map and Fig 5 page 169).

Footloose industries

Most light and high-tech industries are found next to motorways. Look at **Figure 1**. They follow motorway corridors such as the M11, M23, M3 and M4.

There are more footloose industries along that part of the M4 corridor between London and Reading than anywhere else in the UK:

- **Light industries** There are many food companies (e.g. Mars at Slough) and companies making electrical goods.
- **High-tech industries** There are many companies involved with software and micro-electronics for computers and telecommunications equipment. Examples include Digital, Oracle and NEC (**Figure 2**).

General advantages of the M4 corridor for the growth of light industries

Locations next to motorways would suggest that transport is the most important factor. Transporting the finished goods to market is more important than transporting the raw materials to the light industries. The raw materials used by footloose industries are not large or heavy. The richest market is in London and the South East. It is a big advantage to be close to this market. Motorways connect to the rest of Britain. There is also a high speed rail link along the M4 corridor between London and South Wales. Overseas links are easy, using the three main airports around London and motorway (M20) to the Channel Tunnel.

Special advantages of the M4 corridor for high-tech industries

Labour becomes the most important factor for these industries. Skilled research scientists and engineers are needed. Nearby universities (shown by red dots on **Figure 1**) supply graduates. Well paid, skilled workers prefer to live in pleasant places. High-tech companies keep this in mind when choosing a location. Upland areas with scenery worth visiting at weekends are shown in brown on **Figure 1**.

Key
- University
- Airport
- High-tech firms
- Research centres
- Cambridge Science Park
- Scenic upland areas
- Motorway
- Railway line
- Areas with many footloose industries

0   20 km

Figure 1
Industrial corridors along motorways out of London.

Figure 2
Both food and high-tech companies are located in the industrial estate in square 7169 on the OS map.

Figure 3
Part of Reading
at a scale of
1: 50 000
(2cm = 1km).

© Crown Copyright. Licence no. 100000230

Activities

1 Answer all these questions from **Figure 1**.
  a (i) Name the three London airports.
  (ii) Name two university towns close to the M4.
  (iii) Which scenic upland area is closest to Swindon?
  b Give the numbers of the motorways which link London:
  (i) to Bristol **(ii)** to Cambridge and
  (iii) to the Channel Tunnel.
  c (i) In what way is the M25 different from the other motorways on the map?
  (ii) Describe where most of the high-tech firms are located.

2 Write out the title 'The M4 corridor – case study of an area of footloose industries'. Make notes under the following headings:
  a Examples of footloose industries
  b Reasons for their growth (refer to 1 Transport 2 Market and 3 Labour).
  c Draw a large labelled sketch map, based on **Figure 1**, to show the area's advantages for transport.

Figure 4 Lower Earley (square 7570), Reading, 1995.

3 Reading is attracting people as well as industries.
  a How does **Figure 4** show new and recent growth?
  b Describe what the OS map shows about the location of Lower Earley.
  c Suggest two reasons why planners may not want Lower Earley to grow any further south.

The Rhine–Ruhr region

▲ **Figure 1** North Rhine–Westphalia.

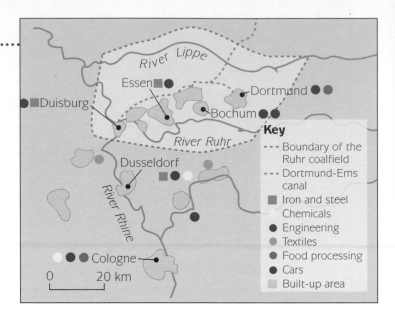

▲ **Figure 2** Industries in the Rhine–Ruhr region.

The state of North Rhine–Westphalia, shaded in brown in **Figure 1**, is the richest and most densely populated state in Germany. The largest town is Cologne on the River Rhine. This region is also the largest industrial area in the EU.

Types of industries

For over a century industrial activity depended upon coal. The Ruhr coalfield, shown in **Figure 2**, is the largest in Europe. Industries, such as iron and steel, chemicals, engineering and textiles, grew up here because they used the coal for smelting or for driving machines. These industries have been in the Rhine–Ruhr region for 150 years or more. Although heavy industries remain important, some consumer industries, such as food processing and cars, have been added to make the list of industries even longer.

Reasons for the growth of industries

There are three main reasons:

1 **Energy supply** is the most important reason. The Ruhr coalfield has large amounts of good quality coal. Heavy industries such as steel use large amounts of energy. By locating close to the Ruhr coalfield they save a lot on transport costs.

2 **Transport on the River Rhine**, the biggest river in Europe. The river is busy with barge traffic. It links the Rhine–Ruhr region to the North Sea and world shipping lanes. Large river barges can move up to 9000 tonnes

at a time. Moving bulky and heavy raw materials by water is much cheaper than using rail or road.

3 **Market** A local market was created as industries that used the steel, such as those making machinery, also set up their factories in the area. The whole Rhine–Ruhr region is the richest and largest market in Germany. Since the region has a central position within the EU, this gives it a wider market of over 300 million people.

Industrial change since 1950

Although coal mining and heavy industry have declined in the Rhine–Ruhr region during the last 50 years, it has been less severe than in the UK because of:

- the amount and quality of coal from the Ruhr field
- the prosperity of German industry
- the region's central position within the EU
- water links along the River Rhine.

However, there have been some significant changes:

1 Decline in the number of workers in coal-mining and heavy industries,

   e.g. 1950 – over 500 000 coal miners
   1995 – 100 000 coal miners.

2 Newer manufacturing industries are now well established,

   e.g. Ford and Opel cars
   1950 – car making was 16th in order of importance
   1995 – car making was 5th.

3 A great rise in the tertiary (service) sector (look at the yellow sectors in **Figure 3**),

e.g. Cologne has become a centre for media (TV, radio, films etc.) with 130 000 media sector jobs. It is an attractive city on the banks of the Rhine with good transport links.

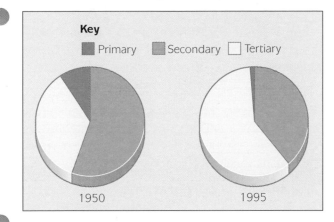

Key
■ Primary ■ Secondary □ Tertiary

1950   1995

▲ **Figure 3** Employment structure in the Rhine–Ruhr region, 1950 and 1995.

The main problems

- Unemployment – it has not been possible to replace all the jobs lost in mining and heavy industry.
- Over-dependence upon mining and heavy industry which are still losing workers.
- Environmental problems – the task of landscaping waste tips and cleaning up water courses, after over 100 years of mining and heavy industry, is massive.

▼ **Figure 4** Changes in importance of different industries in the Rhine–Ruhr region, 1950–1995.

A. 1950 Top eight industries	B. 1995 Top ten industries
1 Textiles	1 Chemicals
2 Coal mining	2 Machinery
3 Food	3 Food
4 Steel and heavy metals	4 Electronics
5 Chemicals	5 Motor vehicles
6 Construction	6 Construction
7 Machinery	7 Steel and heavy metals
8 Electronics	8 Petroleum-refining
	9 Coal mining
	10 Textiles

Activities

1 Use **Figures 1** and **2** to answer these questions.
   a Name two towns located on the River Rhine.
   b Name three towns with iron and steel works.
   c Name one town located in the Ruhr coalfield. Which industries does it have?
   d Of the six manufacturing industries shown in **Figure 2**, name three that are heavy industries.
   e How does **Figure 2** show that Cologne has both heavy and consumer industries?

2 a Give the reasons for the growth of heavy industries in the Rhine–Ruhr region.
   b Describe some of the environmental problems which are caused by mining and heavy industry.
   c State two other problems facing the Rhine–Ruhr region.
   d Why is it often difficult to solve problems like these?

3 Use **Figure 4** to answer the following questions.

   a (i) By how many places did coal mining drop between 1950 and 1995?
   (ii) Which industry fell more than coal?
   (iii) Name one industry which stayed in the same position.
   (iv) Name the new industries in the top eight in 1995 that were not there among the top eight in 1950.
   b (i) Choose one industry that has declined in importance between 1950 and 1995 and suggest reasons for its decline.
   (ii) Choose one that has increased in importance and suggest why it has grown.

4 a Look at **Figure 3**. Work out the percentage differences for primary, secondary and tertiary between 1950 and 1995. Make it clear whether they are + or –.
   b Draw a divided bar graph to show the percentages for 1995.

5 a From **Figure 4** name the primary industry that has declined most.
   b Name a town in the Rhine–Ruhr region with many tertiary industries. Why has it attracted tertiary industries?

Industries in less economically developed countries

Primary industry, mainly farming, remains the most important industry in many LEDCs. Often more than 50 per cent of the workforce is employed in agriculture (**Figure 1**).

In the world's poorest countries, farming is the way of life for almost everyone. The small numbers of people in industry and trade are usually found in the capital city.

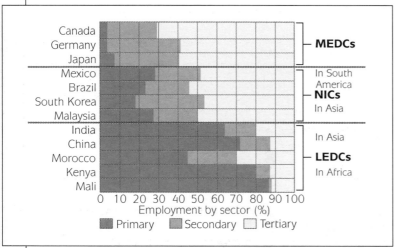

▲ **Figure 1** Employment structures for countries with different levels of economic development.

Figure 2 is called a scatter graph. The percentage employed in agriculture has been plotted against the country's wealth for ten countries in South America. It shows that the percentage employed in agriculture goes down as the wealth of a country goes up.

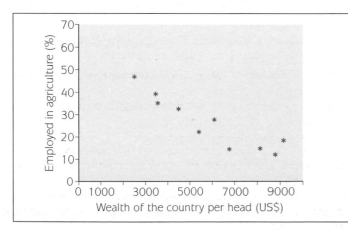

▲ **Figure 2** Relationship between percentage employed in agriculture and wealth in ten countries in South America.

In some LEDCs, secondary and tertiary industries are more important than primary. In **Figure 1**, look for Mexico, Brazil, South Korea and Malaysia. These countries are known as NICs, newly industrializing countries. Manufacturing industry has increased by a lot; so too have service industries.

Figure 3 shows that the largest part of manufacturing output is still in MEDCs, even if the percentage in LEDCs is increasing. Some of this growth is due to investments by transnational corporations (TNCs).

Transnational corporations

These are large companies with businesses in many different countries. The headquarters of many of the largest are in MEDCs (**Figure 4A**). They are global companies, which set up businesses in any country of the world where profits can be made. You will know the names of many of the companies listed in **Figure 4B**, but there are many more, including McDonalds and Coca-Cola.

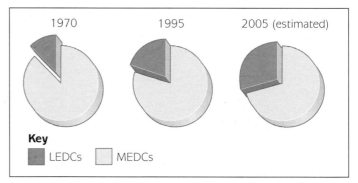

▲ **Figure 3** Manufacturing in LEDCs and MEDCs (% of world output).

Advantages and disadvantages of transnationals
Advantages

*   Money is invested in another country.

*   Industries are started that LEDCs could not set up for themselves (e.g. making cars and computers).

*   Improvements in transport are made.

*   Jobs are created, especially in assembly industries (e.g. electrical goods and electronics) and in light manufacturing which uses a lot of labour (e.g. clothing, sports goods and toys).

*   Exports are increased to markets worldwide.

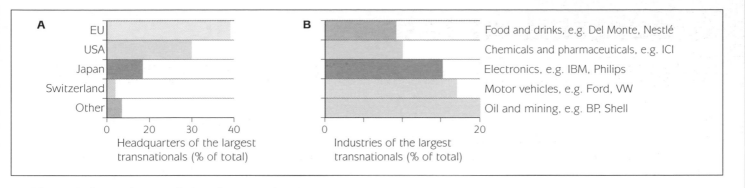

▲ **Figure 4** Some characteristics of transnationals.

Disadvantages

- People usually work for low wages.
- Profits go back to the MEDC where the headquarters is located, so that benefits to the LEDC are reduced.
- LEDCs become dependent upon markets in other parts of the world, which go down during times of economic decline.
- Some have poor safety records and they do not spend enough money on stopping air and water pollution from their factories.

Bhopal, Central India, December 1984

A leak of gas from a factory making pesticides, owned by Union Carbide, an American transnational corporation, killed over 2500 people. It affected the health of up to a quarter of a million people, most of whom were slum dwellers. They had been attracted to the city by its rapid industrial growth and were unaware of the risk of living next to a factory producing toxic chemicals.

The cause of the accident was put down to design faults in the factory's safety systems, made worse by a decline in maintenance standards. Significantly, factories producing these chemicals in the USA are required to be located 50km away from settlements.

Activities

1 a Mix and match. Write out the terms below and match each one to its correct definition.

Term	Definition
LEDC	One that supplies services to people and other industries
MEDC	One that processes raw materials and makes other products
NIC	One that takes raw materials from land or sea
Primary industry	A country in which manufacturing industry is increasing
Secondary industry	A rich country such as the USA and UK
Tertiary industry	A poor country such as Mali and Kenya in Africa

b Look at **Figure 1**.
(i) State the percentages working in primary industry in the following countries: Kenya Brazil Germany
(ii) What is the main reason why the percentages are so different?
(iii) Which one of the countries shown has the highest percentage in secondary industry? State its percentage.
(iv) Which country has the lowest percentage in secondary industry? State its percentage.
(v) Why do you think the percentages working in secondary industry are so different?
(vi) How do the percentages working in tertiary industries change between LEDCs, NICs and MEDCs?

c Look back at the types of services listed in the Information Box on page 167. Suggest why there are more jobs like these in an MEDC (such as Canada) than in an LEDC (such as Kenya).

2 a (i) From **Figure 4B**, write down the names of those transnational corporations you have heard of and state some of the things they make.
(ii) Add the names of three more transnational corporations and state what they make.

b Make a table to show the advantages and disadvantages of transnational corporations in LEDCs.

3 a Read the newspaper report about Bhopal in Central India in 1994.
(i) How could Union Carbide have reduced the risk of a gas leak?
(ii) Why was the loss of life greater in India than it would have been from a similar factory in the USA?

b At the time the factory was being planned, many Indians were in favour of it being built. Suggest reasons why (i) the people of Bhopal and (ii) the Indian government were in favour.

Newly industrializing countries (NICs)

Manufacturing industry is not shared out equally among LEDCs. There is more in LEDCs in East Asia and least in countries in Africa (**Figure 1**).

The advantages of East Asia for industrial location

1 **Cheap labour supply**

This is the most important factor.

- Wages are low by world standards, especially in China (**Figure 2**).
- Asian workers are reliable and willing to work hard for long hours.

2 **Transport**

- There is easy access to the main shipping routes; transport by sea is the cheapest way to transport goods long distances.
- Containers (boxes of standard sizes in which goods are packed at the factory) reduce the costs of transporting manufactured goods by sea.

3 **Market**

- Markets within the Asian countries are increasing as people become more prosperous.
- The main markets in MEDCs are reached by cheap sea transport.

4 **Government**

- Many governments help transnational corporations, e.g. by providing sites for factories.

The four countries that grew fastest were Hong Kong, Singapore, Taiwan and South Korea. They are known as the 'Four Tigers'. Other NICs in East Asia are Thailand, Malaysia, Indonesia and the Philippines. They have a wide range of industries including:

- heavy industries – steel, shipbuilding and petrochemicals
- light (consumer) industries – electrical goods and clothes
- high-tech industries – micro-chips, semiconductors, computers and word processors.

Problems caused by rapid growth

In the rush for growth, no thought is given to workers' health. Health and safety standards in factories are poor.

Environmental effects are not considered. Waste leaves the factories untreated and some rivers are dead because of pollution from industrial waste. Air pollution is a serious problem in those cities with heavy industries. Smog causes severe breathing problems.

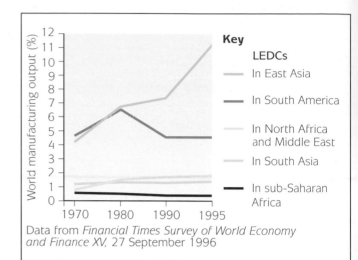

▲ **Figure 1** Manufacturing (% of world output) in LEDCs, 1970–1995.

Data from *Financial Times Survey of World Economy and Finance XV*, 27 September 1996

Germany	
USA	
UK	
Singapore	
South Korea	
Hungary	
China	

Key
⑤ = US$1 per hour

▲ **Figure 2** Labour costs in factories in the mid-1990s (US$ per hour).

▲ **Figure 3** The CBD of Hong Kong – wealth comes from both manufacturing and trading.

Activities

1 With the help of an atlas, on an outline map of East Asia name and shade in **(a)** the 'Four Tigers' and **(b)** other NICs.

2 Look at **Figure 1**.

  a By what percentage did East Asia's share of world manufacturing output increase between 1970 and 1995?

  b State how East Asia is shown to be **(i)** similar to and **(ii)** different from South America.

  c State two differences shown in **Figure 1** between East Asia and sub-Saharan Africa.

3 a From **Figure 2**, state the wage rates per hour in factories in the following countries in the mid-1990s:

  (i) the UK **(ii)** Singapore **(iii)** South Korea **(iv)** China.

  b Approximately how many times greater were wage rates in the UK than in **(i)** Singapore and **(ii)** China?

  c Explain fully why many clothes, sports goods and electrical appliances on sale in shops in the EU are manufactured in East Asia.

Industry in an LEDC – South Korea

► **Figure 4**
South Korea; the main concentration of industries is in and around Seoul.

South Korea is one of the world's top ten industrial countries. All the general advantages for industrial growth for East Asia (page 180) apply to South Korea.

1 Labour – cheap, but people are hard working and efficient.

2 Transport – almost the whole country lies within 100km of the sea for access to cheap transport by sea.

3 Market – the main markets for its goods are in countries around the Pacific Ocean, such as the USA, Japan and Hong Kong.

4 Government – it puts tariffs on imported manufactured goods, which protects South Korea's own industries.

ℹ Problems

* Air pollution from traffic and industrial fumes in Seoul.
* Strikes because of low wages and poor working conditions.
* Faulty goods – so great was the drive for growth that quality sometimes suffered
* Currency crisis in 1997/98 – was growth too fast?

Total population: 44 million
Capital city: Seoul (12 million)

Industrial corporations	Manufactured goods
Samsung	Semiconductors, electronics, shipbuilding, petrochemicals
Hyundai	Electronics, shipbuilding
LG (Lucky Goldstar)	Electronics, electrical goods, petrochemicals
Daewoo	cars, electronics, shipbuilding

Manufacturing industry	World ranking
Shipbuilding	1st
Petrochemicals	5th
Textiles	5th
Cars	6th
Electronics	6th
Steel	6th

▲ **Figure 5**
Information about South Korea.

Activity

Write out a title – 'Case study of industry in an LEDC – South Korea'.

a Draw a sketch map of South Korea.

b Under the sub-heading 'Manufacturing industries':

  (i) List the top six manufacturing industries in South Korea.

  (ii) Write by the side of each one whether it is a heavy industry, light industry or high-tech industry.

  (iii) Choose one of the big industrial corporations (hopefully one you have heard of). What does it make?

  (iv) Give reasons for the growth of manufacturing industry in South Korea.

c Under the sub-heading 'Problems' write about two problems caused by rapid industrial growth.

Changes in industrial location in the UK

1 The growth of out-of-town locations

Old manufacturing industry was located in the centre of towns and cities (e.g. the dye works in **Figure 2** on page 166). If land is cleared for new building in areas in the centre, they are called brownfield sites – sites that have previously been built on.

Most modern footloose industries prefer greenfield sites – sites in the countryside that have never previously been built on. These lie out of town, usually in the rural–urban fringe. Notice the great difference in appearance between the area in **Figure 1** on this page and in **Figure 2** on page 166. Advantages of greenfield over brownfield sites include:

▲ **Figure 1** Worton Grange, Reading

- cheaper land
- closer to motorways
- more space
- less traffic congestion
- easier to create a pleasant environment.

> ### ℹ️ Examples of out-of town locations for industries
>
> **A Industrial estate** – mainly for light industries, e.g. the Slough industrial estate, where Mars is located.
> **B Business Park** – a mixture of light industries, offices, call centres, retail outlets, distribution depots and research centres. Worton Grange is an example (**Figure 1**). It has been carefully planned with open spaces and modern buildings set among landscaped surroundings.
> **C Science Park** – mainly for companies doing research and development. There is always a direct link with a University. One of the largest and most successful of the 40 science parks in the UK is Cambridge Science Park (page 165).

However, new factories, offices, houses and roads would all prefer to use greenfield sites. Without planning controls, would any countryside be left? There is not enough space for all of them, especially in densely populated parts of the UK such as the South-East, where pressure on green land is already very great.

> ### ℹ️ Cambridge Science Park
>
> Opened 1972. Established by the University of Cambridge. Over 50 hectares of land, with lakes and trees between buildings. Nearly 100 companies employing about 2500 people.

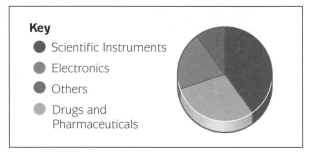

Key
- ● Scientific Instruments
- ● Electronics
- ● Others
- ● Drugs and Pharmaceuticals

▲ **Figure 2** Types of companies in Cambridge Science Park.

> ### Activities
>
> 1 a (i) What is meant by a brownfield site?
>   (ii) In which part of an urban area is it most likely to be found?
> b (i) What is meant by a greenfield site?
>   (ii) Where is it found?
> c A greenfield site was used for Worton Grange Business Park in **Figure 1**.
>   (i) Describe its appearance.
>   (ii) What are the advantages of a greenfield site like this?
>   (iii) Explain fully the disadvantages of using more and more greenfield sites.
>
> 2 Write down the title 'Case study of a Science Park – Cambridge'. Include information about it using these headings.
> a Definition of Science Park
> b Location in the UK (**Figure 1** page 174)
> c Appearance (photograph page 165 and Information Box page 182)
> d Types of companies in order of importance (**Figure 2**)
> e Reasons for growth.

2 Poorer areas of the UK in need of government assistance

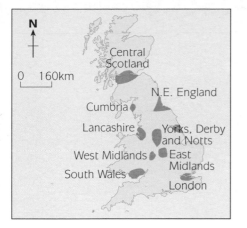

Figure 3 Old industrial regions in Britain.

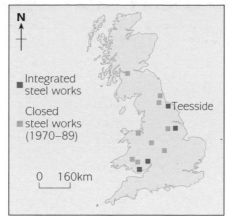

Figure 4 The British steel industry, 1970–1995.

Figure 5 Steel output on Teesside, 1971 and 1995.

Figure 3 shows the old industrial regions of Britain. With the exception of London, all these industrial regions were close to coalfields. During the Industrial Revolution industries went to the coalfields, because coal was difficult and expensive to transport. Although few factories use coal for heating today, the shaded areas in **Figure 3** include some of the UK's important manufacturing regions.

Heavy industries have suffered a great decline. In 1900, the UK was number 1 in the world for shipbuilding; today it is South Korea (page 181). Iron and steel works used to be found on almost every coalfield; today steel making is concentrated in only four places (**Figure 4**). One of these is Teesside (pages 172–3). **Figure 5** shows a great decline in the number of steel workers on Teesside, despite increases in the amount of steel made. Steel workers have been replaced by machines, leading to unemployment.

The problem is that:

- the loss of jobs in coal mining and heavy industries was mainly in the northern and western parts of Britain
- the new jobs from modern footloose industries are mainly in the south and east of Britain.

Look at **Figure 6**. The UK government and the EU give money to the areas shaded red, orange and yellow. They also give help to companies creating new jobs. Without help, Central Scotland, North-East England and South Wales would have become industrial deserts, with even higher rates of unemployment than they have now.

Figure 6 Areas of the UK in 1996 in which government and EU assistance can be given to those setting up new industries

Activities

1 a Explain as fully as you can how:
   (i) Figure 4 shows a large decrease in the number of steel works in the UK
   (ii) Figure 5 shows a big drop in the number of steel workers on Teesside
   (iii) Figure 5 also shows that amount of steel produced has increased. Use values taken from the Figures in your answers.
  b Draw a pictogram to show the numbers employed in the steelworks on Teesside for 1971 and 1995.

2 a Draw or trace a small sketch map of the UK. Mark on it and name where you live.
  b Looking at **Figure 6**, do you live in an assisted area? Yes or No? If yes, what kind?
  c If you answered 'Yes' to (b), explain why your home area needs government help with jobs.
   If you answered 'No' to (b), explain why no government help is needed with jobs in the area where you live.

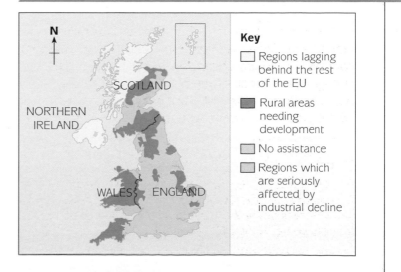

The globalization of industry

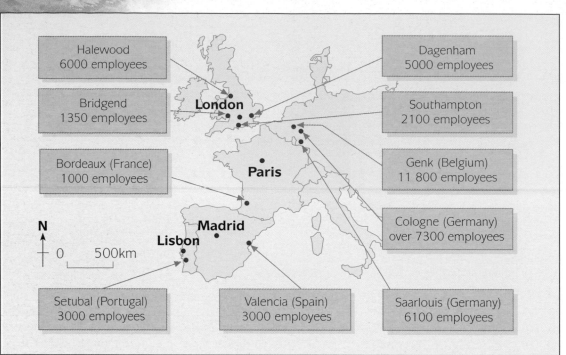

Halewood
6000 employees

Bridgend
1350 employees

Bordeaux (France)
1000 employees

London

Dagenham
5000 employees

Southampton
2100 employees

Genk (Belgium)
11 800 employees

Paris

Cologne (Germany)
over 7300 employees

N

Madrid

Lisbon

0   500km

Setubal (Portugal)
3000 employees

Valencia (Spain)
3000 employees

Saarlouis (Germany)
6100 employees

▲ **Figure 1** Ford's main production sites in Europe, 1997.

Globalization means that industry is becoming more international. This is because:

- Large companies set up factories in more than one country; they sell their goods in countries located all over the world. These companies are the TNCs referred to on page 179. Transnational corporations such as Ford treat the EU as if it were all one country (**Figure 1**).

- Industrial countries exchange goods with other countries; they trade in global as well as home markets.

During the 1990s South Korean companies invested in the UK. For example, Samsung set up a factory on Teesside making microwave ovens. LG chose South Wales in 1996 for a big investment to make TV monitors and semiconductors. Newspaper headlines (**Figure 2**) showed that investments from TNCs were warmly welcomed.

Another worry for the UK is that transnationals will direct future investments into countries of central and eastern Europe instead of the UK.

Hyundai to build £2.4bn plant in Scotland
Fife semiconductor facilities will create 2000 jobs in an area troubled by unemployment

▲ **Figure 2** Newspaper headlines showing that transnational companies were welcomed in the UK.

Wage rates in Hungary (**Figure 2** page 180) are much lower than those in the UK. The rich EU market is not far away. TNCs go where they can make most profit.

This is all part of the globalization of industry, which has its advantages and disadvantages for countries.

Activities

1 a (i) From **Figure 1**, in how many different European countries does Ford have workers?
  (ii) The headquarters of Ford is in the USA. Why does Ford fit the title 'A transnational corporation'?
 b Explain why in the future more TNCs might decide to invest in Hungary than in the UK.

2 a What is meant by globalization?
 b Write about its advantages and disadvantages.

Chapter 12

Managing resources and tourism

Antarctica – the last great wilderness on Earth without permanent human inhabitants. Mineral resources, including oil, are known to exist and tourist numbers are increasing, which is why the existing international agreements are essential to conserve it as a wilderness.

Key Ideas

Management of resources is crucial to sustainable development:
- some natural resources are non-renewable and finite
- the use of finite resources has been increasing as a result of population growth and economic development
- there is an urgent need to conserve finite resources and to develop alternative resources to ensure sustainable development.

Environments offer possibilities for tourism and development:
- some environments offer opportunities for developing tourism
- tourism can lead to economic development but it may also bring problems
- for tourism to be sustainable, management and conservation are needed.

Resources

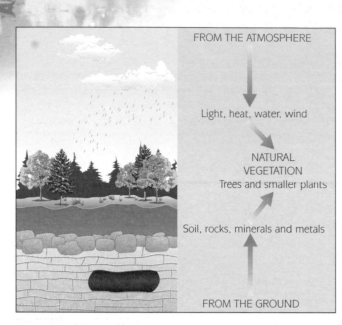

FROM THE ATMOSPHERE

Light, heat, water, wind

NATURAL
VEGETATION
Trees and smaller plants

Soil, rocks, minerals and metals

FROM THE GROUND

▲ **Figure 1** Some of the Earth's natural resources.

The Earth provides many natural resources, without which human life would have been impossible. Some are shown in **Figure 1**.

For the earliest human inhabitants, natural ecosystems provided all their basic needs for survival:

- *Water* came from the atmosphere.
- *Food* was obtained either directly by eating plants and their fruit, or indirectly by eating the animals that fed on the plants.
- *Shelter* was gained from making use of wood and branches.
- *Clothes* for *warmth* were made from plants and animal skins.

For a long time humans survived by gathering and hunting. What people used was quickly replaced by nature. In other words the natural resources from the forests were renewable.

Today, only small groups of people depend entirely upon local natural resources. Indian tribes living in remote parts of the Amazon rainforest are one of the few examples left. Their way of life is **sustainable** because they cause little disturbance to the forest. If not destroyed by people, forests and soils are examples of renewable resources.

◀ **Figure 2** Preston in the 1930s, a classic example of a northern industrial town.

Fossil fuels – questions and answers.

1 Which are the main *fossil fuels*?
Coal, oil (petroleum) and natural gas.

2 What makes them *fossil fuels*?
- They were formed from the remains of plants and animals.
- Their formation began many millions of years ago (e.g. about 300 million years ago for the UK's coal deposits).
- Massive numbers of plants and animals were needed to form tiny amounts of fuel.

3 Why are they *fuels*?
When burnt, they give off heat which can be used directly as a source of power:
- e.g. heat from coal smelts metals
- e.g. petrol from oil drives car engines
- e.g. natural gas heats water in central heating systems.

4 Why are they described as *non-renewable*?
- It takes a very long time to make even small deposits of fuel.
- It will take millions of years to replace the fuels people have already used, e.g. one estimate is that it takes *one million years* of formation to replace the fossil fuels used up by people in only *one year*.

5 Why are fossil fuels also described as *finite*?
Fossil fuels used by people today are not going to be replaced by nature for millions of years. We have **reserves** of fossil fuels. These are deposits that have been discovered, but have not yet been used. More coal, oil and gas are likely to be discovered, but there is only a limited (or finite) amount of these close enough to the Earth's surface to be mined. Every time a tonne of fuel is used, that is one tonne less for future people on Earth to use.

6 For how long will the fossil fuels last?
One estimate is shown in **Figure 3**. Estimates keep changing because they depend on the amount used and new discoveries are being made.

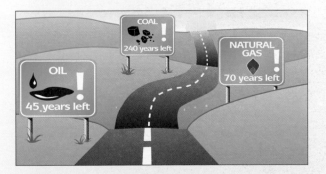

▲ **Figure 3** Life expectancy for known reserves of fossil fuels, at present rates of use.

Loss of natural resources

In most of the populated parts of the world forests and other vegetation have been cleared for farming. As the world population has grown to more than 6 billion (**Figure 1** page 188), pressure on the Earth's natural resources has greatly increased. Population pressure has led to deforestation, soil erosion and desertification, causing the loss of renewable resources such as trees and soil in many parts of the world.

In MEDCs the majority of people live in towns and cities. They grew fast from 1750 as a result of the '**Industrial Revolution**'. The natural resource that made factories and industries possible was **coal**. For example, in the textile mills of Yorkshire and Lancashire, coal heated the water, that made the steam, that drove the machines. Steam trains and ships used to be the main means of transport. Industrial towns in the UK grew near to the coalfields. **Figure 2** shows that old industrial towns were full of factories, smoking chimneys and rows of terraced houses for the workers.

From the UK the Industrial Revolution soon spread to other countries that had their own coal, such as Germany and the USA. Since 1900 the number and variety of manufactured goods have increased greatly, which has led to today's **consumer society** in MEDCs.

Population and industry are still growing; they are consuming the world's natural resources at a fast rate, which is alarming many people.

Activities

1 Four natural resources essential for human life are sunlight, rain, plants and soil.
   a Draw a labelled diagram to show these four natural resources.
   b Explain why each one is needed.
   c They are renewable resources. What is meant by a renewable resource?

2 Fossil fuels are also natural resources.
   a Name the three main fossil fuels.
   b Why are they called fossil fuels?
   c Draw a bar graph to show the information given in **Figure 3**.
   d Fossil fuels are non-renewable resources. What is meant by a non-renewable resource?

3 Use **Figure 2**.
   a Draw a frame of the same size. Make a labelled sketch of the urban land uses shown (e.g. factories and houses).
   b A lot of coal was being burnt. What disadvantages of burning coal are suggested by looking at this photograph?

Resource use

Energy sources are vital for:

- people's everyday needs, e.g. for cooking, lighting and heating
- factory needs, e.g. to operate machines
- transport needs, e.g. cars, trains and planes.

Other natural resources, such as wood and metals, are raw materials from which manufactured goods are made.

World population growth

World population has increased. Look back to pages 106–7 for the reasons for this. The rate of increase has speeded up. **Figure 1** shows this. It took almost 100 years for world population to double from 1 to 2 billion, but then it took less than 50 years for it to double again from 2 to 4 billion. As the world population grows, pressure on the world's natural resources increases.

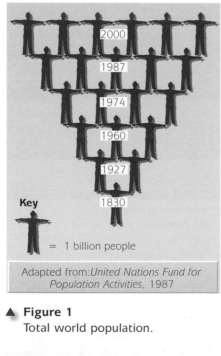

Adapted from:*United Nations Fund for Population Activities, 1987*

▲ **Figure 1**
Total world population.

▶ **Figure 2** World commercial energy consumption, 1973–1998.

World energy consumption

Everyone wants a better standard of living, but this means using more energy. Homes in MEDCs are packed full of electrical goods. Electrical goods do jobs that used to be done by hand, such as washing or washing up. Televisions, stereos and computers are used for leisure and entertainment. Private cars use more energy per person than buses and trains.

Once people in LEDCs become richer, they behave in the same way. After electricity is supplied to their homes, they want at least a television and a fridge. As LEDCs develop economically, more energy is used in factories and offices, as well as for transport.

Figure 2 shows that world energy consumption continues to increase. This is caused by two things pulling in the same direction:

- more people on Earth
- higher levels of economic development.

In fact, world energy consumption is greater than that shown in **Figure 2**. Local energy sources, such as wood, are not included. Wood for fuel is an important energy source in rural areas in Africa and Asia.

Differences in energy consumption between countries

There are great differences. Most energy is used in MEDCs. Look at **Figure 3**. The top ten countries are ranked from 1 to 10 according to the total amount of energy used (the green column). Only two are LEDCs – China and India. Total populations (the brown column) vary greatly. Therefore, it is most important to look at the last column and see how much energy is used per person per year. Only then does it become clear how big the differences really are:

- the average American uses 7.87 tonnes of energy per year
- the average person in the UK uses 3.69 tonnes of energy
- the average person in India uses only 0.24 tonnes.

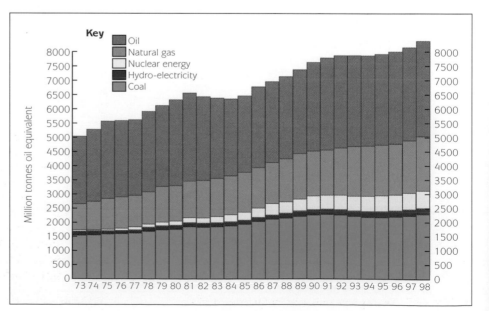

Rank	Country	Total consumption of energy (million tonnes oil equivalent)	Total population (millions)	Energy consumption per head (million tonnes oil equivalent)
1	USA	2070	263	7.87
2	China	833	1218	0.68
3	Russian Federation	624	148	4.22
4	Japan	490	125	3.92
5	Germany	336	82	4.10
6	France	235	58	4.05
7	India	227	930	0.24
8	Canada	225	30	7.50
9	UK	218	59	3.69
10	Italy	152	58	2.62

▲ **Figure 3** The world's ten greatest consumers of energy, 1995.

▶ **Figure 4** Differences in average energy consumption, 1995.

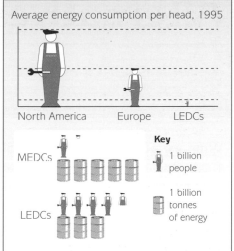

Figure 4 tells a similar story. The top part shows that the energy used by the average American is double that of a European, and at least ten times more than that of someone living in an LEDC. The bottom part shows MEDCs consume more energy, even though a lot more people live in LEDCs.

Differences in levels of economic development explain most of these differences in energy consumption. In MEDCs there is high energy consumption because of:

- many factories and offices
- much transport for goods and people
- high wages
- people having many electrical goods in homes, owning cars and taking holidays.

In LEDCs there is low energy consumption because:

- most are farmers
- farm work is done by human energy, not machines
- many villages do not have electricity
- fuelwood is collected for cooking and is often the only fuel used
- wages are low
- most income is spent on survival.

In MEDCs some energy is wasted as well, especially in the USA. Many Americans still love to drive big cars, known as 'gas guzzlers'. The price of petrol is only one third of that in Europe. Americans tend to overheat their buildings in winter and over-cool in summer. The air conditioning is so effective that visitors to the USA often need to put on an extra layer of clothes when going indoors!

Activities

1 a Use **Figure 2**.
   (i) What was the total world energy consumption in 1973?
   (ii) By how many million tonnes did it increase between 1973 and 1998?
   (iii) List the five energy sources in 1998 in order of importance.
   (iv) Name the three that are fossil fuels.
   (v) Out of the total world consumption of energy in 1998, how many million tonnes came from fossil fuels? Show your working out.
 b What is the main problem of relying so much on fossil fuels?
 c **(i)** Name the main types of energy used by you and your family at home.
   (ii) When do you and your family use most energy? Explain your answer.

2 a In **Figure 3** look at the last column – energy consumption per head. List the ten countries in order of size (greatest consumption = number 1).
 b Using **Figures 3**, **4** and **5** write down information which supports each of these statements:
   (i) more people live in LEDCs than in MEDCs
   (ii) more energy is used in MEDCs than in LEDCs.
 c Give reasons why:
   (i) the USA uses the most energy
   (ii) MEDCs use more energy than LEDCs
   (iii) an African farmer consumes very little energy.

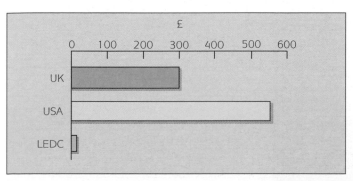

▲ **Figure 5** Average weekly family income, 1997.

Alternative sources of energy

An alternative source of energy is one that can be used instead of fossil fuels. Most are also renewable sources of energy. These are sustainable sources of energy, which will be present long after fossils fuels have run out.

Why are alternative sources of energy needed?

Figure 2 on page 188 shows that over 90 per cent of world energy came from fossil fuels in 1998. Although the amount from nuclear and hydro-electricity has increased over the years, the world mainly depends on oil, coal and natural gas for its energy needs. Fossil fuels are easy to use. Oil and gas are cheaper than other energy sources. Although oil prices go up and down (**Figure 1**), a litre of petrol in the UK would sell for less than 20 pence without tax.

For how much longer can we continue to rely upon fossil fuels?

There are three important points to consider:

1 Fossil fuels have a limited life expectancy (see **Figure 3** page 187). The oil companies keep finding new deposits of oil and natural gas, but the amount of oil near the Earth's surface is finite (limited). There will come a time when oil reserves will start to fall.

2 Burning fossil fuels is causing pollution in the atmosphere and damage to the environment (**Figure 2**):

   • Power stations burning coal (**Figure 3**) and exhausts from cars and lorries cause acid rain.

   • Carbon dioxide is released when fossil fuels are burnt causing the greenhouse effect and global warming.

3 Coal, the fossil fuel that will last longest, is the worst for the environment. More carbon dioxide is released from coal than from oil and natural gas (**Figure 4**). Governments are under great pressure from environmental groups such as Greenpeace and Friends of the Earth to reduce emissions of carbon dioxide.

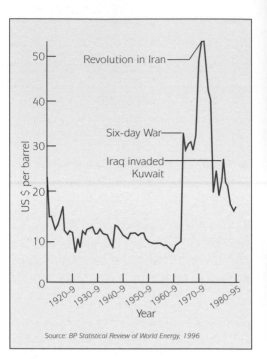

Source: BP Statistical Review of World Energy, 1996

▲ **Figure 1** The price of crude oil since 1920.

"One day, my child, all this could be yours"

▲ **Figure 2** Consequences of burning fossil fuels.

◀ **Figure 3** Ferrybridge power station located next to the Yorkshire coalfield. It is power station number five in the league table for acid rain production in England and Wales.

What alternative energy sources are there?

At one time the big hope was nuclear power. Great amounts of power are produced from small amounts of raw material (uranium). Nuclear Electric made the following claims in its adverts:

> We *don't* contribute to global warming
> We *don't* contribute to ozone depletion
> We *don't* cause acid rain
> Are we the friends of the earth?

The advert is stressing how much cleaner and more environmentally friendly nuclear power is than fossil fuels. These are the good points about using nuclear power. The bad point is what to do with nuclear waste which:

- remains radioactive for hundreds of years
- is dangerous to health and life
- has no safe place for long-term storage.

Scientists say nuclear power is safe. Many people are not convinced. Leaks of radioactive materials have not helped, but what really shattered public confidence in nuclear power was the explosion at Chernobyl in 1986. The survey of the world nuclear industry given in **Figure 5** shows that few new nuclear power stations are being built.

Today, hopes lie with alternative sources that use natural sources of energy, such as sun, water, wind, waves and tides.

Percentage of world electricity from nuclear reactors:	17 per cent	
Total number of nuclear reactors in operation:	447	
Total number of nuclear reactors under construction:	39	

The top five nuclear countries:

Country	Number of reactors in operation	Number under construction
1 USA	110	0
2 France	56	4
3 Japan	53	3
4 Russian Federation	36	3
5 UK	35	0

Nuclear power stations expected to be shut down between 2020 and 2030:

Western Europe	108
Eastern Europe	50
North America	75

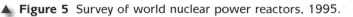
▲ **Figure 5** Survey of world nuclear power reactors, 1995.

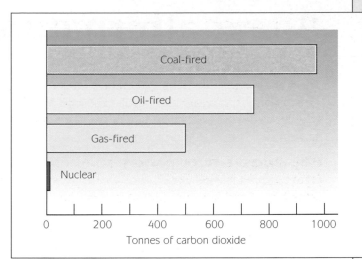

▲ **Figure 4** Carbon dioxide emissions from power stations.

Advantages of using natural sources of energy

- They will never run out, i.e. they are renewable.
- They are clean, i.e. they will cause no new pollution.
- One or more of them is present in every country, i.e. they are different from oil and gas which are found only in certain countries.

Activities

1 a Fossil fuels are dirty.
  (i) Name two environmental problems caused by burning fossil fuels.
  (ii) Use **Figure 4** to explain why use of coal causes more environmental problems than oil and natural gas.
 b Fossil fuels are cheap.
  (i) From **Figure 1**, compare the price of crude oil in 1995 with what it was in 1920.
  (ii) Why are petrol prices in the UK higher than in most other countries?
  (iii) Suggest *one* advantage and *one* disadvantage of lower petrol prices.
 c Fossil fuels are in limited supply.
  (i) Why are fossil fuels non-renewable?
  (ii) Name some alternative energy sources that are renewable.
  (iii) Why are these alternative sources renewable?
  (iv) State two other advantages of alternative energy sources.

2 Make and complete a table with the title, 'Advantages and disadvantages of nuclear power'.

Some alternative sources of energy

The main factor holding up the greater use of alternative sources is *cost*. New technology is expensive to research and develop. Low prices for oil and gas have meant that it was not worth spending too much money on research.

HEP (hydro-electric power)

This is the most widely used renewable alternative to fossil fuels. Running water is used to drive the turbines; the greater force and amount of water, the more electricity that is generated.

Certain physical conditions are needed:

- fast flowing water such as a waterfall
- high rainfall all year
- either a lake as a natural water store, or a narrow and deep valley with rocky sides to create a reservoir store of water.

Once the HEP station is operating, there are many advantages such as:

- continuous production
- no air or water pollution
- low costs
- water can be used again downstream.

Unfortunately, sites with good physical conditions are not found everywhere. The best sites are often in mountains, well away from the cities where the electricity is used. If a dam needs to be built to store enough water, this increases the costs. Flooding the land behind the dam drowns forests, destroys wildlife habitats and forces people off their land. The larger the dam, the greater the problems, but also the greater the saving in the use of fossil fuels.

▲ **Figure 1** Lake Nasser from the Aswan High Dam in Egypt. Electricity from here supplies all of Egypt, including the capital city Cairo. Why do you think so much electricity is produced here?

Wind power

The modern wind turbine stands over 30m high and has fibreglass blades, 35m or more across. When placed close together they form a wind farm. The two most common locations for wind farms are hilltops and along the coast; both are places where strong winds often blow.

Although a wind farm is expensive to build,

- it is cheap to run
- causes no air pollution
- takes up little land as the ground between the turbines can still be used for farming.

Some local people object because of the noise. Others complain that they spoil the scenery. The one big problem is that they produce no power at all on calm days, when everyone has to depend on electricity made from fossil fuels.

CATON MOOR

Activities

1 a How is HEP electricity made?

   b State *three* good physical conditions for the location of an HEP station.

2 Write down the title, 'Case study of an HEP scheme – Three Gorges Dam in China'. Make notes using these headings:

   (i) Location
   (ii) Dam details
   (iii) Advantages
   (iv) Disadvantages.

◀ **Figure 2** Wind farm on Caton Moor in Lancashire.

An HEP scheme: on the Yangtse river

In 1993 the Chinese government began work on the Three Gorges Dam. It will be a 200m wall of concrete, which will make it the world's largest, holding back a reservoir over 600 km long (**Figure 3**).

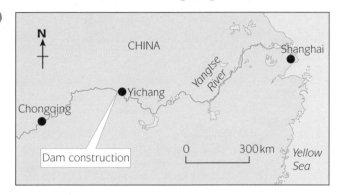

▲ **Figure 3** Location of the Three Gorges Dam.

Electricity from the power station will be distributed to many parts of China by its national grid. The Chinese government says that this extra electricity is essential if China's economic growth is to continue. By reducing the amount of coal that needs to be burnt in other power stations, the government says that it is helping to stop global warming. It is expected to be finished in 2009.

This is a big scheme and there are disadvantages:

* Almost 500 towns and villages will be flooded under the reservoir.
* Over a million people will be forced to move to new homes.
* Habitats for river species (e.g. dolphins) and land species (e.g. giant pandas) will be flooded and lost.

Wind power resources

The UK is one of the best places in Europe for wind-powered electricity. Strong westerly winds are common at any time of the year. Being an island country means that there is a long length of coastline open to strong winds. The upland areas of the north and west, where westerly gales blow most frequently, are rated as excellent for wind power in **Figure 4**, and many other areas are rated as very good.

The aim of the UK government is that 10 per cent of energy needs should come from wind power by 2025. By 1996 there were already 550 wind turbines, producing electricity equivalent to the needs of 400,000 homes. By the time you read this there will be many more; perhaps there are some near to where you live. More companies are now willing to invest in wind farms, because the cost of this source of electricity has fallen below some others (**Figure 5**).

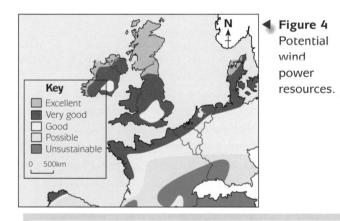

◄ **Figure 4** Potential wind power resources.

Key
Excellent
Very good
Good
Possible
Unsustainable

0   500km

▼ **Figure 5** Average costs of electricity generation in the UK,1997.

Generation method	Cost (pence per kilowatt hour)
Wind power in Scotland	2.7
Wind power in England and Wales	3.1
Power produced from fossil fuels	3.4

Activities

1 a Draw a labelled diagram of a modern wind turbine.
  b Look at **Figure 4**. Describe what it shows.

2 Three different views about wind farms are given below:
  A 'They are eyesores and damage the beautiful areas of the landscape.'
  B 'They produce so little energy it is not worth building them.'
  C 'They are our best hope for stopping global warming.'
  Write about each of these views.

Case Studies – The Three Gorges Dam Project, China/Wind power in the UK

Conserving resources and reducing pollution

Fossil fuels will be the main source of energy for many more years. It will be a long time before renewable sources take over from them. Therefore, plans are needed to:

- conserve resources by recycling
- make better use of energy
- reduce pollution, e.g. to reduce global warming.

Conserving resources

Recycling is recovering waste products and converting them into new materials. One product commonly recycled is the glass bottle (**Figure 1**). Next to the bottle bank in many supermarket car parks are bins for:

- waste paper (pulped down and made into new paper goods)
- clothes and textiles (converted into blankets and covers)
- aluminium cans (melted down and manufactured into new containers).

Recycling aluminium cans is worth doing, because making new from old uses only 5 per cent of the energy that is used to make new aluminium from its raw material (bauxite). **Resource substitution** can be useful as well – this means replacing one product by another. Making more goods out of aluminium, instead of from metals that are less easy to recycle, makes good sense.

Better use of energy

Each person can help to reduce energy consumption by switching off lights when they are not needed, by using low-energy light bulbs and by not using the car when it is possible to walk, cycle or use public transport. Small measures from many people can have a big total effect.

Governments and companies can do even more to save energy. Standards for new buildings have been improved so that less heat is lost through walls, roofs and windows. Combined heat and power schemes are being encouraged; for example, next to some power stations there are glasshouses that are heated by the water that has passed through the cooling towers. Supermarkets use the heat given off by their freezers to heat other parts of the store.

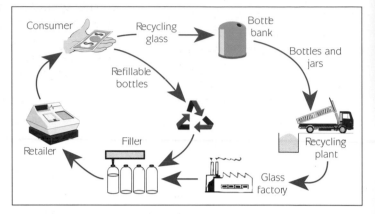

▲ **Figure 1** Recycling glass bottles.

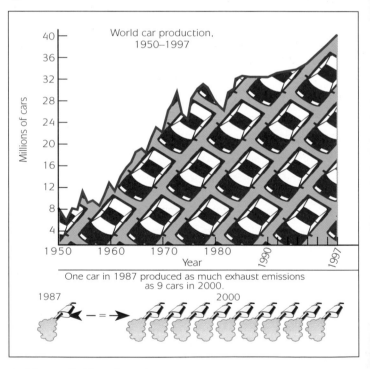

▲ **Figure 2** More but cleaner cars.

People in MEDCs are not going to give up using their cars, but cars are being designed to use less energy and cause less air pollution (**Figure 2**). Fuel consumption is being reduced using improved technology that makes engines more efficient. A petrol car bought in the UK today is 90 per cent cleaner than a car that was made ten years ago. This is mainly because of catalytic converters, which reduce emissions of pollutants (such as oxides of nitrogen and carbon monoxide).

Reducing pollution

Pollution does not stop at country borders; it is an international problem. **Global warming** is a good example. Higher temperatures are being recorded everywhere, not only in countries which burn large amounts of fossil fuels. If pollution is an inter-national problem, the only way to control it is by international agreements between countries, but persuading different countries to agree is never easy.

Many people think that global warming is the world's number one pollution problem. The Earth has been getting warmer since 1900. **Figure 3** shows this. However, not everyone agrees on the reasons why the Earth is warming up, although the majority blame the greenhouse effect (**Figure 4**).

The greenhouse effect works like this (see also **Figure 4**):

- Light rays from the sun reach the Earth's surface and heat it up.
- Heat escapes from the surface, but some is trapped by a layer of carbon dioxide.
- The layer of carbon dioxide in the atmosphere is now thicker than it used to be so more heat is trapped.
- This causes surface temperatures to rise.

The main reason why the layer of carbon dioxide is thicker is because more and more carbon dioxide is being released, as more fossil fuels are burnt. Over 90 per cent of the world's commercial energy supplies still come from fossil fuels (page 188).

What are the possible solutions to this global problem?

Solutions must be international because all countries are affected. The conference on Climate Change in Japan in 1997 led to the Kyoto Treaty.

The Kyoto Treaty says:

- all MEDCs must cut emissions of carbon dioxide so that they are 5.2 per cent lower by 2010 than they were in 1990
- LEDCs need not make any cuts unless they choose to do so.

Is the Kyoto Treaty working?

- Some say that, instead of 5 per cent, a 60 per cent reduction in greenhouse gases is needed if global warming is to be stopped.
- LEDCs that burn a lot of coal, such as China and India, are not required to make any cuts.
- The USA, which is responsible for more carbon dioxide emissions than any other country, is not trying to meet the targets. It has not signed the treaty.

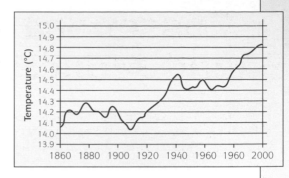

▲ **Figure 3** Average world temperatures, 1860–2000.

Countries that have large areas of low-lying land next to the sea, such as Bangladesh, are very worried, as also are low-lying island countries, such as the Maldives in the Indian Ocean. Both are poor countries. They are disappointed that rich countries are not doing more to try to reduce the greenhouse effect. We do seem to be a long way from moving towards a cleaner planet (see page 208).

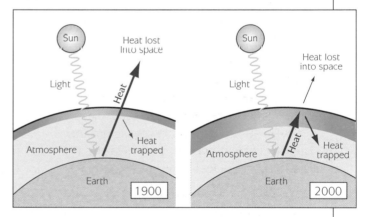

▲ **Figure 4** How the greenhouse effect operates.

Activities

1. **a** What is meant by *recycling*?
    b In your home area,
       (i) which waste products are recycled
       (ii) how is their collection organized?
    c Draw a labelled diagram to show what happens to a glass bottle put into a bottle bank.
    d Do you think that recycling is a good thing? Explain your view on this.

2. **a** Describe what **Figure 3** shows.
    b With the help of labelled diagrams, explain how the greenhouse effect works.
    c State *two* ways in which global warming is an international problem.
    d **(i)** What is the Kyoto Treaty?
       (ii) Give *two* reasons why it will not stop global warming.
       (iii) Explain why solutions to international problems are difficult to achieve.

3. One way to reduce global warming is to replace fossil fuels by alternative energy sources.
    a Name *two* alternative energy sources (pages 192–3).
    b Explain some of the difficulties for increasing the amount of energy they produce.

Energy – a summary

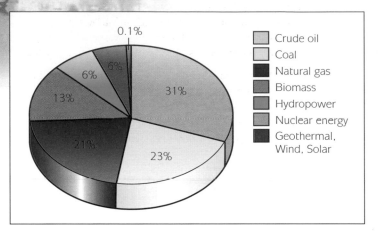

All sources of energy have their advantages and disadvantages. Past and present energy use is dominated by fossil fuels (**Figure 1**). Future energy use will be a better mixture of fossil fuels and alternative sources.

◀ **Figure 1** World consumption of energy (1996), including estimates for non-commercial sources such as biomass.

▼ **Figure 2** Assessment of different energy sources.

1   Fossil fuels

Coal, oil and natural gas

Assessment

Renewable	✗
No release of carbon dioxide	✗
Does not pollute the air	✗
Does not lead to local environmental problems	✗
Safe	✗
Cheap energy source	✓
Known technology	✓
Simple technology for use in remote areas (in LEDCs)	✗
Always available because it does not rely upon the weather	✓

Comment

Economic activities and people's way of life are based on using fossil fuels in most countries.

2   Biomass

Includes vegetation (wood for fuel) and organic materials such as animal dung

Assessment

Renewable	✓
No release of carbon dioxide	✗
Does not pollute the air	✗
Does not lead to local environmental problems	✗
Safe	✓
Cheap energy source	✓
Known technology	✓
Simple technology for use in remote areas (in LEDCs)	✓
Always available because it does not rely upon the weather	✓

Comment

The pollution problems are much less great than for the fossil fuels. It is widely used in LEDCs. For people in rural areas, it is their only source of fuel. However, collecting fuelwood has contributed to deforestation and, in some areas, to soil erosion and desertification.

Activities

1 a Using the information in **Figure 2**, make a table for the advantages and disadvantages of using **(i)** nuclear power **(ii)** biomass.

  b With the help of information from pages 192–3, do the same for HEP and wind power as has been done for the four other energy sources in **Figure 2** on these pages.

2 a Draw a divided bar graph to show world energy consumption in 1996, using the percentages from **Figure 1**. Complete a key.

  b State the total percentage for each of the following from **Figure 1**:
  (i) nuclear power **(ii)** total from fossil fuels
  (iii) total from renewable sources.
  (Note that the three answers should add up to 100.1%)

3 Suggest reasons why
  a fossil fuels are used in every country of the world
  b nuclear power is mainly used in MEDCs such as the USA, UK and Japan
  c biomass is mainly used in LEDCs in Africa and Asia.

4 Using information from elsewhere, choose another example of an alternative energy source (e.g. geothermal or tidal power).
  a With the help of a labelled diagram, describe how energy is obtained from it.
  b Make an assessment of its advantages and disadvantages (as is done in **Figure 2** for other energy sources).

---

3 Solar

The sun's power can be used for generating electricity by using photovoltaic cells (PVs). The main hope for the future is new technology, which will allow the sun's heat to be made into electricity at low cost.

Assessment

Renewable	✓
No release of carbon dioxide	✓
Does not pollute the air	✓
Does not lead to local environmental problems	✓
Safe	✓
Cheap energy source	✗
Known technology	✗
Simple technology for use in remote areas (in LEDCs)	✗
Always available because it does not rely upon the weather	✗

Comment
In some countries, such as the UK, the sun does not always shine due to cloud, and power production is low.

4 Nuclear energy

This is produced by 'fission'. As an atom is split using uranium, the heat produced drives steam turbines to generate electricity.

Assessment

Renewable	✗
No release of carbon dioxide	✓
Does not pollute the air	✓
Does not lead to local environmental problems	✗
Safe	✗
Cheap energy source	✗
Known technology	✓
Simple technology for use in remote areas (in LEDCs)	✗
Always available because it does not rely upon the weather	✓

Comment
Nuclear accidents have meant that public confidence has been lost. There is the problem of what to do with all the radioactive waste that already exists.

Where are the environments that favour tourism?

0   100km

Key

National Park

Area of protection

• Coastal resort

Cairngorm National Park
Loch Lomond National Park
Ayr
Northumberland
Yorkshire Dales
North York Moors
Lake District
Scarborough
Blackpool
Llandudno Southport
Snowdonia
Peak District
Skegness
Brecon Beacons
The Broads
Great Yarmouth
Pembrokeshire Coast
Tenby
Exmoor
Dartmoor
The New Forest
Brighton
Eastbourne
Bognor Regis
Bournemouth
Newquay
Weymouth
Torquay

▲ **Figure 1** Coastal resorts and National Parks in the UK.

In the UK the coastline remains the most important environment for tourism. Sixty per cent of main holidays in the UK in 1996 were taken at coastal resorts. The most popular resorts included the following:

- a beach
- good coastal scenery (such as cliffs, caves, and stacks)
- a reasonable climate. Most coastal resorts are along the south coast of England, where summers are warmest with the highest number of hours of sunshine.

Inland areas with good scenery are becoming more popular. National Parks were created in England and Wales (**Figure 1**). A **National Park** is 'an area of beautiful and relatively wild countryside', which was created for two reasons:

1 to preserve an area's natural beauty
2 to promote people's enjoyment of the countryside.

It is not easy to do both these things, because too many visitors destroy the beautiful countryside that they are all going to see.

Rules and regulations are needed. Each park is managed by its own National Park Authority to check that the rules are being obeyed. Management tasks include:

- undertaking conservation work and planting woodland
- controlling new building
- providing access for visitors, e.g. tracks and footpaths
- setting up visitor facilities, e.g. information centres, car parks and picnic sites.

Worldwide, tourism is growing fast due to:

- increased leisure time
- higher incomes
- cheaper air travel and more package holidays.

◄ **Figure 2** Yorkshire Dales National Park.
A: Improved footpath using local raw materials near Malham Cove;
B: Roadside commercial enterprise, which would be discouraged.

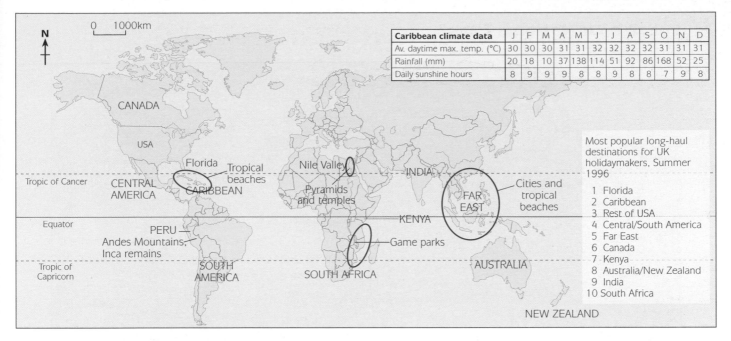

Caribbean climate data	J	F	M	A	M	J	J	A	S	O	N	D
Av. daytime max. temp. (°C)	30	30	30	31	31	32	32	32	32	31	31	31
Rainfall (mm)	20	18	10	37	138	114	51	92	86	168	52	25
Daily sunshine hours	8	9	9	9	8	8	9	8	8	7	9	8

Most popular long-haul destinations for UK holidaymakers, Summer 1996

1 Florida
2 Caribbean
3 Rest of USA
4 Central/South America
5 Far East
6 Canada
7 Kenya
8 Australia/New Zealand
9 India
10 South Africa

▲ **Figure 3** Some popular worldwide destinations.

Tourism was expected to become the world's largest industry by 2000. More people are taking long-distance holidays, either to visit relatives or to escape from the bad winter weather. The peak holiday season in the Caribbean is from December to April, when it is hot and mostly dry (**Figure 3**).

In many LEDCs tourism has been welcomed as a badly needed new source of income. Until large numbers of visitors started going to the Caribbean islands to enjoy the winter sun, countries such as St Lucia relied on the export of bananas, which fetched low prices. Now the money earned from tourists is higher and there is a much wider choice of jobs.

Activities

1 a Look at **Figure 1**.
   (i) Name one part of the UK with many National Parks.
   (ii) Where in England are few National Parks found?
   (iii) Name the National Park closest to where you live.
 b Draw a bar graph to show numbers of visitors to the National Parks named below.

Numbers of visitors per year (millions)

Brecon Beacons	7	Northumberland	1
The Broads	3	North York Moors	11
Dartmoor	8	Peak District	22
Exmoor	3	Pembrokeshire Coast	13
Lake District	20	Snowdonia	11
Yorkshire Dales	9		

2 Choose *one* of the following National Parks:
 • Dartmoor (see pages 22–23)
 • The Yorkshire Dales (see pages 24–25)
 • The Lake District (see pages 58–59)

 a Describe some of the landscape features that attract visitors.
 b Choose *one* landscape feature and explain its formation.

3 a From **Figure 3**, describe the location of the Caribbean.
 b Look at the Caribbean climate data within **Figure 3**. State *one* way in which **(i)** temperature **(ii)** rainfall is different between June and October than during the rest of the year.
 c In Manchester in January, the average temperature is about 5°C, about 50mm of rain is expected and the number of hours of sunshine is less than 4. Why would a person from Manchester spend money on a Caribbean holiday in January?
 d Why is October *not* the best month for going on holiday to the Caribbean?

4 Find out information (from tourist brochures or the Internet) about *one* of the tourist areas named in **Figure 3**, but *not* Kenya. Design an Information Sheet to fit an A4 page which would be useful for a person intending to holiday there.

Case Study – The North York Moors

Focus on a National Park

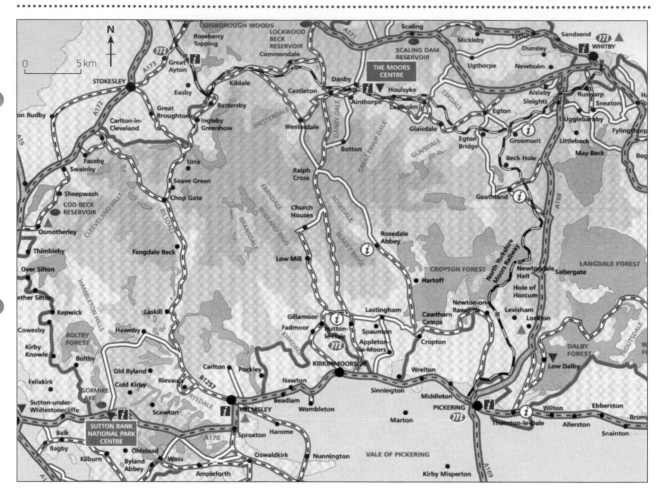

▲ **Figure 1** The North York Moors National Park.

▲ **Figure 2** Inland scene across the North York Moors.

▲ **Figure 3** Rugged coastal scenery, North Yorkshire.

The Park's main problem – pressure from visitor numbers

The Park is close to Teesside, a densely populated urban area. On sunny summer weekends as many as 150 000 visitors may arrive in the Park, mostly by car, which leads to:

- congestion on the roads
- pressure on car parking spaces
- over-crowded villages, e.g. Robin Hood's Bay and Goathland. Places like these that attract many visitors are known as **honeypots**.

The Threat to *Heartbeat* Country

How the popularity of the TV series is harming Goathland

The popularity of the series, which shows a policeman's lot on the North York Moors, has also caused serious problems for the villagers of Goathland, the moorland community in which it is filmed.

Heartbeat's success brings more than a million fans to the village each year, trampling the grass, churning up the roadsides and causing horrendous traffic congestion with their inconsiderate parking. The tourist hordes are eager to see where their favourite show is set. The low estimate is for 1.25 million visitors a year, which means that on a busy day, with a staggering 700 cars parked in Goathland, it can take three-quarters of an hour to pass through the village

The response to the problem has been to deter car parking by significantly expanding the yellow lines in the village and installing kerbs to protect particularly vulnerable roadsides – measures which are starting to prove successful.

David Brewster, the Head of North York Moors National Parks Services, which is partly responsible for tackling the problem, said 'We are not trying to stop *Heartbeat* being filmed here. It does bring income into the area and into Whitby (estimated at £9m. in 1996), but there are also significant problems. We have to do something to reduce their impact.'

Parish council chairman Keith Thompson said, 'We have a concern for the environment and a duty of care for the village. The village grew over a long period of time and we should not spoil it when problems can be dealt with. A lot of people in the middle of the village say they can sit in their gardens and ignore the people milling about outside, but there has been some loss in quality of life. However, I don't think people resent the show, because the visitors provide income and jobs for a lot of people'.

▲ **Figure 4** Adapted from *Yorkshire Life*, April 1997.

ℹ **The North York Moors National Park**

Key facts about the Park
- created in 1952
- about 11 million visitors per year.

Physical features and attractions
- heather-covered moorlands on the higher parts
- woods and farmland on the lower slopes and in the valleys
- spectacular coastal scenery with tall cliffs and wide bays.

Human attractions
- old fishing villages such as Robin Hood's Bay
- churches and abbeys such as Rievaulx Abbey
- long-distance footpaths such as the Cleveland Way
- North York Moors steam railway from Grosmont to Pickering
- moorland villages in scenic settings, such as Goathland, the location for the TV series *Heartbeat*.

Activities

1 a From **Figure 1** page 198, describe where in the UK the North York Moors National Park is located.

 b Draw a frame the same size as **Figure 1** on page 200. Mark on it and name the following that attract visitors:
 - the coastline and the town of Whitby
 - The North Yorkshire Moors Railway
 - The Moors Centre for information near Danby
 - the village of Goathland
 - a large area of moorland without any settlements.

 c Looking at **Figures 1**, **2** and **3**, explain how the North York Moors fits the definition of a National Park given on page 198 'An area of beautiful and relatively wild countryside'.

2 a Make a chart showing costs and benefits of tourism for Goathland.

 b Why do some people in the village object more strongly than others to the great numbers of visitors?

Other problems and conflicts in National Parks

A Footpath erosion

About half the visitors to National Parks never walk more than half a mile away from where their car is parked. Landscape features close to car parks, such as Malham Cove, have footpaths 'almost like motorways' leading up to them (**Figure 1**).

However, many walkers and hikers also visit. Long-distance footpaths such as the Cleveland Way in the North York Moors are well used, which has led to footpath erosion. The thin surface cover of grass is soon removed. Once the bare soil is eroded by people walking over it, it is quickly washed away by the rain. As people look for more comfortable walking on the grass along the sides of the path, the zone of erosion is widened.

One of the management tasks in National Parks is footpath repairs:

- Steps made of local stone are made on steep hill sides (**Figure 2A** page 198).
- Slabs of stone are laid in flatter areas.
- Badly eroded sections are fenced off and re-seeded.
- Wooden rafts are laid across marshy ground.

B Conflicts between local people and visitors

Making a good living in upland areas is difficult. Farmers try to increase their incomes. When some farmers in the North York Moors turned moorland into pasture in the 1980s, environmentalists claimed that the beautiful wild landscape and wildlife habitats were lost.

A lot of people dislike plantations of coniferous trees. However, more money can be made from growing trees than from animals grazing the poor moorland grasses. Nearly 20 per cent of the open moorland on the North York Moors has been ploughed up and planted with conifers in the last 30 years (**Figure 2**). Visitors object less if attractions are provided in the forests, such as forest walks and picnic sites.

Another conflict in National Parks is quarrying, which was dealt with on pages 28–29. This gives work to local people, but they can be eyesores in the middle of splendid scenery (**Figure 3**).

Activities

1. a Explain how footpath erosion is caused.
   b Where is it most likely to occur?
   c How has the footpath in **Figure 2A** page 198 been improved?
   d Describe two other ways of repairing footpath damage.

2. Look at **Figure 2** page 200, and **Figures 2** and **3** on this page.
   a Describe what you can see on each photograph.
   b Which view of the North York Moors do you like best? Explain your answer.

◀ **Figure 1**
The 'road' to Malham Cove in the Yorkshire Dales National Park. At least most of the erosion from people is limited to the line of the footpath.

▲ **Figure 2** Coniferous plantation on the North York Moors.

▲ **Figure 3** Boulby potash mine within the North York Moors Park.

Case Study – Tourism in Kenya

Tourism in an LEDC

KENYA SAFARI and KENYA COAST EXCURSION

- **Day 1** London to Nairobi with British Airways

- **Day 2** Nairobi to Aberdares
  Transfer to the highlands of the Aberdare range and overnight at the Aberdare Country Club.

- **Day 3** Aberdare National Park
  Transfer to The Ark, situated in the heart of the Aberdare National Park. In the evening enjoy floodlit game viewing.

- **Day 4** Aberdares to Sweetwaters
  Transfer to the Ol Pejeta Rhino Reserve and Sweetwaters tented camp, overlooking one of the busiest waterholes in the reserve.

- **Day 5** Sweetwaters to Mount Kenya
  After an early morning game drive, continue to the famous Mount Kenya Safari Club on the slopes of Africa's second highest mountain.

- **Day 6** Mount Kenya
  A full day at leisure at the Mount Kenya Safari Club. Take an optional excursion to the Animal Orphanage or to Mount Kenya or treat yourself to an 'Aerial Safari', a 20-minute scenic flight over Mount Kenya.

- **Day 7** Mount Kenya to Masai Mara
  A short flight takes you to Masai Mara and the Mara Safari Club.

- **Day 8** Masai Mara
  Another full day at the Mara Safari Club with morning and evening game drives. You can also take part in the walking safari or take an optional hot-air balloon ride over the Masai Mara Park.

- **Day 9** Masai Mara to Nairobi to Kenya Coast
  After a short-flight transfer to Nairobi, travel by Kenya Airways to Mombasa. Ground transfer to the Turtle Bay Beach Club located 20km south of Malindi on a white sand beach within the Watamu Marine National Park.

- **Days 10–15** Kenya Coast
  Spend a lively and relaxing week next to the sea. Use of the hotel's water sports and sports and fitness facilities is included at no extra cost.

- **Day 16** Kenya Coast to Nairobi to London
  Fly back to Nairobi to connect with the overnight British Airways flight to London.

▲ **Figure 4** A typical holiday in Kenya.

Nairobi	J	F	M	A	M	J	J	A	S	O	N	D
Daytime temp.(°C)	25	26	26	24	23	22	21	22	24	25	23	28
Rainfall (mm)	88	70	96	155	189	29	17	20	34	64	189	115
Daily sunshine hours	9	9	9	7	6	6	4	4	6	7	7	8

Activities

1 Draw temperature and rainfall graphs (like those used on pages 76–77) to show the climate of Nairobi.

2 a Draw a large sketch map of Kenya. Mark on it places visited by tourists.
  b Look at **Figure 4**. What can visitors do **(i)** at the Ark **(ii)** in the Masai Mara and **(iii)** on the Kenya coast?

3 Draw *either* a pie graph *or* a divided bar graph to show the following percentages.

Tourists to Kenya in 1995:
UK 24%, Germany 29%, Switzerland 8%, France 8%, Italy 8%, USA 6%, others 17%.

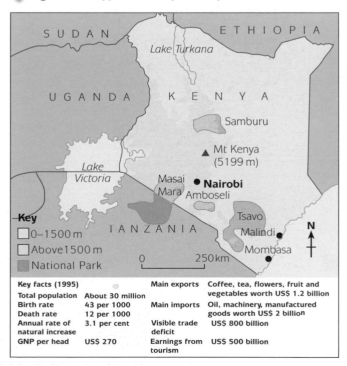

Key facts (1995)		Main exports	Coffee, tea, flowers, fruit and vegetables worth US$ 1.2 billion
Total population	About 30 million		
Birth rate	43 per 1000	Main imports	Oil, machinery, manufactured goods worth US$ 2 billion
Death rate	12 per 1000		
Annual rate of natural increase	3.1 per cent	Visible trade deficit	US$ 800 billion
GNP per head	US$ 270	Earnings from tourism	US$ 500 billion

▲ **Figure 5** Kenya.

Kenya has two different environments attractive to foreign visitors:

- wildlife parks on the plateau
- coastline of the Indian Ocean.

Many visitors spend one week on safari viewing wildlife and one week on the beach, as in the typical holiday described in **Figure 4** on the previous page.

KENYA

One of the 'Big Five' that tourists can expect to see on safari.

Wildlife

Of all the countries in Africa, Kenya has some of the most accessible game parks. Here you can observe some of the greatest examples of wildlife including the 'Big Five' – elephant, lion, leopard, buffalo and rhino. Scenically stunning with vast expanses of savanna grassland and bush across the plateau of the highlands, it is blessed with beautiful mountains such as Mount Kenya, Africa's second highest peak. A tempting option for the more adventurous visitor is to take the three day trek complete with porter, cooks and guides to the 5 000m summit.

Going on a bush safari is one of life's great adventures. We make sure that it is a comfortable one. You will travel in a specially adapted minibus with a guaranteed window seat, be guided by an English speaking driver and accommodated in comfortable lodges. There is nothing like seeing animals in the wild, in their own natural habitat.

Coastline

As for the beaches, the coastal strip from Malindi to beyond Mombasa has mile upon mile of white coral sand, lapped by the warm waters of the Indian Ocean, sheltered in parts by gently swaying palms. Why not take a trip in a glass bottomed boat on to the reef where you can see over 240 species of fish and a wide variety of corals? And if you want something different, visit Mombasa – it's hot and dusty, but there is a buzz of excitement in its colourful bazaars!

▲ **Figure 1** Brochure information about the two tourist environments in Kenya.

Interview with Kenya's Minister of Tourism and Wildlife in early 1997

Q *What has been the main achievement of the Kenyan tourist industry in the last 34 years?*

A Tourism is important for world economic development. In Kenya tourism is our number two foreign exchange earner, accounting for 21 per cent of total foreign exchange earnings. In terms of jobs, over 11 per cent of total wage employment is from tourism. The growth of tourism has encouraged growth in other sectors, such as agriculture and transport.

Comment on the answer
The Minister is stressing the benefits from tourism, both to the economy of Kenya and to the people of Kenya.

Q *What are you doing to ensure that Kenya remains a favourite tourist destination?'*

A We are trying to attract visitors from a wider range of countries. We are hoping to become one of the main eco-tourism destinations by avoiding some of the problems caused by mass tourism. We have recently taken part in tourist exhibitions in Poland, Japan, Hong Kong, Australia and New Zealand.

Comment on the answer
People in other countries need to be shown what Kenya can offer the visitor. Attracting tourists from a number of countries will help to reduce the over-dependence on visitors from Germany and the UK.

The problems

1 Falling numbers of tourists

Visitor numbers have fallen since the peak of 900 000 in 1990 and crashed in the second half of 1997 (**Figure 2**). Everyone concerned with the tourist business suffered – safari lodge owners, hotel workers, minibus drivers, street traders and many others (**Figure 3**).

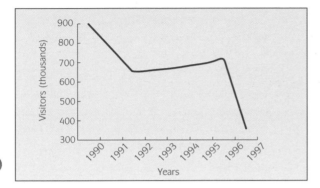

▲ **Figure 2** Number of visitors to Kenya, 1990–1997.

The National Parks are empty

Last week I was almost the only guest at Kilaeuni, a 56-room thatched safari lodge in Tsavo National Park. It is the high season for tourism in Kenya; in a normal year the park would be buzzing with the zebra-striped minibuses with pop-up roofs.

But tourism in Kenya has collapsed. All over the country, parks and lodges are half empty. On the coast, hotels are closing for lack of business; the hawkers and beach boys are starved of their European prey; no one is buying their wooden masks, their polished elephants or their beaded Masai bracelets.

This year's tourist season has coincided, fatally, with the run up to Kenya's election. Violence has already started. After the massacre of tourists at Luxor in Egypt, tourists are taking no chances. In August the violence in Kenya got too close to the tourists. A police station in the coast resort of Likoni near Mombasa was attacked and seven police officers were killed. The members of a band that had been playing in a tourist hotel were murdered.

▲ **Figure 3** From *The Guardian*, 15 December 1997.

2 Damage to the environment

There are also environmental problems. In the game parks (especially the Masai Mara which has many visitors):

- Minibus drivers surround and disturb animals (**Figure 4**).
- They churn up the ground in the wet season.
- The grassland is changed into a 'dust bowl' in the dry season.

On the coral reefs off the coast:

- Boats drop their anchors onto the fragile coral.
- People walk on the coral.
- Some tourists take pieces of coral away as souvenirs.

The Kenya Wildlife Service (KWS) manages the Game Parks. Its workers are poorly paid and have only limited experience of the work. Some take no action against minibus drivers, who go off the roads to move close to the wild animals, because they earn higher tips from tourists. Tourists are often more interested in getting close to the animals than in the erosion they are causing.

▲ **Figure 4** Lions in the Masai Mara, surrounded by tourist minibuses.

3 Conflicts with local people

The Masai, who are the local tribespeople, were driven off their land to make way for the Game Parks and wild animals. Shortages of grazing land and population increase have forced local farmers to move closer to the edges of the parks. Elephants trample their crops. Lions eat cattle. Villagers and tribespeople are injured, or sometimes killed by wild animals, but they are not allowed to kill them. Few of the Masai gain any benefits from tourism.

Hopefully, because of new attitudes associated with **eco-tourism**, there might soon be opportunities for the Masai to benefit for the first time (see page 207).

Activity

Write notes on Tourism in Kenya as a case study using the following four headings (illustrate your answer with maps and diagrams).

- Tourist attractions and their locations
- Benefits of tourism
- Problems
- Changes (you also need to look ahead to page 207).

The impacts of tourism

	Advantages		**Disadvantages**

Advantages

A *Environmental*

- Makes people more aware of conservation of landscapes, vegetation and wildlife.
- Money from tourists is used for conservation and management.

B *Economic*

- The country earns foreign exchange from overseas visitors.
- There is more work in services and in craft industries making souvenirs.
- Public services improve (airports, roads, water and electricity supplies), which also benefit local people.

C *Social* (effects on people)

- Local cultures and traditions are more likely to be preserved..
- Loss of young people by migration may be stopped because of new work opportunities.

Disadvantages

A *Environmental*

- Natural environments are destroyed and wildlife habitats are lost when airports, roads, hotels etc. are built.
- There is pressure on landscapes visited by many tourists, e.g. footpath erosion.
- Pollution problems increase, e.g. litter, noise and untreated waste going into rivers or seas.

B *Economic*

- LEDCs do not benefit fully from what overseas visitors pay for their holidays. Only 15 per cent may reach the country, because goods and trained staff may be imported from MEDCs.
- Numbers of visitors can go down leading to economic decline.
- Many jobs in tourism are unskilled, poorly paid and seasonal (only for part of the year).
- Some local people, such as farmers, lose their land and livelihoods in areas where facilities for tourists are built.

C *Social* (effects on people)

- Local people copy visitors and soon lose local traditions.
- Tourists look down on local people and treat them badly.

▲ **Figure 1** Advantages and disadvantages of tourism.

Tourism has both advantages (positive impacts) and disadvantages (negative impacts) for countries, people and environments. Some of these are shown in **Figure 1**.

The disadvantages are often greater for LEDCs than for MEDCs:

- Environmental – management is more difficult, because governments in LEDCs lack money and workers lack training, e.g. in Kenya (see problem 2 page 205).
- Economic – a lot of what is needed to start tourism has to be imported, e.g. materials for building airports, paved roads and hotels with modern facilities; equipment for providing public services such as water and electricity.

Look at **Figure 2**. Some types of holidays benefit LEDCs such as Kenya more than others.

Small benefit to an LEDC	**Greatest benefit to an LEDC**
• Book and pay for holiday in home country. • Travel on an airline from an MEDC. e.g. British Airways • Stay in luxury hotels owned by American or European companies. • Eat all meals in the hotel.	• Pay for as little as possible in home country. • Travel on an airline from an LEDC. e.g. Kenya Airways • Stay in small hotels or guest houses and pay locally. • Eat in local restaurants.
Example A *Total cost of holiday £1500* *Money benefit to Kenya* £300	**Example B** *Total cost of holiday £1500* *Money benefit to Kenya* £750

▲ **Figure 2** Who benefits?

'Green' tourism (or Eco-tourism)

This is sustainable tourism. For green or eco-tourism protecting the environment is most important. However, involving the local people in tourism is important as well. Taking account of the needs and wishes of local people makes this type of tourism different from others. It is only fair that local people should benefit from tourism.

'Green' tourism in Kenya

Three quarters of Kenya's wild animals live outside National Parks, where a lot of the land is owned by the Masai tribespeople (**Figure 3**). There is now enough wildlife outside the Parks for tourists to be attracted.

Three tented camps have been set up in Kimana, owned and run by Kenyans. They are on an important migration route for wildlife between Amboseli and Tsavo National Parks. (You can see where these Parks are located by looking at **Figure 5** on page 203.) The Masai are paid a rent of about £1000 per year for the use of their land. The local Masai people are important to the success of small tourist developments like this, which have the advantage of causing less environmental damage.

However, there are still problems:

▲ **Figure 3**
Masai tribesperson.

- Only a small amount of tourist money is trickling down to the Masai people. Not being able to read or to understand legal documents, the Masai are often cheated by tour operators.
- The Masai need to carry on with their traditional way of life – planting crops and keeping cattle. These farming activities do not mix well with encouraging wildlife.

The need for management and stewardship

As tourist numbers increase, management is needed everywhere. Often proper management in tourist areas is started only after some damage has already been done. Antarctica is different. It offers tourists magnificent scenery, icebergs and nesting penguins by the million (Figure 4).

Until recently, its remoteness saved it from tourists, but in summer 1995 tourist numbers passed 10 000 for the first time. Most visitors arrive on cruise ships. By living on ships, the chances of damaging the fragile land environment are reduced.

The cruise operators comply with the guidelines from the International Association of Antarctic Tour Operators (IAATO), including the ones listed below.

Visitors must not:

- disturb wildlife in any way
- go within 5 metres of penguins
- leave litter or waste.

Hopefully by such stewardship Antarctica's natural beauty will be sustained, despite the growth of tourism.

▲ **Figure 4** Antarctica, an attractive but different tourist location.

Activities

1 Look at **Figure 2**.
   a How much more money did Kenya earn from holiday B than from A?
   b What percentages of the holiday money paid went to Kenya?
      (i) For A, was it 10%, 20%, 30%, 50%, 66%, 80%?
      (ii) For B, was it 10%, 25%, 50%, 75%.
   c Explain why Kenya and its people benefit more from tourists who take holiday B.

2 a What is meant by green or eco-tourism?
   b Write about an example of green tourism in Kenya.

3 a Describe what can be seen in **Figure 4**.
   b If you were a tourist to the area in **Figure 4**, what would you not be allowed to do?
   c State two reasons why management of tourists is necessary in Antarctica.

Towards a cleaner planet

Industry

- be more energy-efficient
- switch from dirty fossil fuels (coal and oil) to cleaner natural gas.

Electricity companies

- clean up the gases before releasing them
- use more renewables such as water (HEP), wind and solar.

Homeowners

- reduce heat losses from roofs, walls and windows
- do not waste heat or hot water
- choose electrical appliances that use less electricity.

Drivers

- choose small, fuel-efficient cars instead of 'gas-guzzlers'
- switch to public transport when it is available.

▲ **Figure 1** How lifestyles need to change to reduce carbon dioxide emissions significantly.

▲ **Figure 2** Normal traffic levels in one of Santiago's main streets.

◄ **Figure 3** The advert for pure orange juice above all the street traffic.

The Kyoto Treaty does not cover emissions from traffic in LEDCs such as Chile. The streets of its capital city, Santiago, are choked with traffic on every working day (**Figure 2**). The advert above the traffic is from the makers of orange juice, who are comparing their 100 per cent pure juice with the air in Santiago, which they say is almost 60 per cent smog (**Figure 3**).

Much still needs to be done if the planet Earth is not to be left for future generations in the state shown in the cartoon on page 190.

ℹ Global citizenship

This involves people everywhere:
- thinking about the effects of our activities on the world
- trying to preserve and improve the environment
- keeping natural resources for others to use in the future.

Activities

1 Use information from this page and from earlier in the chapter. Make lists of the ways for reducing damage to the environment by
   - industries and companies
   - ordinary people like yourselves
   - governments.

2 a What is meant by *global citizenship*?
   b Why is being a good global citizen difficult?

Chapter 13

Development

Rush hour in a country's capital city. What do you think is this country's level of economic development? Is it a low-income, middle-income or high-income country?

Key Ideas

Contrasts in development are related to economic, environmental, social and political conditions:

- contrasts in development between MEDCs and LEDCs are indicated by factors such as population, health, literacy, housing and GNP
- environmental hazards can contribute to the lack of development.

Trade and aid in MEDCs and LEDCs are important to development:

- the greatest volume of trade takes place between MEDCs within the developed 'North'
- MEDCs exchange manufactured goods for raw materials from LEDCs in the developing 'South', which should make each of them interdependent
- patterns of world trade have disadvantages for LEDCs
- aid is one means of transferring resources from MEDCs to LEDCs but there are some disadvantages in relying upon aid.

Contrasts in development

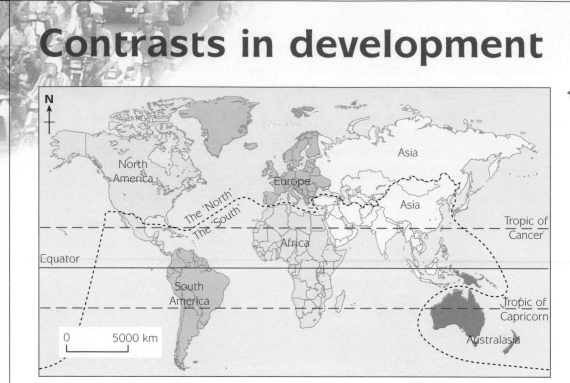

Figure 1
The world divided into MEDCs (North of the line) and LEDCs (South of the line).

You already know that MEDCs are more economically developed countries and LEDCs are less economically developed countries. These labels for countries are based upon splitting the world into two parts – an economically developed 'North' and an economically developing 'South'. The dividing line between the two is shown on **Figure 1**.

Of course, it is not easy to fit some countries into this simple division of two world groups. Even inside a country, there can be big variations in wealth between different regions. Take the UK as an example. It has its own divide between the poor 'North' and rich 'South'. It may be real, but people imagine it to be greater than it really is (**Figure 2**). In LEDCs there are often large differences in wealth between rural and urban areas.

One example of a sharp divide between a MEDC and a LEDC is the border between the USA and Mexico. Although Mexico is better developed than many LEDCs, it is poor in relation to its wealthy neighbour to the north. Some of the contrasts in wealth between them are shown in **Figure 3**. Some of the differences are as follows:

- GNP per head (this indicates wealth) is six times greater in the USA.

- Infant mortality rate (this indicates poor health care) is more than three times higher in Mexico.

- The percentage of people working in agriculture is ten times greater in Mexico; less money is made from farming than from manufacturing industry and services.

With such large differences in wealth and level of development between two sides of a border, it is not surprising that many Mexicans want to migrate into the USA. Some Mexicans can earn the same in one hour in the USA as they would earn in one day at home! Illegal immigrants from Mexico are a major problem along the border.

What is meant by 'development'?
Development means almost the same as wealth.

A developed country (MEDC) is a rich country. After providing for essential needs (food, water, shelter, clothing and heat), most people have money left over to buy consumer goods or to spend on entertainment, leisure and travel. A large service sector grows up to provide for them.

Figure 2 Unemployment in the UK in the 1990s – real or imagined differences between North and South?

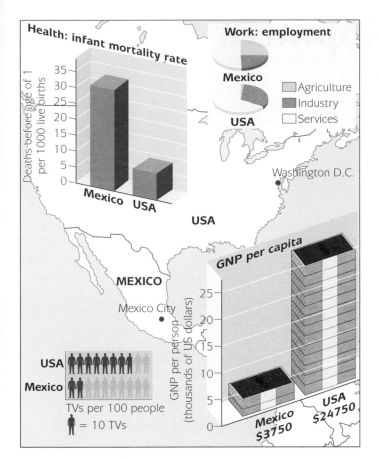

▲ **Figure 3** Contrasts between the USA and Mexico.

A less developed country (LEDC) is a poor country. Many of these countries rely upon farming, which makes little money. A few people are very rich, but for the majority there is a constant battle just to survive.

- Without enough food or safe supplies of water, people's health suffers.

- Proper medical care is limited, which is particularly bad for babies and children.

- Education is also limited, which leads to low levels of literacy.

- Millions in Africa, Asia and South America live in cramped housing without services.

Therefore, a child in an LEDC has little chance to improve on their parents' quality of life. Industries and services are increasing in many LEDCs, but not fast enough to improve the standards of living of many people.

Both economic and social factors are used to measure levels of development (pages 212–213). Wealth is an economic factor. However, a person's wealth also affects quality of life, health, literacy and housing, which are examples of social factors.

Activities

1 a Look at **Figure 1**.
   (i) Name one continent which is on the North side of the line.
   (ii) Name two continents which are on the South side of the line.
   (iii) Describe what happens to the North–South line after it leaves Asia.

   b The table below shows average income per head by continent.

Continent	Average income per head (US$)
Africa	660
Asia	1 980
Australasia	13 540
Europe	11 870
North America	24 340
South America	3 040

You need an outline world map.
(i) Make a box with a key for three groups ($0–10 000, $10 001–20 000 and $20 001–30 000) using darker colours or heavier shading for the high incomes.
(ii) Colour or shade them in on the map.
(iii) Draw in and name the North–South line on your map.

   c How good is this line for showing world differences in wealth?

2 Look at Figure 4.
   a Describe the features of each village.
   b Explain the evidence from the photographs which suggests that:
   (i) there is a lower level of development in village A
   (ii) natural resources are better in the area where village B is located.

▲ **Figure 4** A: A village in Peru.
       B: A village in Malaysia.

Measures of development

GNP (Gross National Product) per head

The most widely used indicator of a country's level of development is GNP. This is an economic indicator, because it measures wealth.

To calculate the GNP:

- add up the value in US dollars of all the goods and services produced in the country during the year

- divide the total value by the country's population

This gives the GNP per head, which can be compared with that of other countries.

As a measure of development, the GNP has advantages and disadvantages.

▼ **Figure 2** GNP per head in the mid-1990s.

Highest GNP per head (above US$20 000 and minimum population 1 million)

Rank	Country	Continent
1	Switzerland	Europe
2	Japan	Asia
3	Denmark	Europe
4	Norway	Europe
5	Sweden	Europe
6	USA	North America
7	Germany	Europe
8	Kuwait	Asia
9	Austria	Europe
10	United Arab Emirates	Asia
11	France	Europe
12	Belgium	Europe
13	The Netherlands	Europe
14	Canada	North America

Advantages of GNP	Disadvantages of GNP
Can be calculated for all countries	Sometimes reliable data is not available
Good indicator of a country's wealth	Output from subsistence farming in LEDCs is not included
Easy to compare wealth of one country with that of another	Countries with a lot of oil and small populations have very high GNPs, e.g. Kuwait (**Figure 1**)

Lowest GNP per head (below US$200)

Country	Continent
Mozambique	Africa
Tanzania	Africa
Ethiopia	Africa
Sierra Leone	Africa
Nepal	Asia
Bhutan	Asia
Vietnam	Asia
Burundi	Africa
Uganda	Africa
Rwanda	Africa

Source: Population Concern, *1995 World Population Sheet*

◀ **Figure 1** GNP per head – the world's highest and lowest in the mid-1990s.

Figure 2 is a world map showing GNP country by country. It gives us a good idea of the world distribution of wealth and shows the global pattern of high and low levels of economic development. What pattern is shown?

- The rich MEDCs (with a GNP over US$ 10 000) are in the continents of North America, Europe and Australasia. Japan in Asia is also in this group. They lie on the northern side of the North–South line.

- The poorest LEDCs (with GNP under US$ 1250) are mainly in the continents of Africa and Asia. They lie on the southern side of the North–South line.

- Middle income LEDCs (with between US$ 2500 and 5000) are mainly in South and Central America.

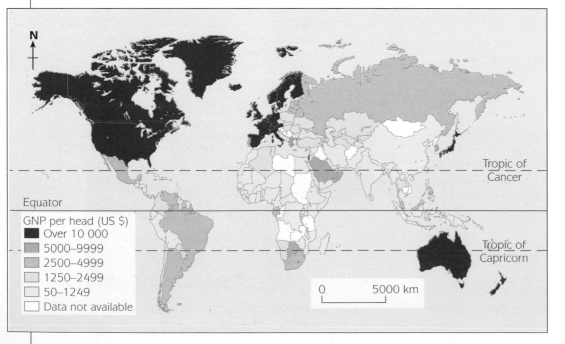

GNP per head (US $)
- Over 10 000
- 5000–9999
- 2500–4999
- 1250–2499
- 50–1249
- Data not available

Equator

Tropic of Cancer

Tropic of Capricorn

0   5000 km

Population characteristics

These are examples of social indicators of development, because they are to do with people. Population differences between MEDCs and LEDCs were dealt with in Chapter 8. A summary of the main ones is given in **Figure 3**.

Taking each indicator of development from **Figure 3** in turn:

- **Birth rate** – a country's birth rate falls as the wealth of a country and its people increases. The government has more money to spend on education and to set up family planning clinics.

- **Natural increase** – as people become richer, the rate of natural increase falls. People do not need as many children to earn money to support them in their old age. Their attitude towards having more children changes.

- **Number of young people** – as birth rates fall, the percentage of young people under 15 goes down.

- **Stage in the Demographic Transition Model** – the poorest LEDCs are in stage 2 of the DTM, described on page 107. Reducing the birth rate allows a country to pass from stage 2 to stage 3. When it falls to a very low level, a country moves into stage 4. MEDCs are in stage 4.

A decrease in the birth rate is the most important change. This happens as countries become richer, i.e. because of increased economic development. Therefore, the population characteristics in **Figure 3** are good indicators of a country's level of development.

Indicator	MEDCs	LEDCs
Birth rate (per 1000 per year)	Low	High
Typical values	10–16	20–45
Natural increase (% per year)	Low	High
Typical value	Below 1%	2.0–3.5% (or more)
People below the age of 15 (%)	Small	Large
Typical value	Below 25%	30–50%
Stage in the Demographic Transition Model	4	2 or 3

▲ **Figure 3** Population characteristics.

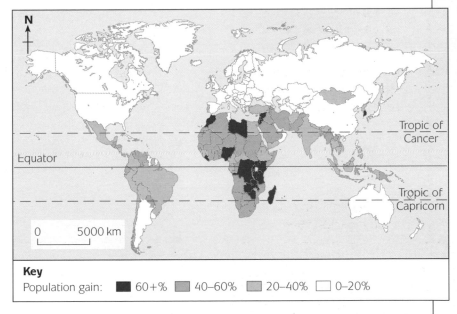

▶ **Figure 4** Population change, 1986–2000.

Key
Population gain: ■ 60+% ■ 40–60% ▨ 20–40% ☐ 0–20%

Activities

1 a Of the 14 rich countries named in **Figure 1**, how many are in **(i)** North America **(ii)** Europe **(iii)** Asia **(iv)** Africa **(v)** South America?

  b Of the 10 very poor countries named in **Figure 1**, how many are in **(i)** North America **(ii)** Europe **(iii)** Asia **(iv)** Africa **(v)** South America?

  c Why are your answers to **(a)** and **(b)** so different?

2 Look at **Figure 2**.

  a Describe the main differences shown between countries in Europe and countries in Africa.

  b What does it show for the wealth of countries that lie in the tropics (between the Tropics of Cancer and Capricorn)?

3 Draw labelled diagrams, graphs or sketches to illustrate the differences in population characteristics between MEDCs and LEDCs in **Figure 3**. Some suggestions are:

- a pictogram for birth rates
- a bar graph for natural increase
- part of a population pyramid for people below 15 (see page 108)
- a line graph for the DTM (see page 107).

4 Look at **Figure 4**.

  a Describe the differences between Europe and Africa shown.

  b Give two reasons why birth rates are higher in African countries than in Europe.

Other measures of development

It is not easy to gather reliable data for comparing levels of development between countries. Therefore it is better to use several measures of development. The social measures of development used most often are shown in **Figure 1**.

▼ **Figure 1** Social measures of development.

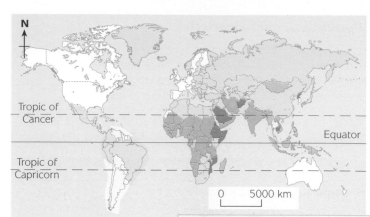

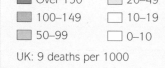

Infant mortality

Number of babies who die under the age of one, per 1000 births

- Over 150
- 100–149
- 50–99
- 20–49
- 10–19
- 0–10

UK: 9 deaths per 1000

HEALTH

- Infant mortality rate (the number of infants who die within their first year of life per 1000 live births)
- Under-5 survival rates
- Life expectancy at birth
- Number of people per doctor
- Number of people per hospital bed
- Percentage of population without access to health services
- Percentage of population without access to safe water
- Average calorie intake per person per day

Enough to eat

Worldwide 800 million people are severely malnourished or starving.

HOUSING

- Number of persons per room
- Percentage of houses without access to electricity
- Percentage of houses with running water

Key

- Health measures
- Education measures
- Housing measures

Clean water

Over 1 million people have no clean water or sanitation. Every day 25 000 people die from water-borne disease

Number of people per doctor

patients per doctor

40 000 —
30 000 —
20 000 —
10 000 —
0 —

Niger | Ethiopia | Nepal | Japan | USA | Spain | Italy

EDUCATION

Nearly one-third of adults in LEDCs cannot read or write. Over 125 million children were not attending school in 1991; two-thirds of these were girls.

Literacy

* Adult literacy rate (proportion of the adult population who can read and write)
* Average number of years at school per child
* Proportion of children who attend secondary school

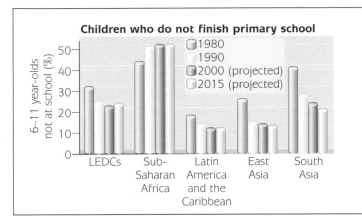

Children who do not finish primary school

6–11 year-olds not at school (%)

1980
1990
2000 (projected)
2015 (projected)

LEDCs   Sub-Saharan Africa   Latin America and the Caribbean   East Asia   South Asia

Many of the different measures are inter-related. Infant mortality rates are high because nearby clinics and hospitals do not exist. Babies catch diseases, such as dysentery and

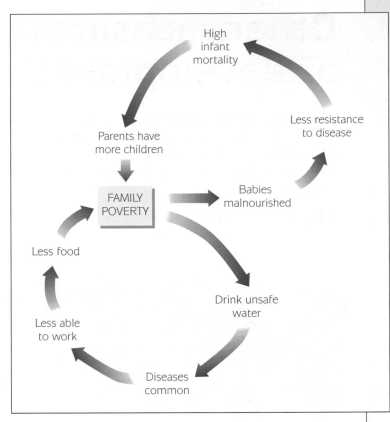

▲ **Figure 2** Poverty cycles.

typhoid, because of the lack of clean and safe water supplies. Little food means that both mother and child are less able to fight off diseases. About 35 000 children die every day in LEDCs from diseases due to poverty. Millions of people are caught in the poverty cycle trap shown in **Figure 2**. Poverty, or lack of wealth, is an economic factor that lowers the social factor – quality of life – for people in LEDCs.

Activities

1 a What is meant by infant mortality rate?
  b Look at the world map of infant mortality.
    (i) Name two continents with low mortality rates (under 10 per 1000).
    (ii) Describe where most of the countries with high mortality rates (above 100) are located.
    (iii) What does the map show about infant mortality in South America?
  c Look at **Figure 2**.
    (i) Draw that part of the poverty cycle diagram which shows how family poverty leads to high infant mortality.
    (ii) Draw another diagram like **Figure 2**, but start this one with RICH FAMILY instead of FAMILY POVERTY. Alter the labels to show why the rich are rich and have a low rate of infant mortality.

2 a Draw a pictogram to show the number of people per doctor, using the values in the bar graph at the bottom of page 214.
    Use one symbol for every 1000 people.
  b Life expectancies at birth for people living in the countries shown are:
    Niger 47 Ethiopia 48 Nepal 55 Japan 79
    USA 76 Spain 77 Italy 77.
    Draw a bar graph to show these.
  c Compare your bar graph with the one on page 214. Are they similar? Are they different? Try to explain your answer.

3 Look at the education section on this page.
  a Describe two ways in which schooling in sub-Saharan Africa is shown to be different from that in South Asia.
  b Suggest how lack of schooling may cause family poverty.

Causes of the lack of development – environmental hazards

Why are LEDCs located mostly in the continents of South America, Africa and Asia? Of the world's one billion people living in great poverty, the majority are in the tropics, where the effects of some natural hazards are strong.

Environmental (natural) hazards

A natural hazard usually causes damage to people and property. Natural disasters resulting from environmental hazards such as drought, tropical storms, earthquakes, floods and volcanoes cause considerable loss of life.

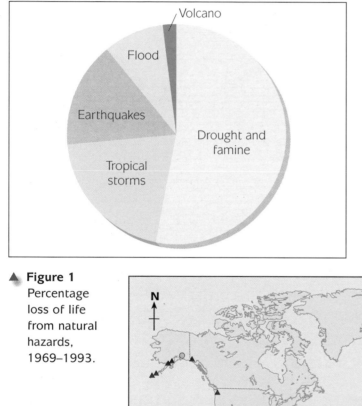

Figure 1 shows the loss of life (as a percentage of the whole population) from these natural hazards during a 25-year period of time. Some hazards (e.g. earthquakes and tropical storms) have an immediate effect upon people and property. Others (e.g. drought) take longer to have an effect, but when they do, can kill thousands through the resulting famines.

Are natural hazards more likely in tropical countries?

- ***Tropical storms*** cause about 20 per cent of the deaths. Whole settlements can be destroyed and plantation crops wiped out by hurricane-force winds. LEDCs are most affected; the only area in the developed world regularly at risk from tropical storms is the south-east corner of the USA.

- ***Floods*** occur when rivers break their banks. There is also coastal flooding due to tropical storms. Bangladesh, with its low-lying coastal location on the Ganges delta, is an example of a tropical country with a high flood risk. The risk is caused both by the River Ganges, which is filled by monsoon rains each summer, and by tropical cyclones, which are driven onshore into Bangladesh after crossing the Bay of Bengal.

▲ **Figure 1**
Percentage loss of life from natural hazards, 1969–1993.

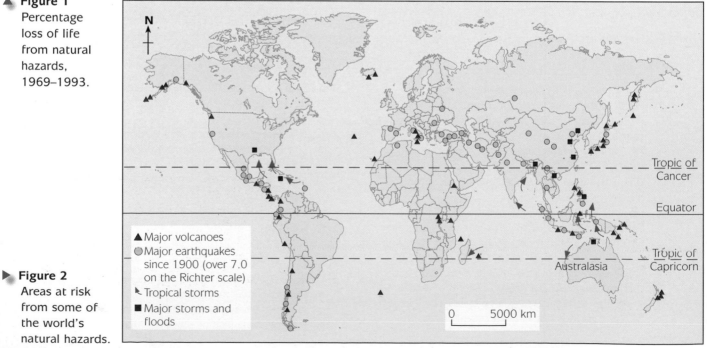

▶ **Figure 2**
Areas at risk from some of the world's natural hazards.

Year	Place	Magnitude on Richter scale	Number killed
1993	Maharashtra, India	6.4	22 000
1995	Kobe, Japan	7.2	5 400

- *Earthquakes and volcanoes* occur along the plate boundaries (see Chapter 1). Major volcanic eruptions and the strongest earthquakes since 1900 are shown in **Figure 2**. Tropical and non-tropical countries alike are affected, but it is poor people in LEDCs in the tropics who are hit hardest. One example of this is shown in **Figure 3**. Although the earthquake in Kobe was stronger than the one in Maharashtra in India, buildings in Kobe were built more strongly and withstood the shaking of the ground better.

- *Drought* occurs in an area when the amount of rain that falls is a lot less than the amount expected by the people living there. There are times when no rain falls for months or even years. Lower than average rainfall reduces the amount of grass and output of crops, so that both animals and people die of hunger. People in rural areas are most at risk of famine, because they depend on subsistence farming.

Many deaths from drought caused famines in the Sahel region in Africa. The terrible effects of the drought upon the people of Ethiopia in the 1980s were shown on TV in MEDCs, which led to food aid on a massive scale (see page 228). A high risk of drought exists in all African countries from Ethiopia to South Africa, should rains fail in the wet season.

Is drought more of a hazard in the tropics? The British drought of 1995–96 was referred to in Chapter 6, pages 86–87. It was expensive for some and a nuisance for many, but it did not cause thousands of deaths, as droughts do in LEDCs. In the tropics, high temperatures mean high rates of evaporation, so that farmland dries out quickly whenever the rains fail. This means that the effects of drought are greater in LEDCs in the tropics where governments do not have the money and resources to help all those affected.

Conclusion

Some natural hazards occur more frequently and have stronger effects in tropical countries. They contribute to the lack of development in LEDCs. However, natural hazards alone cannot explain the size of the gap in wealth and development between LEDCs and MEDCs.

◀ **Figure 3** Two earthquakes compared.

Activities

1 Look at **Figure 1**.
  a Draw a different type of diagram to show the information about loss of life from natural hazards. Finish off your diagram with a key.
  b **(i)** What is meant by drought?
  (ii) Describe how drought leads to famine and large numbers of deaths.

2 a Look at **Figure 3**.
  (i) How much stronger was the earthquake in Kobe?
  (ii) How many more people were killed in Maharashtra?
  b Look at **Figure 2**.
  (i) Name two parts of the world with many major volcanoes.
  (ii) Name two parts of the world with many major earthquakes.
  (iii) Explain why earthquakes and volcanoes cause more deaths in LEDCs than in MEDCs.

3 Look at **Figure 4**. You will also need to look back at Chapter 1.

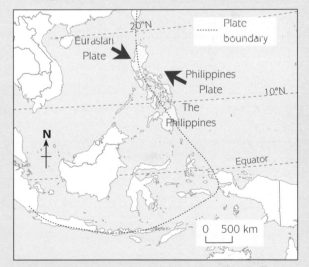

▲ **Figure 4**

  a Name the type of plate boundary which passes through the Philippines.
  b Describe what is happening along this type of plate boundary.
  c Explain why:
  (i) earthquakes are frequent in the Philippines
  (ii) violent volcanic eruptions occur, such as that of Mt Pinatubo in 1991.

Causes of the lack of development – health hazards in tropical countries

The hot, wet climate in the tropics has one big disadvantage for human health – insects and bacteria love it, so they thrive and multiply. Many tropical diseases are associated in some way with water (**Figure 1**).

A Water-borne diseases – diseases spread by drinking or by washing food in contaminated water:

- diarrhoea
- dysentery
- cholera
- typhoid
- hepatitis.

B Water-related insect-borne diseases – diseases spread by insects that breed in water:

- malaria – *from mosquitoes*
- sleeping sickness – *from tsetse flies*.

C Water-based diseases – where the carrier of the disease lives in water:

- bilharzia – *water snails which carry the disease live in streams*
- guinea worm – *worms lay their eggs in water*.

▲ **Figure 1** Diseases in tropical regions associated with water.

Example 1 – Malaria
How do people catch malaria?

- The Anopheles mosquito breeds in standing water in hot countries.
- Mosquitoes seek a blood meal and bite people, usually at night.
- If the female sucks blood from a person already infected with malaria, it can carry malaria to another person.
- Malaria is then passed on to the next person it bites.

What are the consequences?

- It leads to a fever, from which some people die.
- It weakens men and women so that they cannot work; crop output declines.
- Malaria affects 40 per cent of world's population, in over 90 countries.
- It kills four children every minute.
- The most dangerous area is Africa, in countries south of the Sahara.
- 20 million tourists from countries without malaria are put at risk every year; some will not visit countries where malaria is a risk.

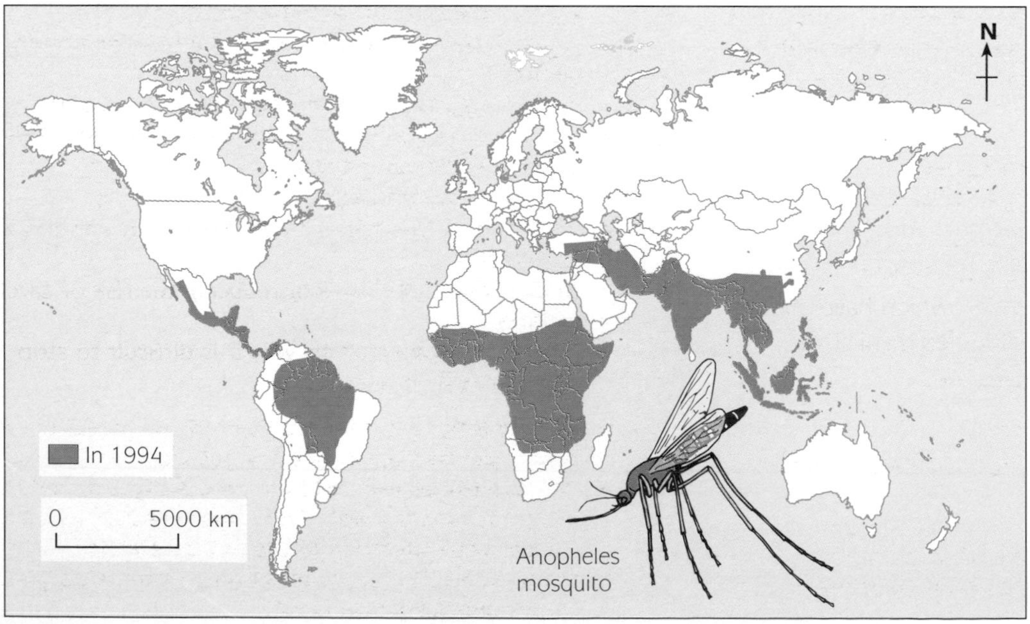

How can it be prevented or cured?

- Drugs can help, but some types of malaria are resistant to drugs.
- The best way is to try to avoid being bitten e.g. by
  - sleeping under mosquito nets
  - keeping as much skin as possible covered by clothing.
- By draining wet areas where mosquitoes breed or spraying them with insecticides.

In 1994

0   5000 km

Anopheles mosquito

▲ **Figure 2** Malaria – areas of the world affected.

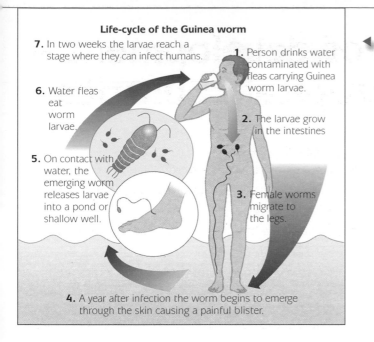

Life-cycle of the Guinea worm

7. In two weeks the larvae reach a stage where they can infect humans.

1. Person drinks water contaminated with fleas carrying Guinea worm larvae.

6. Water fleas eat worm larvae.

2. The larvae grow in the intestines

5. On contact with water, the emerging worm releases larvae into a pond or shallow well.

3. Female worms migrate to the legs.

4. A year after infection the worm begins to emerge through the skin causing a painful blister.

◀ **Figure 3** The Guinea worm in Sudan.

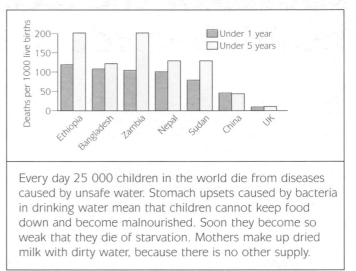

Every day 25 000 children in the world die from diseases caused by unsafe water. Stomach upsets caused by bacteria in drinking water mean that children cannot keep food down and become malnourished. Soon they become so weak that they die of starvation. Mothers make up dried milk with dirty water, because there is no other supply.

▲ **Figure 4** Children's health and mortality rates.

Example 2 – Guinea worm

Sudan in north-east Africa has the world's highest rate of Guinea worm infection. The Guinea worm is passed to people through drinking unclean water. The worm grows below a person's skin and may reach over 60cm long. In the wet season, the worms break through the skin searching for water in which to lay their eggs.

Too much water

The risk of people catching these diseases increases during the wet season. For example, areas of standing surface water are ideal breeding grounds for mosquitoes. This risk is many times greater during floods when there is water everywhere.

The wet season is the time to plant crops. It is the busiest time of the year for farmers, but this is also the time of the year with most insect pests. This means that farmers are not always at their fittest for work, which reduces food production.

Not enough clean and safe water

It is rare for rural people in LEDCs to have a safe water supply inside their houses. Usually water is carried to the house from the open streams, without any treatment. Animals drink from the same streams, which have already flowed past other villages. Many illnesses result from:

• the lack of clean, safe drinking water

• the absence of proper sanitation

• the failure to treat human wastes and keep them separate from water supply.

In many places there is clean water below the ground, but the problem is how to reach it and raise it up to the surface.

Activities

1 Write a title, 'Case study of a water-related tropical disease – malaria'

a Add the sub-heading, 'Areas affected'. Look at **Figure 2**. Of the six continents – North America, South America, Europe, Africa, Asia and Australasia,
   (i) name the three continents with large areas affected by malaria in 1994
   (ii) name the three continents not affected in 1994
   (iii) draw a simple sketch map to show which parts of Africa are most affected by malaria.

b Add another sub-heading, 'How people catch malaria'. Write about:
   (i) where malarial mosquitoes breed
   (ii) how the female carries malaria from person to person
   (iii) why this happens most in hot and wet climates.

c Add the sub-heading, 'Consequences of malaria'. Write about the effects of malaria upon
   (i) people and (ii) the economy of a country.

d Add the sub-heading, 'Preventing malaria and reducing its effects'.
   (i) Describe three ways of reducing the risk of catching malaria.
   (ii) Suggest two reasons why it is difficult to stop people catching malaria.

2 a Why do many people in LEDCs drink water that is not clean? Give as many reasons as you can.

b Why are babies and children more badly affected than adults by drinking water that is not clean?

c Explain why sanitation needs to be installed at the same time as clean drinking water is supplied in homes and villages in LEDCs.

An introduction to world trade

▲ **Figure 1** Hotel resort in the tropics. Tourism is a vital source of foreign exchange for some LEDCs.

ℹ️ Usefulness of trade

1 A country can sell its surplus products.

2 A country can specialize in what it does best.

3 People in a country can eat food or use goods which are not grown or made there.

4 Trade may make a country richer and better developed.

ℹ️ Factors encouraging trade between countries

1 Wealth of a country – rich countries can afford to exchange goods.

2 Highly industrialized countries – they need to import raw materials and energy for the factories. They sell manufactured goods to pay for them.

3 Good transport – needed for easy and cheap movement of goods.

4 Free trade areas (e.g. the EU) – to allow the exchange of goods between countries without any tariffs and quotas.

Trade is the exchange of goods and services between countries.

1 Goods, e.g. raw materials, food and manufactured products, is called visible trade.

2 Services, e.g. money spent by tourists or foreign aid, is called invisible trade.

Pattern of world trade

Many LEDCs export **primary products**:

• Raw materials, e.g. crude oil, iron ore, cotton, from which other products can be made in factories.

• Food, e.g. bananas, coffee and cocoa, from tropical countries.

MEDCs export a greater number and range of **secondary products**. These are manufactured goods, some of which were made from raw materials imported from LEDCs.

Volume of world trade

More than 50 per cent of world trade takes place between the top seven trading nations – USA, Germany, Japan, France, UK, Italy and Canada. These are among the world's richest and most industrialized countries. They have great needs for raw materials and fuels and produce a wide variety of manufactured goods. Goods such as cars are traded across borders between one MEDC and another, because people love to have a choice when buying a new car.

Much less trade takes place between LEDCs. Countries in South America and Africa often grow the same types of crops as their neighbours, so there is little or nothing to exchange. The main transport links by road and rail often lead to ports, not into neighbouring countries, because the tradition is to export crops and minerals to MEDCs.

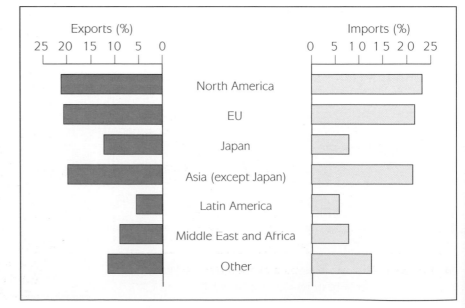

▲ **Figure 2** Shares of the world trade in goods, 1990s.

Figure 2 shows some important features of world trade:

- Rich countries in North America, especially the USA, and countries in free trade areas, such as the EU, dominate world trade.

- Japan is the biggest industrial country in Asia, but it has few natural resources of its own. Trade is vital for importing almost all the raw materials and fossil fuels used by its industries.

- The rest of Asia has been increasing its share of world trade as NICs (newly industrializing countries) such as South Korea, Taiwan and Malaysia have developed (pages 180-181).

- The largest export from some countries in the Middle East and Africa is crude oil.

Trade and economic groupings

By increasing trade, member countries hope to become richer. The aim is to set up a common market, free of tariffs and quotas, so that goods can be exchanged more easily between member countries.

Example 1 EU (European Union)

In 2001 there were 15 member countries (**Figure 3**). Customs controls for goods and people have almost disappeared between these countries. There is a free market in goods. When someone buys a new car in the UK, they often have little idea in which other European countries the parts were made and assembled. Improved cross-border transport links allow free movement of goods. There is the network of 'E' (European) roads, most of them motorways. High speed trains run from France and Belgium into the UK through the Channel Tunnel. More than 90 per cent of the international trade of EU countries is with other EU countries. LEDCs complain that they have limited access into the EU market.

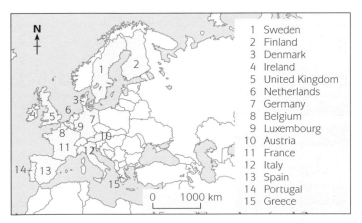

Figure 3 Member countries of the EU in 2001.

1 Sweden
2 Finland
3 Denmark
4 Ireland
5 United Kingdom
6 Netherlands
7 Germany
8 Belgium
9 Luxembourg
10 Austria
11 France
12 Italy
13 Spain
14 Portugal
15 Greece

Example 2 Mercosur

The name stands for 'The Common Market of the South', and refers to South America. By 1995 about 90 per cent of the trade between the four full members (Brazil, Paraguay, Uruguay and Argentina) was free of tariffs (**Figure 4**). Trade has increased with marked increases:

- from Brazil to Argentina of industrial goods

- from Argentina to Brazil of raw materials and farm produce such wheat, apples and wine.

Some of the barriers to movement will take a long time to overcome, such as the lack of good roads and poorly trained, slow customs officials. Problems such as these are only to be expected in the early years.

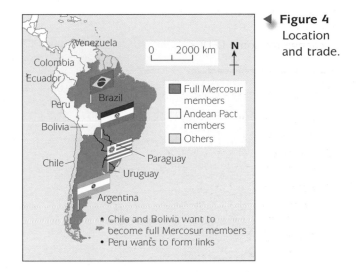

Figure 4 Location and trade.

Full Mercosur members
Andean Pact members
Others

- Chile and Bolivia want to become full Mercosur members
- Peru wants to form links

Activities

1 a What is meant by trade?
  b State the main differences between
    (i) visible and invisible trade
    (ii) primary and secondary products.

2 a List four factors which encourage trade between countries.
  b Give two reasons why a lot of trade goes on between EU countries.
  c What does **Figure 2** show about the EU's share of world trade?

3 a On a large outline map of Europe,
    (i) shade in and name the 15 member countries of the EU
    (ii) using an atlas, mark and name their capital cities.
  b (i) Where in Europe are most of the countries not in the EU located?
    (ii) Suggest two reasons why some of these other European countries want to join the EU.

Causes of the lack of development – the pattern of world trade

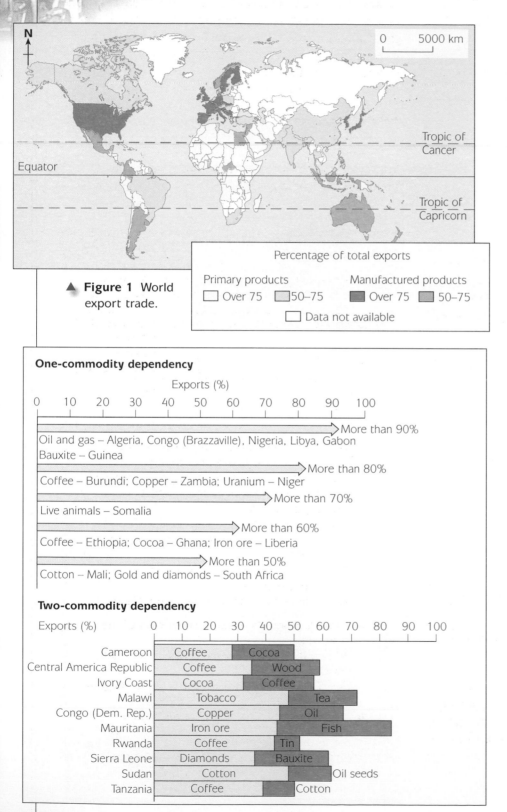

▲ **Figure 1** World export trade.

Percentage of total exports

Primary products
□ Over 75 ☐ 50–75

Manufactured products
■ Over 75 ▨ 50–75

□ Data not available

One-commodity dependency

Exports (%)

0 10 20 30 40 50 60 70 80 90 100

More than 90%
Oil and gas – Algeria, Congo (Brazzaville), Nigeria, Libya, Gabon
Bauxite – Guinea

More than 80%
Coffee – Burundi; Copper – Zambia; Uranium – Niger

More than 70%
Live animals – Somalia

More than 60%
Coffee – Ethiopia; Cocoa – Ghana; Iron ore – Liberia

More than 50%
Cotton – Mali; Gold and diamonds – South Africa

Two-commodity dependency

Exports (%) 0 10 20 30 40 50 60 70 80 90 100

Cameroon	Coffee	Cocoa
Central America Republic	Coffee	Wood
Ivory Coast	Cocoa	Coffee
Malawi	Tobacco	Tea
Congo (Dem. Rep.)	Copper	Oil
Mauritania	Iron ore	Fish
Rwanda	Coffee	Tin
Sierra Leone	Diamonds	Bauxite
Sudan	Cotton	Oil seeds
Tanzania	Coffee	Cotton

MEDCs need the raw materials and energy supplies found in LEDCs to keep their factories working, e.g. the world's largest reserves of oil are in the Middle East. Look at **Figure 1**. Yellow and green are the main colours for the LEDCs in Africa, Asia and South America. This shows there is a large export of primary products (minerals and crops). Without these, MEDCs could not have industrialized and developed their high standards of living.

LEDCs need manufactured goods from MEDCs, because they cannot make some of them, such as cars and computers. They also need to import machinery, technology and know-how so that they can start their own industries and develop economically. Look again at **Figure 1**. Red on the map shows that the USA, the EU and Japan rely most upon exports of manufactured goods.

Both MEDCs and LEDCs should benefit equally from this pattern of trade. Both are obtaining things that they need that they cannot produce for themselves. Since each is offering what the other one wants, MEDCs and LEDCs clearly depend on each other. There is **interdependence** between them.

One problem for LEDCs is that they depend on the export of a small number of different commodities (**Figure 2**). In Africa, for example, there are at least twenty-five countries that depend upon just one or two commodities for their export earnings. When prices are high, this is not a problem, but they suffer badly when commodity prices fall.

◀ **Figure 2** Dependence upon a limited range of exports by countries of Africa.

The pattern of world trade favours MEDCs

There are two problems for LEDCs relying upon the export of primary products:

1 Primary products fetch low prices. Look at **Figure 3**. Only 12 per cent of the price you pay for bananas in the supermarket goes to the farmer and his workers in an LEDC.

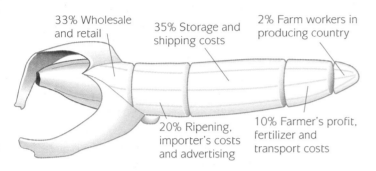

33% Wholesale and retail

35% Storage and shipping costs

2% Farm workers in producing country

20% Ripening, importer's costs and advertising

10% Farmer's profit, fertilizer and transport costs

▲ **Figure 3** Rich pickings – but for whom?

2 The prices of primary products go up and down. The mine owner or farmer has no control over prices. They are fixed by the markets in big financial centres such as New York and London. When demand is low, prices fall. Crude oil is always needed, but even its price fluctuates wildly (**Figure 1** page 190). The world price of oil today is lower than it was in the 1970s. This is bad news for the six African countries, for which oil and gas makes up more than 90 per cent of exports (**Figure 2**). The drop in gold prices in November 1997 (**Figure 4**) was not good news for South Africa, the world's largest producer.

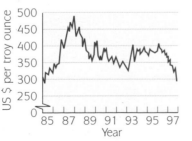

Gold price below $300 for first time in 12 years

US $ per troy ounce — 85 87 89 91 93 95 97 Year

▲ **Figure 4** Gold price information from *The Financial Times*, 27 November 1997.

Therefore, it is risky for LEDCs to depend upon the export of just one or two commodities. Unfortunately, it is the normal situation for many of them, especially in Africa (**Figure 2**), but it is not easy for countries to find alternative commodities to export.

There is another problem for LEDCs when importing manufactured goods. This is because they are more expensive to buy than raw materials. As raw materials are processed, value is added at each stage. When you buy a bar of chocolate, how much of the price is for the cocoa beans from which the chocolate was made? Judging by the banana example above, the answer is about 10 per cent of the bar's price. The prices of manufactured goods tend to move only in one direction – upwards. LEDCs need to export twice as much as they did ten years ago to import the same number of manufactured goods.

Conclusion

The pattern of world trade means that LEDCs export mainly primary products, which are low in price. Imports from MEDCs are high in price. As a result, many LEDCs have big debts.

Activities

1 a Write out the commodities named in **Figure 2** and complete a table like the one started below.

Commodity	Mineral	Crop	Other	Number of African countries exporting it
Oil and gas	✓			6
Bauxite	✓			2

b All these commodities are primary products. What else do they have in common?

c Write about two problems that a country has if it needs to make money from exporting primary products.

d Look at **Figure 1**.
   (i) From where are most primary products exported?
   (ii) From where are most manufactured products exported?
   (iii) Give one reason why they are different.

2 a Draw labelled sketches to show each of the following:
   (i) farmers who grow the crops do not make much money
   (ii) the prices paid for exporting minerals goes up and down.

b Explain why LEDCs stay poor as a result of both of these.

Can poor countries develop economically?

The prospects for most countries are not good. The cartoon below gives one view of development (**Figure 1**).

▲ **Figure 1** Does interdependence between rich and poor countries exist?

In the cartoon:

- MEDCs are milking LEDCs of their foodstuffs and raw materials.
- MEDCs have a strangle-hold over factory owners in LEDCs
- Rich MEDCs become richer while poor LEDCs get poorer.

This suggests that true interdependence (one depending upon the other and having equal benefits) between MEDCs and LEDCs does not exist.

The pattern of world trade, with LEDCs exporting raw materials to be used in industries in Europe, is well established. The reason why the UK set up colonies after the Industrial Revolution was to obtain supplies of raw materials for its growing industries and food for its growing population.

It takes a long time to change established patterns of trade. Caribbean farmers mainly export their bananas to Britain and France, because they were the old colonial countries. A banana boat ready to sail to Europe can be seen in **Figure 2**. Many African countries have been independent for less than 50 years (**Figure 3**) and have not had enough time to find new markets.

Which LEDCs are developing economically?

Two types of country are making better progress than others:

1 Large countries with high totals of population, e.g. Brazil and Mexico.

2 Smaller countries in south-east Asia, e.g. Singapore and Malaysia.

Look at **Figure 4**. It shows how exports from Malaysia changed over 25 years with economic development. The percentage of primary exports (mainly rubber and tin) went down while that of manufactured goods increased greatly. Malaysia is one of the NICs (newly industrializing countries). The photograph on page 209 was taken in Kuala Lumpur, its capital city. It is a middle-income country. Too many people have private forms of transport for it to be a low-income country. In high-income countries motorbikes are replaced with cars as soon as people can afford them.

NICs such as Malaysia are exceptions among LEDCs; many LEDCs need aid as **Figure 5** shows. This is because their debts have increased. Raw material prices have fallen. In some countries the debt is greater than the value of the country's exports in a full year.

◀ **Figure 2** Caribbean farmers carrying bananas to port.

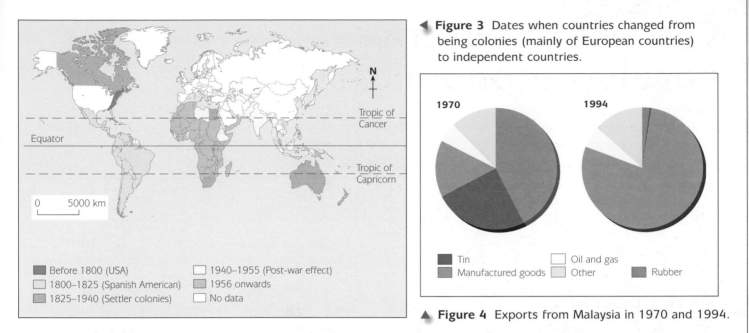

◀ **Figure 3** Dates when countries changed from being colonies (mainly of European countries) to independent countries.

1970   **1994**

Legend:
- Tin
- Manufactured goods
- Oil and gas
- Other
- Rubber

▲ **Figure 4** Exports from Malaysia in 1970 and 1994.

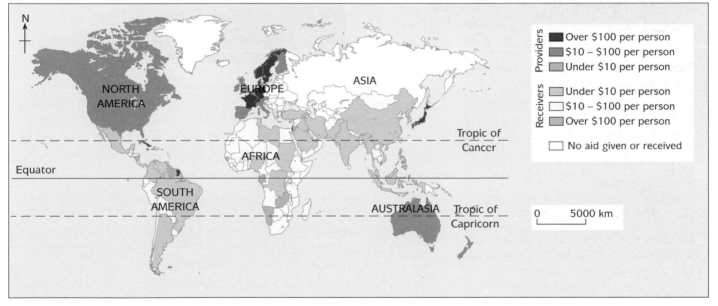

Map legend:

Providers
- Over $100 per person
- $10 – $100 per person
- Under $10 per person

Receivers
- Under $10 per person
- $10 – $100 per person
- Over $100 per person

- No aid given or received

▲ **Figure 5** World distribution of aid.

Activities

1 Look at **Figure 4**.
 a Make two columns for 1970 and 1994. List the exports of Malaysia in order of size from 1 (the largest percentage) to 5 (the smallest) for both dates.
 b How do the changes between 1970 and 1994 show that
 (i) primary industries have declined in importance
 (ii) secondary industries have increased in importance?

2 Look at the photograph on page 209, which was taken in the centre of Kuala Lumpur, the capital of Malaysia.
 a Describe what it shows.
 b State differences between what you can see there and what you would expect to see in the centre of a big city in the UK.

3 Look at the world map in **Figure 5**.
 a Name two continents where countries that provide aid are located.
 b Describe where the countries that receive most aid are found.
 c State two reasons why many LEDCs need aid.

Aid

Aid is a transfer of money, goods and knowledge. Sometimes aid is given as a free gift, but not always. Strings can be attached to the goods supplied and to the help given.

Types of aid

Bilateral aid

Bilateral means 'two sided' – this is aid from one government to another. This is usually tied aid because the country receiving aid has to use the money to buy goods from the country giving aid.

The problem is that what governments give may not be what people receiving the aid need most. For example, large scale projects such as dams and power stations do not always help the majority of people, although they can be of great benefit to a country's economy.

Multilateral aid

Multilateral means 'many sided'. Instead of deciding themselves how the money is to be spent, governments hand it over to international agencies, who decide how the money is spent. Some agencies are run by the United Nations, e.g.

*   WHO is the World Health Organization
*   UNICEF helps children
*   UNESCO looks after education
*   WORLD BANK funds new development projects.

These pay more attention to what is needed than do governments, but they are large organizations. This makes them slow to change and to target the real needs of people in poor countries.

Aid from non-governmental organizations (NGOs)

These are mainly charities. Most are based in MEDCs. Money is raised through voluntary donations and charity shops. They also receive grants from governments, some of which now realize that the NGOs are better at running small community projects. These are more likely to reach the poorest people in greatest need. Oxfam and Christian Aid are examples of NGOs that work in many different countries (**Figure 2**).

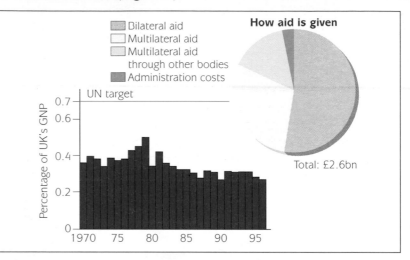

▲ **Figure 1** Aid from the UK. The United Nations' target is for 0.7 per cent of a rich country's GNP to be spent on aid, a target few countries reach.

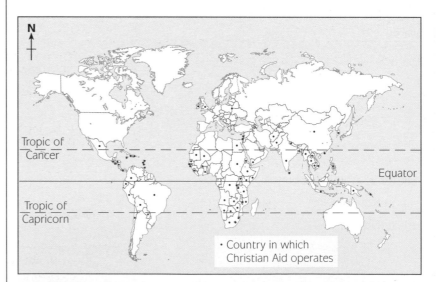

▲ **Figure 2** Christian Aid's global aid programme:
About 50 per cent of its funds are used for long-term projects:
*   agricultural support
*   primary health care
*   clean water projects.
Another 35 per cent are used for emergencies after
*   wars
*   famine
*   other natural disasters.

Short-term (relief) aid

This is used to deal with emergencies. It is a lifeline to people affected by natural disasters such as drought, flood or earthquake. Also people may need help after a human disaster such as a war.

Survivors urgently need food, medical help, clothing, blankets and tents, which are often flown in to the areas affected. These are supplied only for as long as the emergency exists, which is why it is called short-term aid. It gives relief to human suffering,

▶ **Figure 3** Short-term emergency aid in Shindhapalkchock district, Nepal.

which is why it is also known as relief aid. However, a lot of money is spent without any long-term benefits for the people.

Long-term (development) aid

Its purpose is to increase a country's level of development for the future. Much of the work is to improve standards of living and quality of life. Aid agencies of the United Nations carry out a lot of this type of work.

For example – improved health care:

- Immunization programmes against TB (tuberculosis), polio and measles
- Family planning clinics
- Clean water supplies and sanitation facilities.

Long-term aid is most successful when an NGO asks people what they really need. Then it gives them practical help. The aim is to make changes that are sustainable, i.e. the local community will become more self-sufficient, so that after a while it will need no more aid.

For example – help to subsistence farmers:

- Giving advice and support
- Providing good quality seeds suitable for local conditions
- Digging ponds and irrigation systems using low level technology
- Setting up community projects for providing loans for tools and seeds.

This is the best type of aid provided that the schemes are small and can easily be used by the local people. Providing hand-pumps in Bangladesh (**Figure 4**) is a good example.

◀ **Figure 4** A Bangladeshi woman draws safe, clean water from the village hand-pump while another washes clothes. The water pumps are an example of practical long-term aid, which are useful and appropriate to the local community.

Activities

1 Make a full-page version of the table below.
Fill as many of the boxes as you can.

Type of aid	Main features	Advantages	Disadvantages
A Bilateral B Multilateral C NGOs D Short-term E Long-term			

2 Put a title, 'Case study of an aid organization'.
Use Christian Aid (or find out about the work of another organization such as Oxfam or Save the Children Fund).
Write about:
   a How it raises money.
   b Where in the world it works.
   c How it spends its money **(i)** for short-term emergencies and **(ii)** for long-term development projects.

3 a Why do charities prefer to spend aid money on long-term instead of short-term projects?
   b A water pump worked by a diesel engine would not have been as useful to the people in the village. Suggest two reasons why hand-pumps are better than diesel pumps for villagers in Bangladesh.

Ethiopia in the 1980s and 1990s

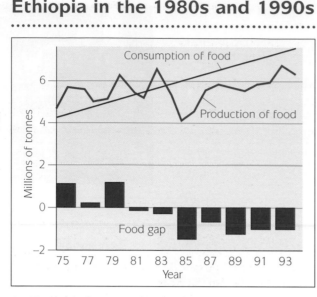

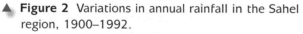

▲ **Figure 1** Food production and consumption trends in Ethiopia.

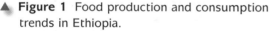

▲ **Figure 2** Variations in annual rainfall in the Sahel region, 1900–1992.

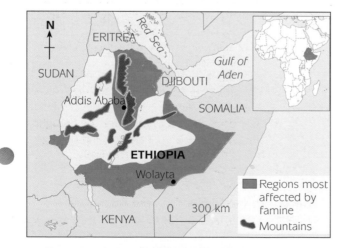

▲ **Figure 3** Areas of Ethiopia in which people were most badly affected by famine in 1984.

The 1980s – the need for relief aid

Figure 1 shows that the last year in which Ethiopia was able to feed itself was 1982. In that year production of food (the red line) was greater than consumption (the black line). The famine was at its greatest in 1984–85, when the food gap was at its widest.

The natural cause of the famine was drought. Look at **Figure 2**. After years of lower than average annual rainfall in the 1970s, the rains failed in 1983–84.

Human factors worsened the effects of the drought on people. There was a civil war and the military government was spending one third of Ethiopia's budget on the armed forces. Although there were food surpluses in some parts of the country, the food could not be moved to where it was needed because of the war.

About 500 000 people died in 1984. People living towards the borders of the country in the north and south were most badly affected (**Figure 3**).

Nearly £15 million was raised in 1984 in Britain alone by the UK Disasters Emergency Committee consisting of Christian Aid, Oxfam, Save the Children and Cafod. Nearly all the relief aid was food aid. Some food aid was plundered by the government for its troops, but most reached the affected areas. From 1984 to 1992 the Ethiopian Famine Relief Fund, consisting of Band Aid and Live Aid, raised £110 million. Ethiopia received a massive amount of short-term aid in the 1980s.

The 1990s – continued need for relief aid

The problem of drought has not gone away. Birth rates are high and there were two million extra mouths to feed in 1994 compared with 1984. Half the population still live in poverty. There are severe food shortages in some areas and many people suffer if the rains fail.

For example, drought affected Wolayta in southern Ethiopia (named in **Figure 3**) in 1994 and about 5000 people died. People's own food stores were quickly used up. Poor road links limited the speed with which the aid agencies could react to the emergency.

Another example is Wollo. Look at **Figure 4**. Villagers can just about exist without food aid in a year of normal rains; food aid is only 5 per cent of their needs. In a drought year many would die without food aid, which increases to 50 per cent of their needs. By cutting down more firewood, soil erosion and environmental damage increase.

Case Study – Aid to Ethiopia

Switching towards development aid

NGOs are setting long-term targets to increase the amount of food produced in a sustainable way. The Catholic agency Cafod, a British NGO, is working with local partners to improve farming. Cafod gives practical help such as:

- supplying high quality seeds which mature even if the rains are poor
- planting drought-resistant trees
- digging ponds and wells
- providing loans for tools
- marketing the surplus produce.

Better drought-resistant varieties of seeds and improved irrigation are giving the local people more security for the future.

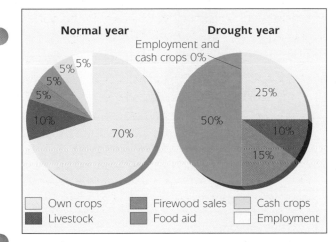

▲ **Figure 4** How people survive in Wollo, southern Ethiopia.

Comments about aid dependency

Food-aid is expensive. People can become dependent upon food handouts and lose the will to produce their own food. Therefore NGOs feel that funds can be better used trying to prevent the problem happening again. This is why they like long-term aid, to try to achieve development that is sustainable for the local people.

Some feel that food should not be handed out free in Ethiopia, but given as a wage. In a typical drought year in Ethiopia one million tonnes of food aid is given out.

It has been estimated that this could pay for the labour for:

- 167 000km of new roads, or
- 2700 earth dams, or
- over 400 000km of irrigation channels.

Each of these would bring long-term benefits and make local communities less likely to suffer in future droughts.

Activities

1 Write a title, 'Aid in Ethiopia'.
  a Add a sub-heading, 'Aid in the 1980s'.
    (i) Name the type(s) of aid received.
    (ii) State the natural causes of the famine.
    (iii) Describe how human factors made the famine worse.
    (iv) Give the year in which the famine was worst.
    (v) Look at **Figures 1** and **2**. Why was the famine worst in that year?
    (vi) How many people died?
    (vii) Where in the country was aid most needed?
    (viii) State one advantage and one disadvantage of giving food aid.
  b Add a second sub-heading, 'Aid in the 1990s'.
    (i) Name the type(s) of aid received.
    (ii) Why was aid still needed?
    (iii) What is an NGO? Look at page 226.
    (iv) How are NGOs, such as Cafod, trying to reduce Ethiopia's need for aid in the future?

2 Look at **Figure 4**.
  a Make two lists, side by side, one for a normal year and the other for a drought year. Show sources of income for both years, working from highest to lowest.
  b Draw a divided bar graph to show how people in Wollo survive in a drought year.
  c Why do you think that income from crops falls more than income from livestock in a drought year?
  d How does the information for the drought year suggest that soil erosion and damage to the environment are more likely?
  e Life is hard for villagers in Wollo in normal years as well as drought years. Write about this as fully as you can.

Country on a delta

	Bangladesh	UK (for comparison)
GNP per head (US$)	220	17 970
Birth rate (per 1000)	36	12
Death rate (per 1000)	12	11
Infant mortality rate (per 1000 live births)	108	7
Life expectancy	55	76

▲ **Figure 1** Development indicators.

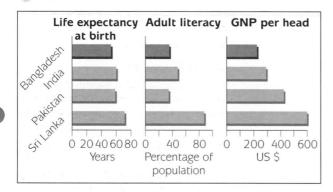

▲ **Figure 2** Level of development compared with other countries in South Asia.

Bangladesh is one of the world's most densely populated countries with almost 800 people per square kilometre. Its 120 million people are crowded onto the delta formed by the Ganges and Brahmaputra rivers. It is also one of the world's poorest countries. Bangladeshis have to live with natural disasters – floods and cyclones (tropical storms). Overseas aid is a vital source of income to the country. Now, more of the aid is being used in local community projects in the villages, in which almost 80 per cent of the country's population still live.

	US$ (millions)
Value of goods exported • garments (clothes) 52% • fresh fish (shrimps) 14% • jute 10% • leather 8%	2600
Value of goods imported	4300
Other sources of income: • money from Bangladeshis working overseas • aid money	944 1675

▲ **Figure 3** Bangladesh's trade in the mid-1990s.

Physical features

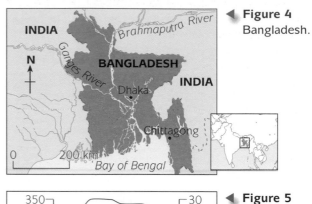

◀ **Figure 4** Bangladesh.

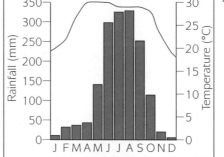

◀ **Figure 5** Climate of Dhaka.

Advantages	Disadvantages
• Hot climate allows all-year crop growth. • There is plenty of water from monsoon rains and large rivers. • Great thicknesses of fertile silt soils. • River floods renew the silt every year. • The wet delta is ideal for the two main crops – rice for food and jute for export. • Farmers regard normal flooding as beneficial for soils and crops. • Fisheries along the rivers are another natural resource.	• Cyclones bring hurricane-force winds and storm surges which cause coastal flooding. • Heavy monsoon rains cause river floods. • Flat and low-lying land (most below 10m) means that almost all the country has a flood risk. • Cyclones (e.g. 1991) and floods (e.g. 1994) have destroyed crops, killed thousands and left millions homeless. • Drinking water supplies are contaminated and outbreaks of typhoid and cholera occur.

Aid from overseas

Most of this is bilateral or multilateral (page 226). Another name for it would be 'project' aid. It is used for building power stations, bridges and roads. There are three main disadvantages of this type of aid:

1 The majority of people, who are poor and rural, feel little benefit.

2 The aid is given as loans that have to be paid back.

3 Not all the money is spent on the projects because of corruption.

NGOs want more of the money to be spent on working in the villages. Staff from NGOs meet the village community and ask for their views. Such surveys reveal the need for:

- better health care
- education for the children
- local job opportunities for the people without land
- better credit facilities from local banks
- flood protection.

Only after talking to villagers do NGO staff prepare an action plan.

A community-based NGO with Oxfam support – Manab Mukti

The community of Manab Mukti has about 5000 households. It is on a low-lying island in the Brahmaputra river. To help them cope with the regular river flooding, they were trained in disaster preparation. They were helped to

- raise their homesteads above regular flood levels
- make platforms on which to keep their livestock
- build toilet blocks
- raise the tubewells above flood levels to ensure supplies of clean drinking water during floods
- make two community shelters for times of great flood.

Measures were also taken to help community development. Training was given to farmers. A credit scheme was set up so that families could borrow money for agricultural purposes, e.g. new seeds for growing crops that withstand floods better.

Although the people remain poor, Manab Mukti is now a healthier, happier and more prosperous community. This example shows how a small investment of funds in the right place at the right time can have a great effect on people's lives.

Activities

1 Physical features and human settlement
  a Describe the main features of the climate of Dhaka (see page 77 for what to do).
  b Draw a sketch map using **Figure 4** to show that Bangladesh lies on a delta.
  c Write about **(i)** two advantages and **(ii)** two disadvantages of living in a delta region.

2 Natural disasters. Flooding is one natural disaster that affects Bangladesh.
  a Explain why flooding occurs in Bangladesh.
  b Describe some of the damage caused by flooding.
  c In what ways are NGOs helping people to prepare for flooding?

3 Trade (Look at **Figure 3**.)
  a **(i)** Draw two bar graphs to show the value of goods exported and imported.
  (ii) How many millions of dollars was the trade gap between exports and imports?
  (iii) Draw a pie graph to show the types of goods exported.
  (iv) When exports are added to other sources of income, what is the total amount of income for Bangladesh?
  (v) Explain why the money from the other sources of income is so important.
  b Some LEDCs earn income from tourism, but Bangladesh is not one of them. Suggest reasons why few tourists visit.

4 Development (Look at **Figures 1** and **2**.)
  a Draw a vertical bar graph to show life expectancy in Bangladesh compared with the other four countries in **Figures 1** and **2**.
  b Describe the economic evidence which shows that Bangladesh is one of the world's poorest countries.
  c Choose one other development indicator and explain how it shows that Bangladesh is a poor country.

5 Aid
  a Give three reasons why aid is important to Bangladesh.
  b **(i)** For what is bilateral and multilateral aid used?
  (ii) State and explain two disadvantages of bilateral aid.
  c **(i)** Describe how NGOs operate in Bangladesh to make sure that they give the type of aid local people need.
  (ii) For one village, give details of how the lives of villagers have been improved by aid.

Chapter 14

Examination technique

The questions

Every Geography GCSE examination question has at least two parts:

1 Command words – what the question is telling you to do.

2 Question theme – what the question is about.

Some have a third part.

3 Where in the world – e.g. in the UK or in a LEDC.

Example of a two part question:

Name two volcanoes.

command words   question theme

Example of a three part question:

State two problems in inner-city areas of cities in MEDCs.

command words   question theme

Command words

A Short and simple

- Name
- State
- Give
- List

These are simple and clear command words, often used at the start of questions.

Questions:

Name one country in which... or Give two ways that...

B Definition commands

- Define the term...
- What is meant by...?
- Give the meaning of...

These command words are asking for definitions. It is important that you look at the number of marks.

For questions worth only one mark, only a brief definition is needed. For questions worth two or more marks, a longer definition is needed. Sometimes it helps to give an example as well.

Question

What is meant by intensive farming?   (3 marks)

Answer from Candidate 1: Getting a lot from the land. A lot is grown and sold by the farmer.

Examiner comment:

- The candidate has only attempted to make two points, yet there are three marks for the answer. The most marks the candidate could possibly be given is two.

- In fact, this answer is only worth one mark, because the two statements are both making the same point, about growing a lot from the land.

Answer from Candidate 2: Intensive means producing as much as possible from the land. To gain a high output from the land, large inputs are needed and the land is carefully farmed so that the farmer produces as much as he can.

Examiner comment:

- This candidate also begins by making the same point twice, for which there is just one mark.

- Then the answer is developed and the candidate makes two other valid points.

- There is now enough for the candidate to be given all three marks.

The lesson to be learnt from this is – always answer as fully as you can. In fact it is better to try to make four points for a question worth three marks, because one of the points you make may not be considered to be worth a mark by the examiner.

C Describe command

- Describe the features of a delta.
- Describe what **Figure 1** shows. (**Figure 1** may be a graph, diagram, map or photograph.)

Describe is one of the most commonly used command words in Geography examinations. You need to write about what there is on a photograph and its appearance, or about what is shown on a graph. You are not being asked to explain. Once again look at the number of marks for the question as a guide to the amount of detail expected.

In physical geography, if the question asks you to describe a landform (e.g. volcano, limestone pavement, waterfall, sea cliff, or corrie), you are being asked to write about what it looks like.

- Write about its shape, size and what it is made of.
- Be generous with your use of adjectives such as wide/narrow, steep/gentle/flat, straight/curved, etc.

Question

Describe the physical features of the landform in the photograph.

Possible answer:

- Name the landform first: *volcano (or even composite volcano)*
- Describe its shape: *cone- shaped*
- Describe other features: *lava flows on its sides*
- Give a more detailed description: *steep slopes on the snow-covered top of the cone; slightly more gentle slopes lower down; bare rock (lava) on the lower slopes*

D Explain command

- Explain the formation of ...
- Give two reasons for ...
- Explain why ...
- Why does ...?

To answer these questions you need to use your knowledge and understanding. Write the answers in as much detail as you can. Try to use information that is precise. When two reasons are asked for, try to make sure that the reasons are different and not the same one stated in a different way.

Question

Why are there great increases in population in LEDCs?

(4 marks)

Answer: *Because birth rates are high and death rates are low.*

Examiner comment:

- This is only the basic answer, it starts to answer the question, but it is not developed.
- It is worth only one of the four marks.
- To gain more marks, the candidate needed to explain why birth rates are high (e.g. because of lack of birth control, many children are useful to parents in their old age etc.)
- The candidate could also have explained why death rates are low (e.g. because of improvements in medicine).

Question

Explain the formation of spits along some coasts.   (5 marks)

Answer: *A spit forms after the longshore drift moves sand along the coast. I have drawn a diagram below to show how it does this.*

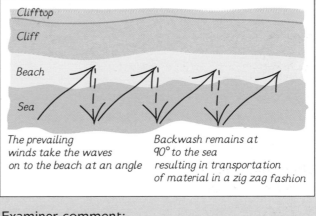

Examiner comment:

- All that is written is correct and the longshore drift contributes to the formation of a spit.
- Although the question did not ask for a diagram, relevant points made on the diagram can be given marks.
- However, the answer can be given only two of the four marks, because only part of a full explanation for the formation of a spit is given here.
- There is nothing in the answer that explains why the spit forms after the longshore drift has transported sand along the coast.

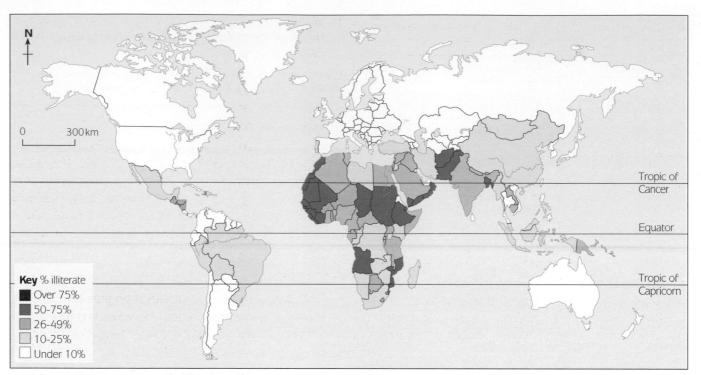

▲ **Figure 1** Percentage of total population unable to read or write.

Questions based on source materials

The main sources used in Geography examinations are:

- maps
- graphs
- diagrams
- photographs
- tables of data
- cartoons.

Most source-based examination questions begin with a series of short questions. You can find the answers by looking carefully at the source materials. A longer question often follows, for which you need more knowledge and understanding.

Questions:

Study the world map (**Figure 1**) which shows the percentage of total population unable to read and write.

a   Name one area of the world with a low rate of illiteracy (under 10 per cent).   (1 mark)

How to approach answering:

- Look at the key for under 10%.
- Name an area (rather than a country) shown in light yellow on the map.
- Answers that would gain the mark include Europe or North America or Australasia.

b   Describe where countries with high rates of illiteracy (above 50 per cent) are located.   (3 marks)

How to approach answering:

- Take note of the command word, which is 'Describe'. This is telling you that the map will show you where the countries are located.
- Look at the key for over 50 per cent; this means that areas shaded in both dark orange and red are to be used for the answer.
- Now look to see where the countries are located.

Answers that would gain marks include the following:

(i)   Most in Africa.

(ii) Almost all of the countries of Africa, except for a few countries in the centre and south, are above 50 per cent.

(iii) A band of countries of very high rates over 70 per cent is found north of the Equator in Africa.

(iv) High rates extend into the Middle East and South Asia.

Any three of the above four descriptions would gain the marks.

c   Explain why rates of illiteracy are high in some countries of the world.   (4 marks)

Some examples of answers that would gain marks are given on the next page.

One mark answer	To make a two mark answer you need to add
• Lack of schools	especially outside cities and large towns.
• Children work on the farms	instead of going to school because their families are poor.
• Few children go to secondary schools	because these schools are too far away from where they live.
• LEDCs are poor countries	and governments cannot afford to build schools everywhere.
• Girls are kept at home	and they are not given the same chance as boys.

Giving short answers such as 'lack of schools' and 'poor countries' would mean that you need to find four different reasons for full marks. If you explain each of your answers more fully, two reasons would be enough.

Using case studies

Sometimes the question wording makes it clear that you are expected to use your case study information.

- With reference to an example you have studied…
- Illustrate your answer by reference to an example.
- For one industrial area in…

In these questions you have little chance of gaining more then half marks, unless you include some case study information in your answer. Look at these examination answers from two candidates.

Question:

For one named area with many footloose industries, give the reasons why these industries have grown in this area.

(5 marks)

Answer from Candidate 1: There are many footloose industries along the sides of the M4 between London and Bristol. One area is on the industrial estate next to the M4 in Reading where there are food processing and high-tech industries. High-tech industries need skilled workers and there is a university nearby in Reading. Rail and road links are very good. I have already said that the footloose industries are along the sides of the M4 motorway, which goes to London. London is the biggest city in England. The M4 goes past Heathrow airport for markets overseas.

Examiner comment:

- This candidate begins well by naming an area of footloose industries.
- The points made in the rest of the answer refer to this area, which is good.

- Some information that is precise is included, such as skilled workers coming from Oxford University, which makes this the best type of answer.
- The answer is worth all 5 marks, because all the information used refers to the case study of the named area of footloose industries. There is enough information for five marks.

Answer from Candidate 2: Lots of workers are needed in footloose industries. There are good roads. The railway lines are also good. There are some high-tech industries. These are making lots of money because everyone is now buying computers. High-tech industries are footloose industries. There are lots of these near London near the M4 because of good markets.

Examiner comment:

- Only at the end of the answer is an area for footloose industries named. However, it is just 'tagged on' without any precise information being related to it.
- Most of the answer is vague with 'good' and 'lots' being used too many times. They could apply to the location of any industry, in any place.
- Although the nature of footloose industries is mentioned, this is not relevant in a question about reasons for their growth.
- Therefore it is a weak answer to the question, worth at most two marks.

From these two examples, notice how specific information about an area greatly improves the quality of an answer. A good way to revise your case studies is to make short lists of key facts about them. One example is given in the Information Box.

---

i Key facts

Area of footloose industries along the M4
Types of industries:
- Light e.g. food processing and electrical goods
- High-tech e.g. computers

Reasons for growth:
1. Transport – motorways e.g. M4
   – railways e.g. high speed line London to Bristol
   – airports e.g. Heathrow
2. Market – near the largest, London
   – EU via Channel Tunnel
   – overseas via Heathrow
3. Skilled labour – from universities e.g. Bristol
4. Pleasant countryside nearby – e.g. in the Cotswolds

Activity

Answers that have gone wrong

What is wrong with these answers?

Write down:

a   what is wrong

b   what the correct answer should be.

Check your answers with those at the bottom of the page. Do not cheat by looking at the answers first. That is not going to help you do well in the GCSE examination.

1   Name a country which has suffered from drought and been given much food aid.   (1 mark)

Answer: Africa.

2   With reference to an area you have studied in an LEDC, explain the disadvantages caused by tourism.   (4 marks)

Answer: I am going to use Costa del Sol in southern Spain. A line of villas owned by rich Europeans stretches 50 kilometres along the coastline. This has made rich what was once one of the poorest areas in Europe. There are many jobs in service industries and young people are attracted from all parts of Spain by the prospects of jobs.

3   a   Measure the distance along the railway line between stations A and B.   (1 mark)

Answer: 2.5

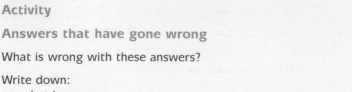

▲ **Figure 1**

b   In what direction would you be travelling if you took the train from station B to station A?   (1 mark)

Answer: Eastwards

4   Study the photograph below, which shows part of the coastline of north-east England. Describe the coastal features shown.   (4 marks)

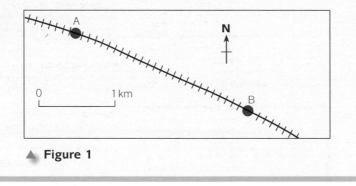

▲ **Figure 2**

Answer: The main features of this coastal area allow us to see where the sea crashes against these rocks. It also allows us to see that the rocks have been severely beaten by the sea in one particular place. Abrasion is one way in which the sea batters rocks. The rocks have obviously been eroded away in one place on the photo.

Answers to what has gone wrong

1   Africa is not a country. It is a continent. Ethiopia, a country in Africa, would have been a correct answer.

2   There are two reasons why this answer could not be given any marks.
   • Spain is an MEDC not an LEDC.
   • The question asks for disadvantages, but the candidate is talking about the advantages of tourism.
   In other words, the candidate did not answer the question set.

3   a   2.5 is the correct number, but 2.5 what? The answer needed is 2.5km to be given the mark. Units must always be stated, otherwise the answer means nothing.

   b   The answer given is for travelling from station A to station B, i.e. the answer is the opposite to the correct answer. Even then a more accurate answer would have been SE rather than E. The correct answer, starting from station B, is NW.

4   The candidate is trying to explain what can be seen on the photograph. However, the command word in the question is Describe. There are no marks for explaining. Instead the candidate should have described what can be seen, such as * two stacks * steep cliffs * caves at the bottom * a beach of stones around them.

Glossary

Contemporary issues new and live issues affecting people around the world, such as recent natural disasters; greenfield versus brownfield sites; or a foot and mouth disease outbreak

Global citizenship to be responsible for ensuring that our individual actions take account of the consequences, not just for ourselves but for the world as a whole, e.g. by reducing air pollution we reduce the risks of acid rain and possible global warming, which would have consequences around the world

Globalization increasing way in which all countries are affected by decisions made in other countries

Political issues those to do with government, for the local level up to national and international levels

Social and economic issues those that affect people and finances; they are often grouped together as socio-economic issues, e.g. unemployment, quality of life

Sustainable development new developments that ensure there will be at least the same amount of resources in the future as there are today – that is, development does not damage the environment or use up resources in a permanent way; examples include green tourism, renewable energy, tree planting, using brownfield rather than greenfield sites in cities

Values and attitudes the ways in which different groups of people and individuals respond to circumstances or events

Chapter 1

Anticline an upfold, like an arch

Basic lava thin 'runny' lava, low silica content, flows long distances

Composite volcano volcano with alternate layers of lava and ash

Compressional plate boundary (margin) where two plates are moving together (destructive)

Convection current change in the flow and pressure of the Earth's mantle affecting plate movement

Core the centre of the Earth

Crust the thin layer at the Earth's surface

Epicentre point on the Earth's surface directly above the focus

Focus point within the Earth's crust where an earthquake occurs

Geosyncline a depression between two plates

Landslide rapid movement of rocks and soil under the influence of gravity

Lava name given to molten magma when it erupts at the surface

Magma molten rock from deep within the Earth

Mantle molten rock surrounding the Earth's core

Passive plate boundary (margin) where two plates are moving alongside each other in the same direction but at different rates (conservative)

Plate section of the Earth's crust

Primary effects (of an earthquake) direct effects of an earthquake, e.g. buildings collapse

Richter scale measure of the strength (intensity) of an earthquake

Secondary effects (of an earthquake) indirect effects, e.g. fire, tsunami, disease

Sedimentary rock formed from sediments laid down under water

Seismograph measures and records the intensity of an earthquake

Shield volcano large volcano formed from basic lava spread over a large area

Subduction zone where a plate is sinking and melting

Syncline a downfold

Tensional plate boundary (margin) where two plates are moving apart (constructive)

Tsunami huge 'tidal wave' caused by a submarine earthquake

Vent opening through which lava flows from a volcano

Chapter 2

Aquifer underground store of water in permeable or porous rocks

Cavern underground chamber in limestone, larger than a cave

Chalk escarpment landform with both a steep scarp slope and a gentle dip slope

Chemical weathering break-up of rock by processes such as solution by causing changes in the minerals that form the rock

Clay vale large area of low land (larger than a valley) which tends to be wet because of the impermeable clay

Clint flat-surfaced block of rock in a limestone pavement

Dip slope the gentle slope on a chalk escarpment

Dry valley V-shaped valley without any stream flowing in the bottom

Freeze–thaw break-up of rocks by alternate freezing and thawing of water trapped in joints in the rock

Gorge steep-sided rocky valley with a stream flowing in the bottom

Gryke vertical gap between blocks of rock in a limestone pavement

Igneous rock rock that began as magma in the interior of the Earth

Karst scenery area in which several typical Carboniferous limestone landforms are found

Limestone pavement level surface of bare rock broken up into separate blocks

Limestone solution process of chemical weathering that dissolves limestone rock

Metamorphic rock rock whose shape or form has been changed by heat and/or pressure

Physical weathering break-up of rock by processes such as freeze–thaw without any changes in the minerals that form the rock

Pillar (of limestone) column of lime from floor to roof in a limestone cave or cavern

Scarp slope the steep slope on a chalk escarpment

Scree pieces of rock with sharp edges below rock outcrops

Sedimentary rock rock that began as sediments, usually on a sea bed

Spring point where water from underground reaches the surface

Stalactite column of lime hanging down from the roof in limestone caves or caverns

Stalagmite column of lime built up from the floor in caves or caverns

Swallow hole funnel-shaped holes in limestone down which surface streams disappear underground

Tor block of rock outcropping on top of a granite plateau such as Dartmoor

Weathering breakdown of surface rock by weather without any movement of the rock

Chapter 3

Alluvium river-deposited material (sand and silt)

Attrition process of river erosion whereby the load rubs against itself

Channel the feature in which a river flows

Confluence where two rivers meet

Corrasion process of river erosion where the load rubs against rocks (abrasion)

Corrosion process of erosion caused by the solution of minerals, e.g. salt

Delta often triangular-shaped flat land jutting out into the sea at the mouth of a river

Discharge amount of water flowing in a river, measured in cubic metres per second (cumecs)

Distributary stream channel in a delta resulting from division of a larger channel

Drainage basin area of land drained by a single river

Estuary drowned river mouth in a lowland area

Gorge of recession steep-sided narrow valley created by a waterfall/river retreat

Hydraulic power process of coastal and river erosion caused by the force of water

Hydrological cycle cycle of water between the air, land and sea

Interlocking spurs spurs of high land which overlap in the upper part of a river valley

Meander bend in the middle and lower courses of a river

Meander scar dried-up ox-bow lake

Mouth where a river enters the sea or a lake

Ox-bow lake semi-circular lake formed by a meander being sealed off from the main course of a river

River cliff steep river bank on the outside of a meander

Saltation small particles 'jumping' along the river bed

Slip-off slope gentle slope on the inside of a meander

Solution a form of chemical weathering

Source the starting point of a river

Suspension small particles of clay and silt carried along in the river

Traction boulders rolling along the river bed

Tributary small river which flows into a larger river

V-shaped valley river valley in its upper course, steep-sided and narrow

Velocity the speed of a river's flow

Volume the capacity of a river

Watershed the imaginary line that surrounds a drainage basin

Whinstone a hard, resistant igneous rock

Chapter 4

Abrasion (glacial) process of erosion in which rocks carried in the bottom of a glacier wear away the surface rock

Arête sharp-edged two-sided ridge on the top of a mountain

Boulder clay all materials deposited by ice, usually clay with boulders of different sizes within it

Cirque another name for the circular hollow of a corrie

Corrie circular rock hollow high on a mountainside surrounded by steep, rocky walls

Drumlin egg-shaped small hills made of boulder clay

Erratic large boulder dropped by a glacier, of a different type of rock from the rock now below it

Glacial trough flat-floored, steep-sided valley, usually described as a U-shaped valley

Glacier large moving mass of ice

Ground moraine boulder clay deposited by glaciers which gives a hummocky surface

Hanging valley a tributary valley left hanging high above the main valley floor, usually with a waterfall at the bottom end

High-level bench flatter area high on the valley side above the steep sides of a U-shaped valley

Honeypot place that is especially attractive to many visitors/tourists

Ice sheet moving mass of ice that covers all the land surface over a wide area

Lateral moraine line of glacial deposits along the side of a valley

Medial moraine line of glacial deposits down the middle of a valley

Misfit stream small stream in a large glaciated valley

Moraine all material deposited after having been transported by ice

Pleistocene Ice Age time when most of the British Isles were covered by ice, about 20 000 years ago

Plucking process of erosion in which blocks of rock are torn away from the bedrock as the ice moves

Pyramidal peak three-sided slab of rock which forms a mountain peak

Ribbon lake long, narrow lake on the floor of a glaciated valley

Rock bar outcrop of hard rock between rock basins made of softer rocks

Rock basin hollow on the valley floor eroded by glacial abrasion and plucking

Snout furthest point reached by a glacier, where all the ice melts

Snow line above this point the land is covered by snow

Striation deep groove in rock outcrops made by abrasion as the ice flowed over them

Tarn small circular lake that fills the bottom of a corrie after the ice has melted

Terminal moraine ridge of boulder clay dumped by a glacier as it melted

Truncated spur projection in a river valley that has later been eroded away by a valley glacier so that the lower valley sides are now vertical

Valley glacier moving mass of ice confined within a valley

Waterfall (glacial) fall of water down the side of a U-shaped valley from a hanging valley

Chapter 5

Arch a rocky opening through a headland

Backwash backward movement of water down the beach after a wave has broken

Cave area that has been hollowed out by waves at the bottom of a cliff

Coastal management attempts by people to maintain or alter the natural features of the coast to their own advantage

Constructive wave gentle wave with strong swash and weak backwash which deposits material

Destructive wave high wave with strong backwash which breaks frequently, causing erosion

Fetch the length (distance) of water over which the wind has blown, which affects the size and strength of waves

Longshore drift the current that transports material along the coast in a zigzag

Spit long ridge of sand and shingle, attached to the land at one end but in the open sea at the other end

Stack piece of rock surrounded by sea, now standing away from the coast

Swash forward movement of water as a wave breaks

Wave-cut platform area of gently sloping or flat rocks exposed at low tide

Chapter 6

Altitude height of the land has an effect on temperature and precipitation of a place

Climate average weather conditions of a place over many years

Cold front boundary between a cold air mass and a warm air mass, where the cold air mass moves under the warm air in front of it

Convectional rainfall heavy rain formed by the cooling of moist air as it rises above a heated surface

Front the dividing line (boundary) between two air masses with different temperatures, as a result of which air rises to give rain

High pressure air in an anticyclone sinks to create an area of high pressure at the Earth's surface

Hurricane powerful tropical storm affecting the Caribbean and some other tropical ocean areas

Insolation heating of the Earth's surface by the Sun's rays

Latitude distance from the Equator; has an effect on the temperature of a place

Leaching minerals washed out of the soil by high rainfall, making the soil less fertile

Low pressure air in a depression rises, leaving an area of low pressure at the Earth's surface

Precipitation all forms of moisture from the atmosphere: rain, snow, hail, fog, mist

Prevailing wind direction of the wind that blows most frequently at a place

Relief rainfall rain formed by the cooling of moist air as it is forced to rise over high land

Temperate maritime climate the warm wet climate of the UK

Warm front boundary between a warm air mass and a cold air mass where the warm air rises up over the cold air in front of it

Weather the day-to-day conditions of temperature, precipitation, cloud, sunshine and wind

Chapter 7

A horizon the top layer in the soil profile

B horizon the second layer in the soil profile, found in

soils where the minerals have been washed down from the layer above

Biodiversity great numbers of plants and animals in one ecosystem; greatest in tropical rainforests

C horizon the third layer in the soil profile, made of materials weathered from the rock below

Ecosystem the living community of plants and animals and the physical factors upon which they depend, such as climate and soil

Hard pan soil layer in which minerals washed out from higher up the profile, such as iron, have been compressed

Latosol the red and yellowish-red soil that forms under tropical rainforests

Leaching water moves downwards from the A horizon through the soil, carrying organic material and minerals with it

Podsol soil type under coniferous woodland

Soil profile layers of soil between the ground surface and the solid rock below

Sustainable conserved and able to be used for many years into the future

Sustainable management of forests the forests are not destroyed, so forest resources and products can continue to be used by people in the future

Chapter 8

Age- and sex-selective migration migration often involves younger males in LEDCs, so it is both age- and sex-selective

Census collection of data on a country's population character-istics, usually every 10 years, in the form of a questionnaire

Choropleth map map that uses shading to show density, e.g. of population

Conurbation large continuously built-up area

Core the heart of a country; often the richest, most successful region

Counter-urbanization people move back into the countryside from the towns

Densely populated large numbers of people per unit area

Desertification land turning into desert

Dot map map that uses dots to represent numbers, e.g. of people

Economic migrant Person who has moved in search of work, e.g. a Mexican moving into California

Emigration when people leave a country

Forced migration people forced to move, e.g. as a result of natural disaster or war

Internally displaced migration within a country usually forced by persecution or civil war

Life expectancy average number of years that a person is expected to live

Migration the movement of people

Migration balance the difference between the number of emigrants and immigrants

Natural increase increase or decrease in a population: birth rate minus the death rate, usually expressed as a percentage

Overcultivation crop growing so intensively that the land loses its fertility

Overgrazing too many animals grazing an area so that the vegetation cover cannot support the number of animals

Perception a person's view

Periphery the edge of a country; usually the poorer regions

Polder an area of land reclaimed from the sea, especially in the Netherlands

Population pyramid graph to show age and sex structure of a population

Push and pull factors factors that force a person away from one place and to another place

Refugee person forced to move from one country to another, often as a result of war or famine

Rural to urban migration movement from the countryside to the towns

Salinized when soils are made salty

Sparsely populated few people per unit area

Transmigration policy Indonesian government policy to encourage people to migrate from the country's core to the periphery

Urban depopulation movement of people out of towns and cities

Voluntary migration people choose to move to a new place

Zero population growth when the birth rate is equal to the death rate so that the population neither grows nor declines; also known as the replacement rate

Chapter 9

Bridging point settlement located where a river is forded or bridged

Burgess model a model of urban structure for towns in MEDCs

Central Business District (CBD) the heart of a city where the financial and business interests are (shops, offices, entertainment)

Commuter or dormitory village settlement on the edge of a town or city

Comparison goods goods that are expensive and bought less frequently, e.g. furniture

Convenience goods goods that are cheap and bought frequently, e.g. papers, food

Core (of the CBD) the heart of the CBD where the large department stores are located

Dry-point site site of a settlement which avoids land that is likely to flood, e.g. a gravel mound or side of a valley

Frame (of the CBD) the outer area of the CBD with smaller shops and offices

Green belt land around a large town or city which is protected from development, in order to halt the expansion of the town into the countryside

Hinterland the area surrounding a settlement, port, etc.

Industrial estate zone of light industry, often on the edge of a town

Informal sector in LEDCs many people work in the informal sector as shoe-shine boys, servants, etc.

Inner city the urban zone of MEDCs outside the CBD – a zone of mixed land uses

Megacity city with over five million people

Millionaire city city with over one million people

Morphology arrangement of land uses in an urban area, usually in distinct zones

Periferia housing zone in São Paulo where shanty towns have been upgraded

Recreational facilities sports fields, clubs and leisure complexes

Route focus where many communication routes (roads, railways) meet

Rural–urban fringe area at edge of an urban area, beyond the suburbs, where there is a mix of rural and urban land uses

Self-help scheme people in shanty towns in LEDCs are given basic services by the government, and some of the means to build their own homes

Site land on which a settlement is built

Situation settlement in relation to its surrounding area
Suburb mainly residential area outside the inner city of an MEDC
Urban land use use of the land in towns and cities
Wet-point site place where a settlement is close to a water supply such as a spring on a chalk escarpment
Zone area where land uses are similar

Chapter 10

Agribusiness farms operated by large companies, e.g. Findus, Bird's Eye
Appropriate technology technology that is appropriate to the needs, skills, knowledge and wealth of the people
Arable growing of crops, e.g. wheat, barley
Cash crops crops that are grown to be sold for profit
Chagras a clearing in the Amazon rainforest
Climate the average weather conditions of an area
Commercial the sale of farm products for profit
Double or multiple cropping where two or more crops are produced on the same land in one year
Extensive farm farm system with low inputs and outputs per land area, usually practised over a large total area, e.g. shifting cultivation in the Amazon Basin or hill sheep farming in Wales
High-yielding varieties (HYVs) crops that have been specially developed to produce very high yields, e.g. IR8 rice
Inbye the flatter land close to the farm in the valley floor in hill sheep areas
Inputs physical and human raw materials that go into a farming system
Intake enclosed fields (usually with dry-stone walls) on lower slopes of upland farms
Intensive farm farm system with high inputs and outputs per land area, usually practised on a small area of land, e.g. market gardening in Kent, rice growing in Asia
Inundation canal channel used to direct water from a river onto the cropped land nearby
Irrigation the artificial watering of land, using sprinklers, canals, sprays, etc.
Jengka Triangle Project a scheme to grow more oil and rubber in Malaysia

Machete primitive hand-held axe used by tribes in the Amazon Basin
Mixed farm single farm where crops are grown and animals also reared
Monoculture growing a single crop on a large scale, e.g. rubber, coffee
Monsoon season of heavy rainfall in countries such as India and Bangladesh
Multinational or transnational corporation (TNC) large business operating in many countries, but usually with its headquarters in an MEDC
Nomadic movement of people with their animals to find good grazing
Open fell the high, unfenced moorland on an upland farm in the UK, usually used for sheep grazing
Outputs the end products of a farm system
Pastoral the rearing of animals
Processes the activities required to turn inputs into outputs
Relief the height and shape of the land
Self-sufficient when people can produce all the foodstuffs they need
Soil the thin layer of weathered material and organic matter on the land surface
Soil conservation techniques needed to maintain soil fertility and prevent soil erosion and leaching
Soil erosion loss of topsoil through erosion by wind and water
Staple crop main food crop, e.g. rice in Bangladesh
Subsistence farmer produces just enough food to feed the family
Tube well modern deep well
Well means of taking water from the water table below ground-level
Yield amount produced by growing crops or rearing animals

Chapter 11

Brownfield site urban area cleared of old industry and housing and now available for new developments
Business park attractive area of offices, research establishments and light industries, usually on the edge of an urban area
Footloose industry light or high-tech industry which has considerable freedom in location

Greenfield site rural open land that has not previously been built on
High-tech company firm that researches, develops and makes technological goods, e.g. semiconductors and microchips
Industrial estate area where several manufacturing companies are located, often on the edge of an urban area
Labour the workforce
Light industry industry producing small-sized items that do not require bulky raw materials
Market place where goods are sold
Newly industrializing countries (NICs) LEDCs where manufacturing has grown very rapidly leading to economic development
Primary industry one that takes raw materials from the land or sea, e.g. mining, forestry, farming
Quaternary industry high-tech industry that researches, develops and makes technological goods, e.g. semiconductors and microchips
Raw materials the things needed to make goods in a factory
Science park attractive landscaped area for high-tech companies which may be linked with a University
Secondary industry manufacturing industry that processes raw materials and makes them into other products
Tertiary industry activity that supplies services to people and to other industries
Transnational large corporation operating in many countries, but usually with its headquarters in an MEDC
Transport movement of raw materials to the factory, or goods from the factory to market, by road, rail, sea or air

Chapter 12

Alternative source of energy one that can be used instead of fossil fuels, usually renewable, e.g. wind or solar power
Benefits economic or social advantages for people
Coal fossil fuel made from trees and plants
Consumer society one in which people are wealthy enough to buy many different goods for themselves and for their homes

Eco-tourism form of tourism in which protection of the environment and the way of life of the local people is considered to be important (same as Green tourism)
Green tourism *see* Eco-tourism
Honeypot place that attracts many visitors and experiences visitor-pressure
Industrial Revolution period of great industrial growth and change
National Park area of beautiful scenery which is managed to preserve its attractive features, and for visitor recreation
Nuclear power energy released from uranium and plutonium
Recycling recovery of waste products by converting them into materials that can be used again
Renewable resource that is replaced naturally and so never runs out
Reserves fuel supplies that have been discovered and could be used in the future
Resource substitution using one product in place of another, e.g. aluminium (which is cheaper and can be recycled) instead of tin and steel cans
Sustainable activity that has a good future because the environment/resource upon which it depends is not being destroyed
Sustainable tourism tourist activities and locations that have a good future because neither the environment nor the way of life of local people are being destroyed
UK England, Northern Ireland, Scotland and Wales

Chapter 13

Aid transfer of money, goods and expertise from one country to another either free or at low cost
Desertification land turning into desert
Gross National Product (GNP) total value of all the goods and services produced by people and companies from one country in one year
Interdependence when two or more countries have a shared need to exchange one another's goods
Invisible trade exchange of services and transfers of money including aid and foreign exchange from tourists

Primary products those obtained from the land or sea without being processed or made into another product, e.g. food, minerals, wood
Secondary products manufactured goods
Trade exchange of goods and services between countries
Visible trade exchange of goods that can be counted, measured or weighed

TOWER HAMLETS LIBRARY

Index